The Learjet Diaries

By Greg Madonna

Cover Design by Bruce Borich

Back cover photo by Taimy Alvarez

Cartography by Julie Witmer, Custom Map Design, juliewitmermaps.com

Middle River Press
1498 NE 30th Ct
Oakland Park, FL 33334
www.middleriverpress.com

ISBN: 978-1-946886-15-6

Library of Congress Control Number: 2020912365

First Edition

The Learjet Diaries

By Greg Madonna

MIDDLE
RIVER
PRESS

To My Fellow Aviators

Table of Contents

Preface

About half of this book is 90% true. For instance, it is true that when I flew the Learjet, I was a punk ass kid who survived on luck instead of any good judgement. It's also true that I almost smeared a perfectly good airplane against the side of a mountain in Colombia. And it's sort of true that I almost left a smoking hole in the slums of Port-au-Prince, and that lying became second nature. But all of that is beside the point.

The point is… well, I'm not sure exactly what the point is, other than to say that this is just a story I felt needed to be told.

You see, I was a Learjet pilot flying charters out of South Florida. It was a time when jet flying was new to aviation and even newer to general aviation pilots more accustomed to flying slower and more forgiving prop driven airplanes. Many of us didn't know what we were doing. I certainly didn't. When I was a new copilot I was young and experienced and I was way out of my league. Training was virtually non-existent. As advanced as we thought we were at the time, we had no modern navigational aids, no licensed flight dispatchers to watch over us, no Crew Resource Management tools and only the most rudimentary training. As a new captain on the Lear they tossed me the keys to the jet with a bag of money, an itinerary, and told me to call when I got back home from a trip. We were utterly on our own and we rarely went anywhere with enough fuel. Once we took off on trips to South America we traveled back in time to a region unlike anything I had previously known. It was only with a combination of just raw skill and luck, mostly the latter, that I was able to survive.

This book began as a story about flying but then it became something more. It became a story about people and how they interacted with each other. It also became a coming of age story and forced me to examine myself and my own motives.

I had led a mostly sheltered childhood and I was mostly unprepared for the harsh world of adulthood. As I left my innocent childhood behind I still thought the whole world was like a Hollywood movie where everyone did the right thing and the good guys always won. I was especially unprepared to enter a world where people dealt in self interest and where corruption was rampant. I saw people get killed and almost got killed myself...several times. My initial reaction was to look at the people in this new world with more than a small amount of disdain. I thought myself above all that kind of dirtiness in life. Over time, I came to realize they were just doing what they needed to do to survive. And, in order to survive myself, I became like them.

One note is that during the course of the book, I refer to the airplane sometimes as a Lear Jet (two words) and sometimes as Learjet (one word). The reason is that the airplane was originally registered as a "Lear Jet" by Bill Lear but once the company was purchased by a corporate giant, the moniker was changed to simply "Learjet."

Of course, I must include the disclaimer that none of what you will read in this book is the truth. Instead, it is a more interesting version of the truth. In other words, it is a work of fiction. All plots, themes, dates, events, locations, organizations, persons, conversations and characters contained in this book are fictional. Therefore, any resemblance to people, or events that may have actually happened, is purely coincidental and unintentional.

Prologue: Desire

I was on my way to the airport but first, I had to stop and buy a carton of cigarettes at the convenience store. I was only going to be out of the country for a few hours and I certainly didn't need an entire carton for myself. However, in my past travels I learned that it was helpful to keep some extra packs in the back of the airplane. That's because cigarettes were useful to bribe airport bureaucrats while traveling through South America.

Well, perhaps, bribe is too strong of a word. Small gifts like cigarettes or bottles of scotch were more a gesture of goodwill to ensure things went smoothly. No, that's not right either. Actually, it was more of a tip and Americans were all about tipping to improve performance. Yes, I've got it right now…it was a tip. And tipping generously always made things happen more to our liking. Well, most of the time, anyway.

I stopped at a red light waiting to turn left into the parking lot. It was 1 AM and the 17th Street Causeway in Fort Lauderdale was dark and empty of traffic. As I waited, I listened to the engine in my ancient green Plymouth labor at idle speed. I waited meekly for the light to change like I was taught as a teenager but then thought that deference to a traffic law designed for midday rush hour was senseless. I looked around to see if there was a cop nearby and then accelerated through the red light towards the bright fluorescent lights of the storefront. At this hour, the store was empty so I quickly ran in and out to grab a carton of Marlboro Reds. They had to be Marlboro Reds, and they had to be in the hard flip top box. That was important; no other type of cigarettes would do.

I was running late so I left the car engine running. Being in a rush wasn't unusual for me because in the world of Learjet charter flying we were always running late. Each customer almost always seemed to call at the last minute with some urgent mission for us.

Tonight, we had instructions to get down to Port-au-Prince as quickly as possible for a pickup and the voice on the other end of the phone line said it was imperative that we had to get there and to get back out of Haiti before sunrise. Those orders may have seemed odd but I had gotten used to unconventional directives. I had been flying the Lear now for a while now, half of the time as captain. During that time, I must admit the flying had changed who I was as a person. For one thing, I cared a lot less than I used to. Not to mention some other things that I'd rather not admit. The changes probably weren't altogether for the best but that's just how things had worked out. Things don't always end up the way you expect.

You see, at the age of 24, I fell in love and I did things that I shouldn't have because of her. But I couldn't help myself. I was smitten by her immediately. She was sleek and she was muscular and she outclassed me in every way. At the time, I didn't realize she was a known killer but it wouldn't have mattered. All I cared about was that she was everything I was not; and I wanted her.

We had an affair that lasted for three years and one day. And looking back on it now, I have to admit that I didn't really fall in love with her, as much as I fell in love with what she represented. She was to be my escape to a different life. Forty feet long with a tail that stood tall and proud, she was a Learjet, Model 24B.

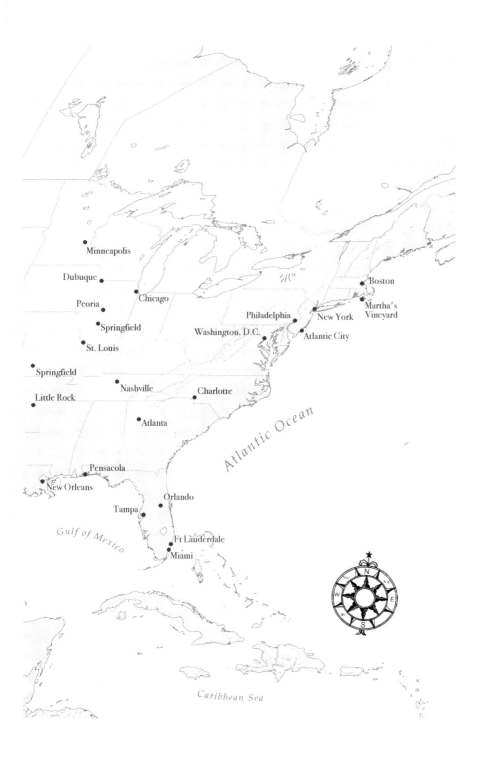

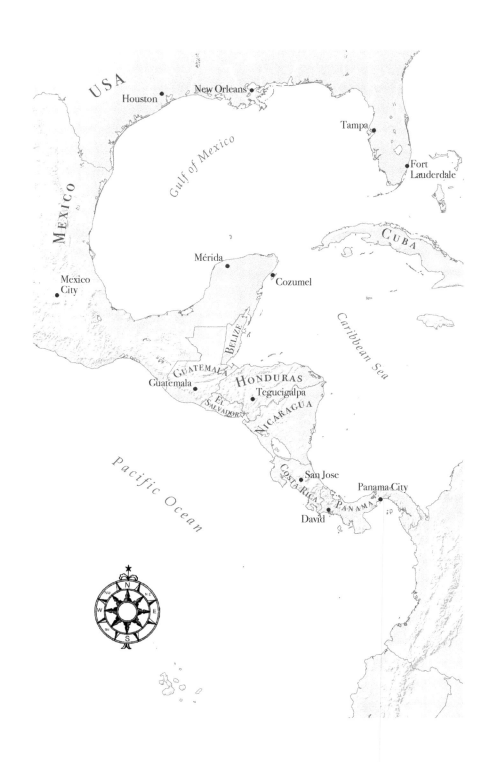

Caribbean Sea

Atlantic Ocean

PANAMA

VENEZUELA

Caracas
Maiquetia
Barcelona

Medellín

GUYANA
SURINAME
FRENCH GUIANA

Bogota

COLOMBIA

ECUADOR

Guayaquil

Manaus

Iquitos

BRAZIL

PERU

Lima

BOLIVIA

La Paz

Arica

Santa Cruz

CHILE

PARAGUAY

Rio de Janeiro

Asunción

Pacific Ocean

ARGENTINA

URUGUAY

N
NW NE
W E
SW SE
S

Chapter 1

....

The Beginning

Whether I was running away from something or running towards something, to this day, I still cannot tell you. Although, does it matter? The main point is that I was just running without thinking things through.

You see, I had been trying to escape my whole life. I had grown up in the 1970s in the dying town of Atlantic City. And everything about that decaying place was reflected in my own life. The city had for decades been the premier resort town in all of the United States but had then gone into decline starting in the 1950s. My father had once been a successful restaurant owner but his own fortunes had followed those of the city. As the city died, its ultimate fate was obvious to everyone and many businessmen moved to the more promising climes of Miami, but my father doggedly stuck it out all the way to bankruptcy and his own early death.

During my formative years, Atlantic City had nothing positive to offer, only sadness and desperation. No culture, no educational centers, no vibrant business community, no sophistication, only melancholy. Without a confident future ahead of me, I spent most of my time exploring the uglier parts of the city looking to find any affinity I might have with others who were also searching for a firm place in society. And it was there where I found myself increasingly attracted to exploring the darker side of life. Every chance I had, I was out of the house. By bicycle as a child, then by bus, or car as I got older. I would go anywhere at any time by any method. It didn't matter; it was just important for me to be on the move, to experience something new... to explore... to escape...to find a place where I belonged.

It wasn't all bad, though. I must admit, there was a simpler time in my boyhood where I was satisfied with spending summers at the beach, frolicking in the ocean with my friends, and enjoying my mother's unconditional love at the end of each day. Home was a sanctuary but I still found myself gravitating towards the unknown. As I got older, high school held no special attraction for me, because, by then, I had developed a perverse hostility towards authority and I was too embarrassed by my father's failure to be part of any social group in school.

In my senior year of high school, I did have a brief affair with a local beauty queen from a school two towns away. Sherry was her name. She favored white T-shirts that stretched tight over her breasts and then followed the curve of her belly, disappearing below the beltline of her hip hugging bell bottom jeans. She was nice looking, of course, but more than that, she was kind. I was surprised when she agreed to go out with me.

As you would expect from a beauty queen, she was statuesque. I was over 6 feet tall myself and when she wore heels, we were eye to eye. But, as it turned out, that would be the only time we saw things equally. One summer day, we found ourselves lying by each other's side in the fragrant grass as we watched the fluffy clouds take various shapes and we shared our vision of the future. It was late in the afternoon and the bright sun melted us into each other. She rolled over and laid her head on my chest. Her wavy black hair felt good against my bare skin and I didn't want to ever leave her. Or maybe, I didn't want her to leave me. I dreamed out loud of a life of adventure but her vision of the future didn't look beyond the local neighborhood so we split up without any emotion. At the time, I moved on without much more thought, although, today, her parting words sear in my memory. Our brief relationship was dead but I guess she still cared enough to say the words.

"You know, Greg...you are a loner. I hope you find happiness but you will never find it by running away."

She was probably right but, despite what she said, I ran away anyway. As for Sherry, she took her own advice. I heard later that she married a local doctor, and raised a happy family.

After spending some time in Europe I found myself in Fort Lauderdale where I completed my university studies, reveling in the anonymity of a large student body. And it was during my college studies, I took flying lessons and earned all the necessary federal qualifications to become an airplane pilot. After a few more failed attempts at relationships, I realized that airplanes were not only more reliable partners but they also offered me another path for adventure.

After graduation from the university, I made a modest living on the quiet side of the executive airport in Fort Lauderdale, teaching a handful of students the basics of airmanship in slow and plodding prop planes. I took the job because I had a vague idea that I would like to be an airline pilot and flight instructing was an initial step in that direction. My life at the time was pleasant and easy, even idyllic. My students viewed me as a great aviation expert although, in reality, I was just a novice myself. I would fly an occasional charter to the remote parts of the Bahamas and I found this gratifying for a while. But my sense of unease began to build again and I looked around for something new.

The more I longed to be an airline pilot, the more I realized I faced a major obstacle. That is because in aviation, pilots for the big air carriers were at the top of the pyramid. They held a job that was glamorous and paid well but I knew my longing would go unfulfilled. None of the airlines were hiring. Worse yet, there were tens of thousands of other much better qualified pilots vying for the very few spots that were available so I put that dream out of my mind. Instead, I hoped I could find comfort again while dating again, but I didn't have many prospects there either. Like so many other pilots, I was away from home too often for any real relationship to develop so work became my main relationship.

At my airport, there were several charter companies that flew the Learjet and it was there where I first saw her. She was the brainchild of Bill Lear, the great genius of American aviation, but she looked as though the gods themselves had created her. In her formative years, she was originally designed to be a fighter jet for the Swiss Air Force. However, Mr. Lear purchased the blueprints and transformed her into a passenger jet with a small cabin just barely large enough to carry two pilots and six passengers. The Lear Jet was the first jet airplane available as personal transportation and her siren call was strong to everyone who knew her. Once transformed into her new civilian role she would gain immortality as the wealthy and the famous flocked to her. And although she now wore civilian clothes, she was still not fully domesticated. People said she was the fastest and most demanding civilian airplane in the sky. And it was true; she still had the primal heart of her progenitor.

The Lear was powered...overpowered really, by two engines, each too large for her frame. People said that except for the fighters down in Homestead Air Force Base, she was the fastest airplane in Miami. That power gave her heart-stopping performance but also an insatiable appetite for jet fuel. And keeping her engines properly fed with that fuel was a maniacal obsession for her pilots. She had a nose strong and aquiline, with a windshield that curved back like wraparound sunglasses. She was a fearsome combination of both the feminine and masculine and she looked spectacular from every angle. I would stand in the hot Florida sun next to my simple and slow trainer airplane and envy those pilots as they passed me by on their way to exotic destinations.

As much as I wanted what they had, I am ready to admit to you that I was intimidated by the Learjet. The airplane had a reputation as being extraordinarily difficult to fly. It was clear that her pilots were better men than me and I regretted that I did not stand a chance to enter their rare fraternity. However, through an improbable twist, I suddenly found myself standing in front of the desk of one such man. His name was Ragsdale.

Chapter 2

The Inquisition

I stood in his sad and unremarkable office at the Fort Lauderdale airport while I waited for his acknowledgment. He sat at a large military surplus desk. Smoke plumed from a cigarette in his right hand and each squeak from his ancient chair aggravated the uncomfortable silence.

Ragsdale was 60 years old, six feet tall and lanky with the body of an athlete himself. It was said that as a teenager, he ran away from his home in Indiana to fly airplanes. Beyond that not much was known about him other than some improbable rumors. The only thing certain was that he had been flying deep into South America for decades and that he was a legend among pilots in South Florida.

Ragsdale, or "Rags" as he was known, swiveled towards me.

"You have been recommended by one of our other pilots."

He paused to glance down at the pilot roster lying on his cluttered metal desk and swept away some cigarette ash from the sheet. His bony finger ran across the names written on the page and he paused halfway down the list.

"Andrews is his name. I have flown with him before… another inexperienced pilot of doubtful abilities."

Rags was wearing a brown suit, threadbare from too many trips to the dry cleaner. His beige shirt and brown striped tie were equally tired and out of fashion. His thick bifocals were of the type that magnified the size of his watery gray eyes. Compared to my thin logbook, he was aviation royalty with tens of thousands of hours in the air and his craggy, lined face was testimony to untold numbers of sunrises seen through airplane windshields. The average age of the Lear pilots in South Florida was about 30 and by that standard Rags was ancient. His overall demeanor was more like a humorless financial auditor than one of the most storied pilots in South Florida.

He reached for a white styrofoam coffee cup with the same hand that was holding his cigarette. The smoke from the coffee and cigarette intertwined and rose to the ceiling. He raised the cup and took a sip before setting it back down on the battered metal desk.

"Your flight experience is pitiful. What makes you think you are qualified to work here?"

I jutted out my jaw slightly, just enough to portray confidence but not so much as to be threatening.

"Captain Ragsdale, I have all the necessary qualifications. I have been a flight instructor for the past year and I have an Air Transport Pilot rating."

In truth, that was hardly a qualification at all to fly a Lear and he saw through my ploy with a snort.

"Well, that is commendable young man."

And he drew again from his cigarette.

"I do see you have a piece of paper issued by the US government stating that you are qualified to fly the Learjet, but that is just a piece of paper. You only think you know how to fly airplanes. That paper is only just a license to learn. You are no more a Learjet pilot than an owner of a house cat is a lion tamer."

I didn't know if he was trying to shame me but I felt the skin on my neck redden and became even more conscious of inadequacies.

But I couldn't fail at this. More than anything I wanted my name to appear on the pilot roster that he so casually held in his hand.

"I know I'm inexperienced but I'm a fast learner. I won't disappoint you, sir."

Ragsdale barely gave me a glance through the swirl of cigarette smoke and continued to make me wait.

My eyes wandered around the room. It was last decorated in the mod style of early 1970s with cheap wood paneling, a couple of side chairs with beige tweed upholstery and green shag carpeting. Or maybe it was brown carpet that had faded to green. I couldn't be sure. A beat up metal filing cabinet occupied one corner of the room. The decor was as worn as his suit.

I waited patiently and as my shame receded, I felt the room's single air conditioning vent blow cold on the back of my neck. I also noted that it was odd, that a man who had spent so many years in the sky would inhabit an office with no windows.

"I have stack of resumes right here with people much more qualified. Why should I choose you?"

For the first time, he made full eye contact with me and held it while he waited for my answer.

Then, it was my turn to make him wait and I returned his stare.

"They may have dropped off a resume, but I am here right now; they're not. I know I can do the job. Give me a chance. That's all I am asking."

He paused again, to draw a deep breath through his unfiltered cigarette, and studied my resume through his bifocals. He already knew my qualifications. Now, he was just making me sweat.

He leaned back and the chair squeaked, which only aggravated the awkward silence.

He drew again from his cigarette and we both played the waiting game.

"Very well. Despite your embarrassing lack of experience, I will give you a chance because we need someone right away. More importantly, business is slow right now and you are willing to work for a pittance of a wage that more qualified pilots will laugh at. Just remember, you will be a burden to all the captains here. Stay out of their way and don't do anything to scare our passengers. Check with the dispatcher for details but I am putting you on the roster to fly with me tomorrow to Nassau. We are flying over to pick up the owner."

Rags paused to take another drag on his cigarette.

"Zero Five Thirty takeoff. Be here by 4:30 and don't be late…And by the way, I suggest you spend some time with the airplane operating manual tonight."

He then dismissed me with a wave of his nicotine stained hand.

Chapter 3

Mentoring

I walked out of Ragsdale's dark inquisition chamber into the bright heat of a Florida afternoon and saw Andrews leaning against the tip tank of one of the company Lears. He was wearing a lemon yellow polo shirt, brown corduroy stubbie shorts, and deck shoes. It was the unofficial uniform of off duty Learjet copilots and each copilot adopted a color combination that favored their unique style. I ended up being more of a khaki shorts and navy blue shirt guy myself. The uniform offered just the right blend of sophistication and cavalier casual. Andrews looked as if he could have been on his way to the Fort Lauderdale yacht club, that is if he wasn't as broke as I was.

Andrews was an entirely different sort of man than Ragsdale. He was young and handsome with curly black hair and a million dollar smile. Everything came easily to him and everyone in the hangar naturally gravitated towards his sunny demeanor.

He was chatting with one of the line boys. He was leaning on an airplane that had just arrived from a trip and it sat alone on the ramp, waiting to be pushed back into the hangar. In the hot midday sun, its crisp white paint glistened in sharp contrast against the black asphalt. It was a 24. The B model with the high performance upgrades; the airplane I had longed to fly; the very airplane I was to fly tomorrow. The registration number "N855W" was emblazoned on the tail in a metallic powder blue.

Andrews flashed his smile and waved me over. As I walked out of the shady hangar and into the sun my eyes squinted in pain from the hot light.

"So what did you think of Rags?"

"He was kind of harsh."

Andrews chuckled.

"Don't take it personally. Rags thinks all the copilots are out to kill him. He will watch you like a hawk, and he won't even let you fly the airplane, but at least he isn't abusive like some of the other captains. If he calls you 'tiger,' take it as a compliment. It means he doesn't think you are a total idiot."

He pointed casually to the airplane he was leaning on and referred to it like an old friend. "55 Whiskey just came in from a trip." He used the phonetic alphabet terminology for the letter "W."

"I'll have the line guys pull it inside and we'll spend some time in the cockpit. Coming right off props you've got a lot of catching up to do. The captains here are not used to flying with new guys, so you are going to need the basics and then a lot more, otherwise the captains will eat you alive."

Andrews was just slightly younger than me but he had already been on the Learjet a few months. This brief time difference placed him enormously higher on the aviation hierarchy than me. I was the barest of neophytes and my current pitiful standing as a new copilot was as tenuous as a grease pencil mark on the scheduling board. My existence could be erased with a single swipe of the eraser, just as easily as Ragsdale had just added it. Although, as I was to later find, the standing of all the other copilots was as equally as tenuous as mine. Each copilot guarded their standing and jockeyed for favor. Each at the mercy of the scheduling gods and each at the whim of the chief pilot. They all kept a close eye on the scheduling board to ensure no one pilot had an advantage in trips awarded. As a result, ensuring an equal distribution of flying hours was an obsession for many and a common source of conflict among copilots.

You see, we were all in competition. Some years ago, all of us had taken an irreversible step towards a career in aviation and we all courted our love with jealous attention. Almost every pilot in the hangar was an aspiring airline pilot and each of us were building experience towards an airline job. In our little fishbowl, hours of jet time in one's logbook were priceless commodities. If one copilot faltered for whatever reason and was taken out of the rotation it was so much better for the others; for they would feast on his trips, just as jackals would feast on the carcass of a fallen animal. Therefore, Andrews was being enormously magnanimous by volunteering his time in order to help me along. It was an early lesson in friendship and camaraderie. At the time, I didn't realize that it was also an introduction into the pilot fraternity. A fraternity that was competitive but, once a mutual respect was earned, also rewarded each pilot with devotion and loyalty to each other. I immediately recognized the dynamic and I swore to myself that, unlike my experiences with university and innumerable old girlfriends, I would not squander this opportunity. I would excel and I would be successful no matter what it took.

The line boys hooked up the old World War Two era tug to the airplane and pushed the airplane back into the hangar. I stood there alongside Andrews and as we watched it slide languorously back into the shadows as we followed behind it. The tradewinds coming off the nearby Atlantic Ocean flowed through the wide open doors and made the hangar a relatively cool and pleasant oasis.

Andrews followed the airplane close behind. Once it came to a stop, he laid his hand on the nose of the airplane.

"Let's jump in the jet, but first thing, you have to learn how to climb in gracefully."

Even though the Lear was much larger than anything I had flown before, it was still a small airplane. It was designed for speed more than anything else and much of its size was devoted to its engines and fuel tanks. It only had a small cabin and the cockpit was even more snug. The main cabin door was more of a hatch than a doorway but I ventured a guess.

"It doesn't seem that hard to get in the airplane."

"Well, it's relatively easy to get in. You don't walk into a Learjet, you have to squeeze in. Although, that is the easy part. The real trick is closing the door and then climbing in the cockpit. You have to do both gracefully.

"The passengers get in first, then you board last, and you have to close the door with them watching you. There is no privacy in the airplane. They see everything you do and remember, appearances are everything. You really have to make it look effortless. You can't look like an amateur. You'll lose all credibility right off the bat."

Once Andrews was inside the cabin, he climbed into the cockpit in one fluid motion. He crouched head first towards the windshield, thrust one leg forward under the instrument panel, then deftly swung his other leg around before plopping his butt on the left seat. It only took him three seconds.

I followed suit in a clumsy fashion, getting stuck halfway through in a crouched position before having to resort to pulling my last leg around with my free hand. The process was exasperating and took me about 30 seconds. Once I squeezed into the right seat, I noticed we lost the breeze. The cockpit was ten degrees warmer and stifling. I felt the heat rising from my shirt collar and pulled my tie down with two fingers.

I gazed with wonder at the instrument panel. Outside, the airplane glistened white and beautiful but inside the cockpit was where her true nature showed. She was a working airplane. A few things looked familiar but this was a serious airplane that was designed for a serious mission. My first clue was the airspeed indicator, with a redline of over 300 knots and an altimeter that read up to 45,000 feet. The instrument panel was painted dark grey. Ten years old, she was in her early middle age, well worn from the hands of experienced pilots. The cockpit smelled of worn leather, hot plastic, and sweat.

Andrews began my tutorial.

"OK, let's start with the important stuff.

"There are two things that will kill you in this airplane…

"I take that back. There are a lot of things that will kill you but there are two things that you can easily avoid: battery overtemps and Mach tuck, so don't be stupid like some other pilots. Pay attention to them.

"First, the batteries. The Lear has Ni-Cad batteries. The Ni-Cads hold a lot of energy and they can give you all that power all at once. They provide a lot of current for starting the engines. And that's what you want. You'll need strong batteries when you're flying in South America. A lot of airports down there don't have starter units so you'll end up doing a lot of battery starts."

He paused to reflect for a moment.

"Well, it's not as though they don't have them. Sometimes they have them but it's either they are broken or sometimes they just won't let you use them unless you bribe the right person. And sometimes, you just need to get the hell out of dodge fast, so you can't wait for a starter unit.

"Anyway, the problem with the Ni-Cads is that because they hold so much energy, they are high strung. They have two problems: If you lose your engine generators and you revert to battery power, they are designed to run at full power for a while but then they just die without warning unlike other batteries that slowly run down to give you a warning. If you are down to battery power only, you have only thirty minutes to get on the ground before they die. You might think you have more time because everything is running great, then all of a sudden…nothing.

"The other problem with the Ni-Cads and this is the big problem, is all that concentrated energy means they are susceptible to overheating if they are overcharged. 'Thermal runaway' is what the engineers call it. There was a Lear 25 that crashed in North Carolina just a few years ago. They were up at 41,000 and the airplane just came apart. The investigation board said there was an explosion in the aft fuselage. A 'low order explosion' they called it. Probably, the batteries overheated. No one knows for sure. But whatever it was, it blew the tail of the airplane off."

"From just a hot battery?"

"Well, they just don't get hot, there's a lot of nasty chemicals in the batteries and they vent off explosive gases. Hot and explosive. Not a good combination."

He drew a deep breath and sighed.

"As if it mattered to the five people on board whether it was low order or not. They're just as dead."

He then pointed to a small sliver of space on the instrument panel in front of my knees.

"The battery temperature gauges are located right in front of the copilot. After a couple of catastrophic overheats they were installed as an afterthought. There isn't much extra space on the Lear instrument panel and that was about the only free space on the instrument panel."

I glanced over at them. They look innocent enough. The indicator was color coded red, yellow and green. The needles were resting at 90 degrees, the same temperature as the outside air and well inside the green band.

"Alway keep an eye on them to see if they're creeping up. Just like everything else about the Lear, you always have to stay ahead of the airplane. Never fall behind. That's true of every airplane but the Lear is especially unforgiving. I can't emphasize that enough. You always have to stay ahead of the airplane."

Andrews continued in this manner for the next few hours, and painstakingly went through every switch and indicator stopping at each one to describe its function during normal conditions; what could go wrong and how a careless pilot could make a mistake.

The more I learned from Andrews the more I realized how little I knew. After repeating what he said each time as a question, even the normally good natured Andrews had enough.

"Look, you are just getting the barest basics. You are going to have to pick up a lot of the rest on your own. All I am doing is making you an assistant to the captain. Just follow their orders."

For the first time in a while, I looked outside and noticed the sun had set long ago and the hangar was dark.

But I had one last question.

"What about Mach tuck?"

"What about it?"

"You said it was one of the things that would kill you in the airplane."

Andrews chuckled.

"Yeah, but we don't have time for that now. The captains will watch out for you and you'll learn about that soon enough. But whatever you do, just never exceed the max Mach speed. The redline on the Mach meter is there for a reason."

I wanted to know more and I frowned.

"Don't worry though. The airplane has a reputation as hard to fly. But it's not the airplane that's the problem, it's the weak-dick pilots that can't handle her. It's a sweet and honest machine. Just follow the rule book, respect her limits and you'll be OK. I gotta get going but good luck tomorrow."

Properly admonished now by both Ragsdale and Andrews, I headed back to my meager apartment with a naivete unique only to those untested. My first trip was in just a few hours but, filled with excitement and anxiety, I found myself unable to sleep.

Chapter 4

Entering a New Life

It was 4 AM as I steered my ten-year-old car to the lonely northern end of the airport. The streets leading to the Fort Lauderdale International Airport were empty and I turned into a small parking lot and chose a parking spot at the far end of the lot. I turned off the ignition and the elderly engine clattered to a stop.

The spot I selected was the furthest away from the entrance of the hangar because my lowly status as a brand new copilot did not allow for a reserved parking spot. But more importantly, most of the Lear captains who got to park right up front were making decent money and were driving a variety of glistening German sports cars. A few years ago I had owned a nicer car myself. But that was then. I had sold my own sports car to pay for my flying lessons. Selling my car to raise the cash was an investment in my future but the investment hadn't yet paid off. In the years following my decision to pursue an aviation career, the economy had turned sour and there were very few flying jobs available. So arriving incognito and parking in the back was fine given the embarrassing state of my life.

After the engine had come to a stop, I was left alone in the morning silence. I stepped out of the car and glanced at my watch for the tenth time in as many minutes. I was too early so I paused in the darkness. Even at this hour, the early morning air was hot and heavy with humidity. The bright white sign on the top of the hangar facing the perimeter road glowed in the tropical mist and created a shadow of me standing by my car. The sign read "Graf Jets" and the buzz from the high voltage electricity that fed it was the only sound at this hour. I looked up at the tall hangar wall next to me. On the other side of that imposing blue aluminum wall were millions of dollars worth of sleek jet airplanes nestled together in the quiet night. And I was actually going to fly one today.

I paused again. I didn't want to appear overly eager by coming in too early but my stomach was churning so I figured I need to get started to get my mind off it. I looked down the length of the airport perimeter road towards the west. Andrews and I used to drag race fuel trucks along this very road when we worked here as line boys just a year ago. It seemed like fun at the time but in retrospect, tearing along a narrow road with 5,000 gallons of jet fuel strapped to your back was probably not the best idea. I regretted my youthful recklessness but I promised myself that I would be much more prudent in the future. With my own counsel in mind, I walked towards a side gate in the chain link fence. And I pushed on it to enter into my new life.

Chapter 5

Preflight

Bright light emanated from inside the hangar and I squinted from its harsh white light. Inside, I saw a collection of gleaming corporate airplanes each owned by a different member of the Fort Lauderdale wealthy class. The hangar seemed larger at night, maybe because each airplane reflected off the mirror polished white floor. Right in the front, by the open door, was my airplane for the day. It was 55W and I nodded. The line boys had just pulled a tug up to her. They were in the process of connecting a long metal tow bar to her nose wheel in order to pull the airplane out of the hangar. The cold steel of the tow bar clanked on the concrete floor as they slid, knees first, onto the floor to make the necessary connection. Once fastened, the tow bar was an ugly knob on her otherwise perfect body.

I looked out across the ramp to survey the rest of the airport. The entire airport was dark and quiet. Fort Lauderdale was officially designated as an international airport but unlike Miami, we were just a sleepy backwater. There were a couple of Eastern DC-9s parked for the night, cuddled together under the dim lights of the passenger terminal. With the exception of an occasional mosquito buzzing by, we were the only activity. I walked past the line boys with only a passing acknowledgement and I slipped through a side door to find Ragsdale in the flight office. This room used for flight planning was down the hall from his own bleak office and was decorated in the same faded style. It doubled as a pilot lounge although it had no lounge chairs. It contained only one long table, four hard office chairs, and a worn out green tweed sofa. The walls were covered with aeronautical charts for all of North and South America and the charts were peppered with pins representing destinations of the company's various charters over the years. I studied it briefly and committed myself to visit as many of those pinned places as possible.

Rags didn't look up to greet me.

"Good morning Mr. Ragsdale." I tried hard to sound efficient and professional.

"Morning, tiger." He still hadn't looked up. Rags was wearing the same brown suit and tie as yesterday. However, his shirt was freshly laundered and starched. There was a steaming hot cup of coffee on the flight planning table.

"I'm just finishing up here. Go ahead and do the walkaround and preflight the inside of the airplane. Then wait for me out there. Nassau is only about a 50 minute flight so we don't need a full load of fuel. I told the lineman I only wanted the wing tanks and the tip tanks filled.

"If he asks you again, just tell him 'wings and tips.' He'll know what that means."

"OK, Mr Ragsdale."

"I also want you to calculate our takeoff weight with 4,000 pounds of fuel. Figure the speeds and required runway length for that weight."

"Yes, sir."

"Be ready for a 0600 wheels up."

He still hadn't looked at me, so I left to go back outside to the dark ramp to begin my preflight chores without even an offer of coffee. No matter. My first flight in the Lear was getting closer and I bounded out of the flight planning office to begin an ancient ritual in the morning heat.

The preflight walkaround was originated by the Wright Brothers and had been repeated over the decades millions of times by every pilot worldwide. Even though the airplane had been checked and rechecked by a team of expert mechanics, it was the pilot who did one last visual check of the external components, small and large. In single pilot airplanes, the pilot himself performed the task. However, in airplanes with two or more pilots, the lowly task was usually relegated to the copilot. And that is how we did it here too.

By now, the airplane had already been pulled out of the hangar and had been fueled by the line boys. I wanted to get close to her right away but I stopped to take the airplane in. She sat there, expectant, facing east, parallel to the mouth of the hangar doors. The lights of the hangar were only partly illuminating her, with one side of the airplane in the light, the other demure in the dark. The jet fuel pumped into her tanks had been fresh and cold and in the humid air, the chilled fuel had created a dewy condensation on her wings. Viewing her, I became aware of my own awkward self. My brand new shirt scratched my skin and my pants were too short. Compared to her sleek beauty, I was still an adolescent mess.

I approached and remembered the instructions given to me by Andrews for the preflight. I started at the nose to inspect the windshield. I placed the palm of my hand on the curved panels of the nose and paused again to take in the whole of the airplane. I then continued clockwise around the perimeter of the airplane, dutifully checking each item. Nothing was too insignificant to overlook, for when traveling close to the speed of sound the slightest imperfection could lead to disaster.

I stopped on the right side of the airplane and slid my fingers across the wingtip tank. I marvelled that something so sleek could contain almost 200 gallons of fuel. I ensured the refueling cap was snugly in place and I recalled Andrews's earlier warning.

"Remember, there's a lot of mass in the tip tanks. More than 1200 pounds when they're full. Even when empty the tanks are a lot of mass. Be careful of over controlling the ailerons, especially on landing. The airplane is super sensitive in roll. You have to be firm with the airplane but also be very gentle in your control inputs. Don't jerk the controls around. And whatever you do, do not ever get too slow on landing. The wings will start rocking back and forth. You'll build up momentum in the tips and your control inputs will get out of sync with the airplane. You can catch a tip on landing and cartwheel."

I walked around to the tail of the airplane. There was a hatch located on the belly of the airplane, which led to a compartment located between the engines. The Lear Jet company said its official name was the "Tailcone Access Door" but all the pilots called it the "hell hole." It contained all the dirty and noisy parts of the airplane, electric motors, hydraulic pumps, pressure accumulators, and flight control cables. It was also home to the treacherous batteries I had been warned about.

I opened the hatch by pressing a series of quick release latches with my right index finger. Nine of them altogether. With each press, the silence was broken by a loud release of the spring. Nine finger presses, nine snaps. The spring tension was hard. Each latch was a design masterpiece in and of itself, and I marveled at the quality of the engineering even in this mundane part of the airplane. By the time I released the last one, my fingertip was tingling from the effort. The hatch was hinged on the front and it swung down creating an opening about 24 inches square. I squatted down to line myself with the hatch and then I stood up with the top half of my body in the hell hole.

Inside, it was pitch black and smelled of oil and acrid electricity. It was much too dark to wait for my eyes to adjust, so I flooded the hell hole with a beam from my flashlight.

Bathed in the artificial light I could then see all the inner workings of the airplane. Nestled in the forward portion of the hell hole was the pneumatic accumulator. It held a charge of high pressure air, which was held in as a back-up source of pressure reserve to blow the landing gear down in case of a failure of the main hydraulic system. The remaining air in the bottle could then be used to power the wheel brakes after landing. It was probably the most important backup system on the airplane. I checked the air pressure that was indicated by a gauge on the bottle and its needle showed solidly in the middle of the green arc.

Overhead, I checked to ensure the flight control cables were taut in their pulleys and there was nothing loose in the compartment. I then looked down at the bottom of the hell hole towards the back and there they were…

Two of them…

The batteries I had been warned about.

Slightly bigger than car batteries. I shined my flashlight on them. They were two slabs of molded plastic. I thought it incongruous that they were both colored pink. Nonetheless, knowing their reputation, they looked intimidating. I touched them. They were cool to the touch, which I found reassuring and I was satisfied they were in no danger of overheating. At least not, now.

The hell hole was even hotter than the outside. I was a visitor in a sinister underworld and I was ready to get out of it. Satisfied with my checks, I ducked back down, snapped the hatch shut and took a deep breath of the humid morning air. I tried to be careful but as I stooped back down I rubbed against the hatch and ended up with a cut on my arm and streak of grease on the shoulder of my brand new shirt.

I then went to continue my walkaround but I had to maneuver around the starter cart parked behind the airplane. The starter cart, manufactured by the Hobart Corporation, was sometimes called the ground power cart. It was a diesel powered generator on wheels designed to assist with starting the engines. The batteries on the Lear were powerful enough to start the engines by themselves but doing so was an unnecessary strain on them. At well equipped airports, like in Fort Lauderdale, a power cart did the work for the batteries. When I worked as a line boy I had used them often. They were loud and smoky creatures but for now, the cart just sat silent and waiting.

As I circled the airplane I marveled that the Lear looked spectacular from every angle. And unlike many other beautiful things, she looked even better up close. The airplane was painted in a brilliant glossy white that glowed even in the dark. Unlike other corporate airplanes of the early 1980s, that were painted with garish and elaborate paint jobs, 55 Whiskey sported only a simple thin powder blue stripe along her length.

I walked back towards the front of the airplane and a shadow approached. It was the chief line boy and I expected him to report everything was in order. Instead, his arms were on his hips and he was blocking my path.

"Hey Stud, is this your first trip?"

"Yeah, Captain Ragsdale hired me yesterday."

"That's what you think. He didn't actually hire you..."

He was wearing navy blue work pants and a white work shirt. The shirt had a red and blue vertical racing stripe on the left side. Unlike most linemen who had a disheveled look, his uniform was perfectly tailored, laundered, and pressed. He was about 30 years old, 5'7" with pale skin and white hair with a razor straight part. His shirt had two chest patches. One said "Graf Jets," the other, "Benny."

He was only about 12 inches in front of my face and I backed up to get him out of my space. He used the opportunity to step forward again to fill the gap I had just opened.

"There are no full time copilots around here. We work at the pleasure of the captains. OK?"

He stomped one foot down to emphasize his point.

I stepped back and he again came forward into my space.

"By the way, don't you have an iron? Your shirt is a fright."

I had to admit that our respective uniforms seemed in reverse. Compared to his crisp work uniform, I was a rumpled mess.

"Yeah, it's brand new. I just unwrapped it and didn't have time to iron it."

Satisfied that he made his point, he grunted.

"Well, just remember that this was supposed to be my trip."

"I thought you said that we only worked at the pleasure of the captains?"

I was pretty pleased with that remark.

"Nice comeback, stud. I was in the rotation to fly next. Instead they put you on it. Just remember that. You owe me."

"Well, I guess you have to take it up with Mr. Ragsdale, then." And I brushed past him.

Chapter 6

Coming to Life

Satisfied everything on the outside was in order, I climbed into the airplane and paused before entering the cockpit. I tried to remember how to enter the cockpit without embarrassing myself as I was just instructed the day before. I looked around and saw no one watching so I climbed in and found myself again stuck halfway on the seat. One of my legs made it to the floor tunnel near the rudder pedals but the other leg was stretched back towards the passenger cabin like a gymnast doing a split. I was stuck and in order to settle into the seat, I had to pick up my ankle again and drag my leg over the center console placing it in the footwell. I did this as inelegantly as was possible and finally settled into a normal sitting position in the seat.

The cockpit was small. I fit but just barely. I was squeezed in tight like a matron wearing a pair of shoes one size too small. The airplane was originally designed as a single seat fighter before Bill Lear remade her. Everything in airplane design is a tradeoff and Lear and his engineers only widened the fuselage barely enough for two people sitting side by side with a narrow aisle. They had no intention of building in comfort at the cost of speed and efficiency. The passengers in the back were cramped in a cabin only five feet wide and and four feet high, Front to back was only nine feet. But it was up front, in the cockpit, where the torturers decided to do their most demonic work. The pilots were squeezed into an even more narrow space, into a tiny cockpit where the fuselage tapered sharply towards the nose. There was little spare headroom and each pilot's shoulders rubbed against the other pilot on one side and against the side of the windshield on the other. There was an old joke that when looking at a Lear Jet crew that you could tell which was the captain or the copilot by which way their heads were permanently tilted having to conform to the curve of the windshield.

As tight as the shoulder room was, the area for each pilot's feet was even more narrow. There was just a slot for a pilot's feet leading to the rudder pedals. In the future, on longer flights, I would long to be able to shift my legs and stretch but instead, each Lear pilot was trapped in his own iron maiden. But even with that, the tormentors were not yet done with their sadistic work. On the copilot's side there was a red aluminum handle protruding into the area that should have been occupied by the copilot's left knee. It was the lever that controlled the emergency air brakes. It was a lever that was for the captain to use in an emergency but the engineers apparently decided the copilot's comfort was less important than that of the captain. Thus, it was perfectly positioned for constant torture on the copilot's knee. And because there was no room to move my left leg, that piece of metal would press relentlessly to add enormously to my discomfort on long legs. Over time, it would leave a lasting imprint on my knee cap. However, in my not too distant future I would find the need to actually use the emergency brakes and be more than happy to trade off physical comfort for the safety back up it provided.

Once I settled in, I began the process of waking up the airplane and flipped the battery switch to ON. Instantaneously, I was greeted by the escalating sound of gyros as they spun to life. In front of me, a host of lights on the warning panel illuminated to advise me the airplane was only being partially powered by the batteries. In flight, this would have indicated a major power loss but on the ground they were meaningless so I ignored them.

The ground power cart wasn't connected yet, so in order to conserve battery power, I quickly ran through all the required preflight checks to ensure all of the airplane systems were operating normally. The airplane was maintained impeccably and everything was in order, so my checks went quickly until I had only one task left. It was also my job to get our clearance from Air Traffic Control.

In the world of jet travel, our flights were highly regimented and strictly controlled. When flying a high performance jet, unlike my previous carefree days, a pilot just didn't jump in the airplane and fly wherever the mood struck. No. ATC had to know where you were going, and when, and at what speed and altitude. And once they approved of your flight plan, you had to then adhere to your pre approved route and altitude strictly. It was all highly regimented especially when crossing international boundaries. As I would also find out, military air defense commanders and customs agents were rather finicky about airplanes showing up on their borders unannounced.

I picked up the microphone and paused. I reviewed in my mind the preferred verbiage exactly as it was printed in the pilot controller glossary. I had done it countless times before with my students in training but this was different. I was now in a Lear Jet and I wanted to sound like a seasoned professional. The microphone was still in my grip, but now sweaty. I cleared my throat and then pressed the mike key firmly.

Chapter 7

Anticipation

'Fort Lauderdale clearance, this is Learjet 855 Whiskey, requesting ATC clearance to Nassau."

Across the runway, located in the center of the airport was a squat beige concrete control tower located on top of the passenger terminal. It had tall glass windows all the way around and offered its sole occupant a commanding view of the airport. The terminal building and control tower were both relics from the 1950s but they did the job.

Working the tail end of the midnight shift was a man probably wearing the uniform of air traffic controllers around the world, a pair of nylon pants similar to those worn by an office worker, a short sleeve dress shirt and tie. He stood in the dark tower cab and he was bathed in the green light emanating from a console of radar screens. At this early hour, the screen was blank as the radar beam swept around an empty sky. He was surrounded by banks of radios, phones, and push button control panels. And he was tethered to this electronic world by a long cord leading to his headset. At the sound of my voice, he turned towards my corner of the airport and peered into the darkness. He squeezed his own microphone button to reply.

Instead, I was surprised to hear a woman's voice. She sounded cute and I suppressed a smile as I wondered if she was attractive. Most people would invariably date those who they met in their workplace; however, there were so few women in aviation that didn't work out for most pilots. I wondered if I could meet her under the pretense of an orientation tour of the control tower.

Without much going on at that hour, she had probably been watching our activity from her perch and answered immediately and in rapid fire. "Lear 855 Whiskey you are cleared to Nassau via Bahama Route 55 Victor... Climb initially to 3000 feet. Expect Flight Level 410 in ten minutes. Contact Miami departure on frequency 126.05. When ready for taxi call on frequency 121.9."

She responded so rapidly that my pencil was barely able to keep up as I copied the clearance on my notepad. I looked down at the scrawl and then obediently read back the clearance. It was a strict protocol followed around the world to ensure we both heard each other correctly.

"Readback correct. When ready for taxi call ground control on frequency 121.9."

Our conversation was then over and I placed the microphone back on its clip, leaving me with just one more task.

The main responsibility of a copilot is to make the captain look good. At most of the Lear operators in Fort Lauderdale, it was standard procedure for the copilot to ensure all of the cockpit switches were pre-positioned in preparation for engine start. This minimized the number of switches the captain had to position himself. The idea was that he could just jump in and go. This also expedited matters for the passengers as well. Many of our customers liked having the first engine start the moment their foot alighted on the stairs. It not only saved a few seconds but they loved the ego boost of having the airplane waiting for them and them only. In doing these chores, I was the modern version of a medieval squire, preparing my lord's horse. With the lowly chores completed by someone else, he only had to mount his steed and go.

In the remaining few minutes, I set the initial altitude into the altitude reminder window, tuned the navigation radios to the proper frequencies, and dialed in the proper outbound course onto the captain's compass, which on a modern jet had the fancy name of horizontal situation indicator. Everything was then set to take us along our cleared route. I swept my eyes across the instrument panel and I was then satisfied that I was done.

Anxious to conserve battery power, I turned off the battery switch and sat again in the darkness listening to the gyros spool back down. Once the gyros were completely run down, I continued to sit in the dark silence, waiting, with only the rapid ticking of the instrument panel clock to keep me company.

I didn't have long to wait.

Off to the left, I saw a shaft of light pierce the dark ramp as Rags opened a side door. He strode confidently and ramrod straight towards the nose of the airplane and waved breezily to the line boys. He was holding a newspaper and he continued to the side of the airplane pausing by the cabin door.

Before he entered the airplane, he stood at the foot of the stairs and tossed the newspaper onto a passenger seat. I glanced back to see the banner. El Nuevo Herald, the Spanish language version of the Miami Herald. He then removed his suit jacket and folded it with care, placing it gently on a passenger seat by the entrance door.

He took a step onto the airplane stairs and the nose strut yielded to his weight, dropping the nose down a couple of inches. As he entered the airplane, he crouched down in the cabin and turned to close the door, which was yet another art form I had not yet mastered.

The main cabin door on the Lear was a simple clamshell affair but closing it required an elaborate ritual involving several steps.

First, he turned to face the door and pulled a wire lanyard to lift the lower clamshell, hooking it loosely in place. He then swung a large handle in the lower clamshell to lock it tightly. Next came the most precarious part of the ritual where pilots had been known to lose their balance and topple out of the airplane. He reached out and up for the top clamshell while holding himself inside the airplane by gripping the seat cushion next to him. Hanging half of his body outside the airplane, he pulled both the top half of the clamshell door down and his own body back inside the airplane. He did it in one graceful motion so the top clamshell then rested lightly on the bottom sill.

At this point the door appeared closed but it was only lightly resting on the door jamb. He then toggled a switch that drove electrically powered hooks that clamped the two halves tightly together.

The hooks gripped down on each other with a zipping sound and the electrical motor wound down under the strain like an electric screwdriver grinding to a halt. Ragsdale then swiveled a second handle to pin the upper panel in place with a definitive twist of his arm and the door latched with a clunk of a bank vault.

And just like that, we were locked inside the airplane.

It all seemed like a complicated and vulnerable bit of engineering but it was one of the strongest parts of the airplane. In the trips to come while taking a break to stretch my legs, I would find myself seated comfortably on that hatch with nothing but a couple of inches of aluminum structure between me and the earth eight miles below.

Chapter 8

The Lessons Begin

Ragsdale made a half a turn towards the cockpit and slid into his seat effortlessly just as Andrews had earlier instructed me. We were about the same size and broad shouldered. In the tiny cockpit our elbows bumped into each other as he buckled his harness.

We were an odd couple. He was the master aviator in a well tailored suit and his black laced up shoes were polished to a mirror finish. I was a raw neophyte in my off the shelf copilot uniform of black polyester pants, a wrinkled pilot shirt, a pair of used epaulets, and some old dress shoes left-over from high school. I had hurriedly found the shoes in the back of my closet the previous night and had to brush off a few years of accumulated mildew to make them presentable. He smelled of coffee and fresh laundry and I hadn't had breakfast yet.

The door had been closed for some time now; without any air condition-ing the cockpit air was getting stale and confining. I was eager to get the en-gines started and get the cabin air conditioning running but Ragsdale didn't seem to be in a rush.

Instead, he drew a pack of cigarettes out of his shirt pocket. They were Pall Malls; soft pack, unfiltered; and a pang of regret rose in my gut. Those are what my dad smoked. As a child, I urged him to stop smoking but he never did. He died when I was just 19. I was an adult legally when he died but really, I was still just a child.

Ever since his death, I always wondered what it would have been like to have known my father as a fellow adult. I had grown up without much mentoring from him or any other male role models in my life. I had always been on my own. Even as a young adult, I never received much mentoring from anyone. It was something I always craved. Although, who knows, maybe people tried but I rejected it.

Rags drew a cigarette from the pack and placed it in his mouth. He flicked open a battered Zippo lighter and angled his head to light the cigarette with pursed lips. He then took a long draw with a grimace and simultaneously clicked the lighter shut with a flick of his wrist. He held his breath for just a moment and exhaled.

We both sat in a swirl of his smoke.

Satisfied he had my attention, he pointed to the top center of the instrument panel with his right hand. He was holding his cigarette in the gnarled fingers of that same hand.

"Watch this line I am drawing."

He then pulled his hand down zigzagging around various switches on the instrument panel, dragging a plume of cigarette smoke behind his pointed fingers. Most of the important switches were on his side of the imaginary line.

"Everything on this side of the line is mine. Don't touch them. Everything on the other side is also mine but you have permission to touch those. Got it tiger?"

I mumbled an affirmative.

Ragsdale glanced around the cockpit and satisfied I had done the preflight correctly, turned his attention to the outside of the airplane. Benny had been standing in front of the airplane waiting patiently for Ragsdale to signal him and the time had now come. Ragsdale looked to Benny and signaled him to start the ground power unit. In turn, Benny signaled to the second lineboy manning the power unit at the rear of the airplane. In the quiet, we heard the ground power unit roar to life and stabilize at idle. After a moment, the lineboy then accelerated the power unit engine to full power providing the airplane with the power we needed to start the engines. The roar was now loud even inside the airplane, and Benny signaled a thumbs up to Ragsdale. I couldn't see it but behind us the power unit was streaming hot exhaust straight up into the morning mist.

Ragsdale sat motionless on his throne and turned on the battery switch causing the instrument panel to come to life again. He then called for the Before Starting Engines checklist. Everything was already prepositioned so I just turned on the fuel pumps and the rotating beacon, and reported the checklist was complete.

Once we got the all clear, Ragsdale reached towards the center instrument panel and moved the starter switch for the left engine to the "start" position.

Even with the ground power unit supplying us with extra electricity, the lights in the cockpit went dim. The starter motor on the engine was the equivalent of a 56 horsepower engine and it greedily sucked in electrons to spin the engine to life. I sat silently to take it all in. Andrews's tutorial from the day before included everything up to this point. I was now on my own. But that was OK. Ever since I was a child, being on my own was something I had become accustomed to.

As the engine began to spool up, the needle on the left engine tachometer began to spin. The igniters then began their work, snapping a spark in the combustion chamber. Even in the cockpit, I could hear their loud clickety clack audible above the din.

Ragsdale began his callouts like a sportscaster reporting what the viewer was already seeing on the screen.

"There's N1 rotation."

But he wasn't ready to do anything yet. He was following a carefully engineered sequence of events to start the engine. And he was careful to follow the sequence exactly for a reason. Jet engines are simple in concept and they are much more rugged than piston engines in almost all areas. However, during start they are susceptible to overtemping and don't react well to mishandling.

The tachometer gauge read in percentage. And as the engine gained speed the tach needle struggled higher, first coming off of zero, then jumping to 5%, and hanging momentarily at 7%. The spinning engine rotors were a heavy load on the starter motor and the ground power unit was straining to provide the power. Even with the assist of ground power the cockpit lights dimmed even more as the engine starter labored to spin even faster. Without the starter cart, the strain on the batteries alone would have been enormous.

Ragsdale called out "10%!"

Satisfied there was enough airflow through the engine to prevent a hot start, he then called out to no one in particular.

"Fuel!"

And he lifted the left thrust lever to open the fuel valves.

With the opening of the fuel valves, high pressure fuel entered the combustion chambers to meet the spark of the igniters. A few more seconds went by and then the entire airplane shuddered as the fuel caught fire and exploded in the combustion chamber. The Exhaust Gas Temperature gauge (EGT), which measured the temperature of the exhaust gas coming out of the tailpipe, jumped to life passing 300 degrees Celsius almost instantaneously. And Ragsdale called it out.

"Light off!"

The EGT continued climbing as the engine continued to accelerate slowly and assuredly. Behind us, a faint blue flame licked out of our tail pipe.

The fuel burning inside the combustion chambers created more heat, and more heat transferred into more rotational energy, and as the engine rotated faster, the cycle began feeding on itself; faster and self sustaining. The EGT gauge climbed steadily and the faint blue lick of flame was replaced by a roar of searing gas out of the tailpipe. The EGT peaked at about 500 degrees and then stabilized at 450 degrees as the rush of air sucked into the intake cooled the exhaust ever so slightly.

Inside the cockpit there was an increased excitement but things were relatively muffled. Outside, though, the serene morning of the Ft Lauderdale airport was interrupted by the exploding Jet-A fuel slamming into the still air.

Satisfied the engine was running on its own, Ragsdale moved the starter switch from "Start" to "Gen," which did two things. It cut out the starter circuitry and engaged the engine generator. It did those two things simultaneously because in Bill Lear's obsession to simplify and reduce weight, we didn't have a separate starter and a separate generator. It was all contained in one unit and by switching to generator mode, the internal circuitry was simply changed over. With the flip of that switch the left starter began to act as a generator providing electrical power to the airplane.

Ragsdale then turned on the airplane inverters, which supplied AC power, and with the inverters now powered, more systems came online. Benny was still standing in front of the airplane although he had stepped back from the airplane to avoid being sucked into the engine. It was an occupational hazard of line boys around the world. Working on an airplane ramp was a maze of invisible hazards. Jet engines could either suck you into the engine or blast you across the ramp depending on what side of the airplane you happened to be on. Whirling propellers and helicopter rotors were even worse, ready to eviscerate the unaware. Invisible and deadly, they were all things that had claimed the lives of even the most cautious ramp worker.

Ragsdale signalled to the line boys to disconnect the ground power unit.

And once they did, the lone engine generator was then powering the entire airplane. Ragsdale gave me an order.

"Call for a taxi clearance."

I dialed a new frequency on the VHF radio and keyed the microphone again.

"Fort Lauderdale ground, this is Lear 55 Whiskey, ready for taxi."

The same voice as before responded.

"Lear 55 Whiskey you are cleared to taxi to Runway 9 Left, via taxiway Alpha. Altimeter setting, 30.15 inches. Call when ready for takeoff."

As the controller gave us a new altimeter setting, we both reflexively leaned forward and adjusted a small knob to calibrate the local barometric pressure on our respective altimeters.

Rags gave Benny a thumbs up signaling we were ready for taxi. He then gave Ragsdale a salute, which Ragsdale then returned.

That salute was another universal custom in aviation. The signalman would salute the captain on the airplane indicating that all the last minute outside checks were completed; that the airplane was clear of obstacles and free to launch. At the same time, like a military salute, it was a display of respect. Afterwards, the captain would return the salute, acknowledging the release and returning the show of respect.

After that bit of theater, Benny signaled for us to begin a right turn out of the ramp area.

Ragsdale pushed up the left throttle. The shriek of the engine rose noticeably and the wheels broke free. As we began to move forward, the linemen stepped back again to avoid what they knew was about to come.

Satisfied we had enough momentum to keep on rolling, Rags then brought the throttle back to idle and turned the airplane hard to the right to head out to the taxiway. As we turned away, the area behind us was scoured by the blast of our engine and the line boys faced away from us, hunched over to protect themselves from the scorching air.

As we headed towards the runway, Ragsdale started his own preflight ritual, one that I would find common to every Lear Jet pilot, and one I would later follow slavishly as well.

He reached down with his right hand to the fuel panel between our knees. On that central console was a single fuel gauge that was used to indicate the fuel level in the five different fuel tanks. There was only one fuel gauge because, again, when designing the Lear Jet Bill Lear was obsessed by two main design criteria, saving weight and reducing complexity. He was once heard to say that he would trade his grandmother for a weight savings of just one pound. And in the design studios of the Lear factory, engineers were often heard to say things like, "Changing to this lighter component is worth four grandmothers." So, in the interest of saving maybe just half of a grandmother, there was only one fuel gauge. And in order to see the level in each of the five tanks there was a selector knob that showed the fuel level in each individual tank on the single gauge. Rags fingered the fuel selector knob and toggled it between the five tanks. With each selection the fuel needle jumped and then quivered to a stop to show the fuel in each respective tank.

The reason for this ritual was that early generation jet engines, like the ones installed on the Lear 24, had an insatiable appetite for fuel. They were only efficient at very high altitudes. Taxiing out we were burning as much fuel as we would be at cruise altitude. The joke among Lear Jet pilots was that you were already fuel critical just taxying out. But it was more than a joke. Fuel conservation was a life or death business in the Fort Lauderdale charter business. In order to maximize profits, most of the operators often flew the airplane to the very extreme end of its range. Fuel stops were an expensive luxury.

As a result, minimizing time on the ground was the main imperative of every Lear Jet pilot. In just the last few minutes, we had already burned 300 pounds of fuel, which at altitude would give us about another 15 minutes of endurance.

Rags noticed my curiosity.

"Remember tiger, there are three useless things to a pilot, the runway behind you, the altitude above you, and fuel you don't have in the tanks."

As a common fuel saving technique, Rags was taxiing on only one engine. The airplane was so overpowered that we still rolled easily on one engine. This technique saved us maybe 200 pounds of fuel. It doesn't sound like a lot and for our short flight to Nassau we had plenty of fuel, but as I would someday find out, every drop counted. In the Lear Jet business, it was good to get in the habit of fuel conservation.

It was dark and the airport was still quiet. Satisfied we would be number one for takeoff. Rags reached over to the start switch for the right engine and moved it to the "Start" position.

Clearly this was a one man show; my job was to only talk on the radios and follow his orders.

The right engine started quickly and with the extra thrust coming from the second engine the airplane strained even harder at her leash. Ragsdale squeezed the brakes lightly to slow our momentum.

As we approached the end of the runway, he commanded:

"Switch to tower and call ready for takeoff, I don't want to have to stop."

It was an easy task and well within my meager capabilities.

"Hello, Lauderdale tower, this is Lear 55 Whiskey. We are ready for takeoff."

The airport was quiet and no other airplanes were around. Our controller had likely been watching us the whole time anticipating my call and answered again with no hesitation.

"Lear 55 Whiskey, you are cleared for takeoff, Runway 9 Left. Climb and maintain 3,000. Call Miami departure on 126.05 once airborne."

I read back the clearance and before I even released the mike button, Rags called out with some urgency. "OK tiger, let's go. Give me the Before Takeoff checklist."

I read through the checklist with one finger on the paper checklist and one finger touching each switch as I read.

"Trim?… Check,

Flaps?… Set,

Transponder?… On,

As I continued to read, the urgency in my own voice rose.

Ignition?… ON!

Stall warning?…ON!"

And I dutifully reported "Before Takeoff Checklist complete!"

Just as I finished the checklist, Rags swung the airplane onto the active runway. We were facing directly east now and I noticed the orange rays of the rising sun peeking above the horizon.

In the past, I had done flights on 9 Left in my Cessna trainer but at those times, I was always an interloper, given the barest of acknowledgement by the controllers. They allowed me to land because the regulations said I had a right to be there; but in reality I was a trespasser, intruding on airspace needed for more important airplanes. In the past, they were eager to shoosh me away. However, on this morning, things were different. Now, I belonged.

Chapter 9

First Flight

We lined up on the runway and Rags braked to a stop. The airplane was now in the starting blocks. The white runway lights extended into the distance, piercing the morning mist.

I waited.

He again toggled through the five fuel tanks. It was then that I began to realize this wasn't a ritual to determine our fuel load, as much as it was a nervous tic. On our short flight, we had plenty of gas. But continuously checking the fuel was an involuntary habit for every Lear Jet pilot.

The moment for nervous energy was past and it was now time to go. One last glance to ensure everything was in order and Rags pushed throttles up to 70% of available RPM. It was just enough to allow the engines to spool up and stabilize. This pause at 70% allowed the air passing through the inside of the engine to combust smoothly and exit out the tailpipe. Older jet engines were susceptible to surge and compressor stall if the throttles were advanced too rapidly. When that would happen, all hell would break loose inside the engine, shaking the whole airplane, and flames would shoot out the front of the engine, creating a dramatic display even for the most casual observer. I would learn quickly that we needed to baby the engines in the 20 series Lears. Of course, in cases of extreme duress, that was not always possible and we had to sometimes ask from the engines more than they could give.

I felt the push against my seat as the airplane began to roll. Just slowly at first. The acceleration pushed me back in the seat but nowhere nearly as forceful as when I had practiced aerobatics. Satisfied the engines were stable and the air was flowing properly through the engine, Rags then quickly powered all the way up to 100%. The tachometers spun crazily up to their redline and the EGT on each engine surged up to 650 degrees Centigrade. The engines responded in full throat and I gasped as I was pushed back in the seat. The airplane was now a fully alive and fire breathing animal, and I found myself only along for the ride.

Andrews didn't tell me about this. We were light, just two pilots and half a tank of gas. The whole idea behind a jet engine is to suck a large volume of air through the intake and blast it out the tailpipe at a much higher velocity. The engines on the Lear were now doing exactly that; and with magnificent results. As I was pushed back in my seat, I was only able to fixate on the white runway stripes as they streaked underneath the nose. We were eating them up faster than I had ever seen. I glanced at the airspeed indicator. In just a few seconds we were already accelerating through 100 knots. And I realized I had missed the 80 knots call out.

Befuddled, I stumble out a few words.

"80 knots, no… a hundred." But by then we were well past 100 knots.

At that point, we were going as fast as I have ever been before in an airplane, and we were still on the ground, and accelerating.

We passed V1, the Go/NoGo speed. And, again, I missed my required call out. Not that it mattered. At this light weight and high power setting we could have stopped and taken off again on the remaining runway again and still have had concrete to spare. We were quickly up to flying speed. Rags then pitched the airplane up. As we leapt off the ground I was pressed more deeply into the seat cushion.

Things came even more quickly then. Rags didn't need me to make the runway callouts but he needed me to accomplish some other chores and he called out in rapid succession.

"Gear up!

"Yaw damper on!"

Things were moving so fast, I could barely hang on. We were already passing three hundred feet of altitude but I felt like I was still on the runway. Ragsdale pitched the nose up even more steeply to a crazy angle. I was disoriented by this steep climb but I had enough sense to quickly bring the gear up. However, I fumbled for the yaw damper and engaged it much later than I should have.

The yaw damper was a vital engineering workaround. Airplanes with swept back wings were inherently unstable and the yaw damper was a computer that automatically modulated the rudder to dampen unwanted oscillations. It was a critical component to the Lear's stability. But you would never have never known it. Ragsdale held the wings rock steady.

He again pitched the nose up even more steeply and he reduced the power to 90% to slow our climb and keep below the 200 knot speed limit around the airport. Flying a Lear was all about maintaining momentum and unnecessary throttle movements were the hallmark of an amateur. However, Rags was certainly not an amateur and he was perturbed when my stupefied pace broke his momentum.

"Call departure!"

This one I knew, and I called Miami departure without delay and they responded quickly.

"Roger, this is Miami departure, You are radar contact. Climb and maintain 16,000 feet. You are cleared to Nassau as filed. Turn right to a heading of 120, fly direct to Bimini when able. Standby for higher."

I was still badly behind the airplane but I was able to catch my breath and get a sense of what was happening around me. Rags did have to level off momentarily at 3,000 feet and I went light in my seat for a moment as the power came off. But as soon as he added power again I was pressed right back into my seat and we were levitating like an angel soaring into space. Even as we accelerated to 250 knots, the altimeter was winding up in a way unknown to me. A quick glance at the vertical speed indicator revealed it was pegged. We were climbing at least 6,000 feet per minute, probably even more.

I looked over my left shoulder, back through the large porthole window on the left passenger side. I recognized Port Everglades and the shore line passing behind us. But it was from an angle I have never seen before. It was as if I was looking straight down, with the wing of the airplane acting more like a fin on a rocket than a lifting device. This just aggravated my sense of being behind the airplane even more, so I pledged not to look backwards again.

As I turned forward, I noticed we had climbed into the sunrise and the dim morning light cast a ghostly shadow on Ragsdales's craggy face. In the dark sea below us, I saw the weedline where the murky coastal waters met the cobalt blue Gulfstream current. A few fishing boats were already out patrolling the shallow reefs.

Chapter 10

Entering the Stratosphere

We passed 10,000 feet and entered high speed airspace. Above 10,000 feet were then able to accelerate unencumbered by ATC restrictions. Rags pitched the nose down and the airspeed needle swept quickly up to 300 knots, although our climb was hardly impeded.

He was hand flying the airplane rather than using the autopilot and his stick and rudder skills were flawless. The airplane continued straight and steady without even the slightest wobble, as though we were still on the ground. His comment from yesterday was right; I was in way over my head. Despite what I thought was a reasonable amount of experience, I was barely able to understand what was happening. And I was only barely able to follow his orders. Thinking ahead of the airplane and making my own decisions was just not happening. The best I could do was to just stay out of his way.

Rags squeezed off a little power to slow our climb and said "Call Miami Center."

Miami Center was the ATC facility that controlled a huge chunk of high altitude airspace between Orlando and all the way down to Puerto Rico. Our short trip from Florida to Nassau was in their purview and we needed their permission to continue climbing.

I had never flown in this high altitude sector so I fumbled again with the Fort Lauderdale departure chart looking for the right frequency.

"That's the wrong chart tiger. That's for Miami departure control. We need the frequency for Miami Center. Go to the high altitude chart."

He paused a second and recalled the correct frequency from his immense memory. "Forget it, just call them on 133.0."

I obediently dialed the new frequency on the left VHF radio and called.

"Miami Center this is Lear 855 Whiskey passing through 16,000 feet."

About 40 miles away in North Miami alongside the Palmetto Expressway was a squat concrete building sprouting with antennas. Inside were an array of radar consoles manned 24 hours a day by a different breed of controller. Unlike the controllers standing in the control tower, scanning the horizon and pirou-etting their dance all day long, these high altitude controllers were glued to a chair for the entire shift and never saw the light of day. They hunched over their control panels watching green blobs move lazily across their radar screens. And one of those blobs that morning was us. It was their job to keep the green blobs moving in the right direction and to keep them from blobbing into each other.

He keyed his mike using a foot switch.

"Roger Lear 55 Whiskey, This is Miami Center. You are radar contact. Climb to and maintain Flight Level Two Three Zero."

"Roger, cleared to 23,000 feet."

Rags simultaneously added the power to begin climbing and admonished me as the G-forces again pushed me back in my seat.

"Hey Tiger, it's not feet. Everything 18,000 feet and above is referred to as Flight Level. It's Flight Level Two Three Zero, or Two Three-Oh. Get it right next time."

"Sorry, Mr. Ragsdale."

Up ahead, there was a building thunderstorm. It looked to be about 28,000 feet high although I had never seen one from this high of a vantage point making it harder for me to judge. The morning sun prismed a rainbow off of its rain shaft. I shifted in my seat. In my prop airplanes, I would have given this cloud a wide berth. I looked at Ragsdale. I knew he saw the rain cell. His head was nodding up and down slightly as he adjusted his line of vision above and below his bifocals. But he remained nonplussed. We were headed straight for the center of the cloud. We weren't going to be able to climb over it. I knew that much but Rags made no motion to deviate around it. He didn't even bother to turn on the weather radar. Another second went by and the morning sun blanked out as we flew under the cloud's shadow. Another sec-ond or two and we were going to be in the dark belly of the cloud.

Yet, Rags maintained his course.

Rain splattered on the windshield with a fuzzy sound and we sliced into the gray cloud. The horizon disappeared and we were on instruments. The cockpit darkened and I reached over to turn up my cockpit lights. The en-gines sucked in the rain and the cabin pressurization filled the cockpit with the cloud's sweet and humid air.

There was a slight burble as we roiled through the convection. At this time of morning, the convective clouds were mostly benign, and the Lear pierced through the cloud effortlessly. At 300 knots we were out the back of the cloud in just a few seconds and just like that our trip through the storm was over as quickly as it began.

We blasted out of the cloud back into the full face of the morning sun and a few rivulets of water streaked off the windshield as the moisture sheared off the airplane. At our speed the airplane was swept dry in a matter of seconds.

In my old plodding trainer airplane, a deviation around that storm cell would have taken 15 minutes; in the Lear it took all of about 15 seconds and we continued to rocket to altitude.

Bimini now appeared on the horizon. At this altitude, the island chain appeared to just float on the ocean surface. North and South Bimini sat only a mile apart from each other. Just to their south was a tiny spit of land called Ocean Cay. It was a man made island made of slurry from an aragonite mine dredged from the shallows of the Great Bahama Bank. Just a few weeks ago I had a part time job flying an ancient Islander cargo plane supplying the island with fresh supplies and workers on shift change. The island, if you could call a 1500 foot square of packed sand an island, was home to a few shacks, a massive steam powered dredge, and that was it. It didn't even have a runway. We just operated along an unoccupied strip of packed calcium carbonate.

Further off to my right was Cat Cay or just "Cat" as it was colloquially known. Each island was in sight of each other but they couldn't have been more different. Ocean Cay was the least lovely of all the Bahamian Islands; just a stark industrial facility, whereas Cat Cay was one of the most exclusive resorts in the world. Centuries earlier, Cat was briefly home to the pirate Blackbeard but more recently, a group of wealthy industrialists had turned it into their own lush tropical playground.

The shallow aquamarine water formed a halo around each island and was in sharp contrast to the deep blue of the Gulf Stream. The waters here were familiar to me. Years ago, before my family's fortunes turned and I was relegated to flying cargo to Ocean Cay, we had visited Cat Cay a few times. My uncle also used to take me fishing around the Biminis when I was a boy and it was there where I first tasted a Cuba Libre, the traditional Caribbean elixir of rum and Coca-Cola. Family lore had it that during prohibition my uncle would go on fishing trips to Bimini and return not with coolers full of grouper but crates of illicit Cuban rum. His boat was called the Imp and it was powered, overpowered really, by two old military Liberty aviation engines, each one alone, too big for her hull. He claimed it was the fastest boat in Miami. And if he couldn't outrun trouble, he was known to have used his fists as a substitute.

Rags broke my reverie.

"Call Miami and get switched to the high altitude sector. Hurry up. Tell him we want higher. We're light and I don't want to have to level off at twenty three." Again, he reduced power slightly to give me some time but I was still slow and inept and he had to pull the power all the way back, almost to idle.

As the engines rolled back, the cabin air flow decreased markedly as the bleed air from the engines dropped. The deceleration was abrupt and the negative g-force lifted me against my seat belt.

As I was to later find out, it was a matter of pride among Lear pilots, to fly as smoothly as possible and make as few power changes as possible. As a result, they would time their climbs and descents so they would only have to set the power once. The Lear Jet community in Fort Lauderdale was small and each pilot had a reputation. Pilots would talk about each other's abilities or sometimes lack thereof. Being labeled a good stick by one's fellow pilots was a high honor. The expression was rooted in old fashioned airplanes that had simple sticks for control instead of car-like yokes. Smoothness on the controls was just one marker of a pilot's ability. Excessive throttle movements tagged one as a "throttle jockey" or worse yet, "not a good stick." Rags prided himself on being a good stick and thus far, I had spoiled his technique on two separate counts.

After some more fumbling again on my part, I found the right frequency and Miami Center cleared us to FL 450. I had sworn to not make the same mistake twice. By now, I got the nomenclature right and read back our clearance correctly as a Flight Level Four Five Zero.

But that was only a small victory. Rags reminded me I was still behind on another of my myriad duties. "Watch the cabin pressurization, we're climbing so fast, don't let the cabin fall behind."

As we approached cruise altitude, things slowed down a bit and I felt like I had a second to catch my breath. We leveled at 450. I checked the clock. We had taken off just 15 minutes ago. That was a stunning rate of climb, equivalent to fighter jets and placed us higher than all the airliners. At this altitude, we were well into the stratosphere. And it was at FL 450 where I first saw the curvature of the earth.

But my copilot duties still took precedence. The flight from Fort Lauderdale to Nassau was so short that no sooner than we had leveled off it was time to start right back down. Rags again broke my dream state.

"We're about to start down. Get the Nassau weather and calculate our landing speed."

I knew I had some chores to accomplish but I had already forgotten everything Andrews told me. I tried just going step by step trying not to make any more mistakes in front of Rags. But I was still befuddled. I thought that maybe he would feel sorry for me and coach me along but Rags was too old school for that. In his world, copilots were an encumbrance more than anything and had to survive on their own. He left me to fumble through the descent checklist unaided.

As I floundered my way through my duties, I glanced over at Rags. His cigarette was hanging casually from his mouth and he was flying with just one hand. Andrews warned me about the airplane's sensitivity but Rags was handling the jet effortlessly.

Miami Center gave us a clearance to descend and then handed us over to Nassau Approach Control. The distance measuring indicator showed 125 miles to Nassau. The sky was clear this morning and at this altitude I could look down and see New Providence Island, home to the capital city of Nassau. It was barely visible on the horizon. In my old airplane, 125 miles out would still have been an hour away. Instead, in the Lear we were in range and about to begin our descent.

Rags gently pulled the throttles all the way back to idle. In jets, the idea was to stay as high as possible, as long as possible, to take advantage of the fuel efficiency afforded at high altitude; and then come down at idle power. At low altitudes the Lear burned gas like water going over a fall and we wanted to spend as little time as possible maneuvering around down low. Ideally, a pilot would make the entire descent at idle and wouldn't have to add power again until spooling up the engines again on final approach.

As Rags reduced power, the airspeed decreased imperceptibly and in order to keep our speed up, he gently pitched the nose down and increased speed.

Now, Rags felt like chatting, "The ideal descent profile is to pitch down, accelerate to redline and come down like a speeding bullet. In a prop you come down at a medium speed. In the Lear, it's all about maximizing speed. You want to stay as high as possible, and as fast as possible, for as long as possible. Let the wings do most of the work, not the engines."

We were planning on landing to the southeast in Nassau, into the prevailing tradewinds. Since we had been on a southeast heading ever since taking off from Fort Lauderdale, we were already lined up on the runway as Nassau approach controller cleared us to use the Instrument landing System (ILS) to Runway 14.

I had already tuned the ILS so Rags would have a radio beacon to home in on. Once the radio was tuned, two needles dropped into view onto his compass indicator, giving him both lateral and vertical guidance. The lateral needle was already centered showing that without any guidance from the ground Rags had already lined us up perfectly to the runway.

As we got closer, the dark green vegetation of New Providence with its stark white beaches became clearly visible. Just like Bimini, it was an emerald jewel floating in the aquamarine Bahamian water. We descended through 10,000 feet and Rags slowed the jet to 250 knots. At idle power, the engine noise was replaced by the rush of air past our windshield. We were now essentially gliding towards the ground and it was peaceful. This was flight as it should be. Like the birds, sleek, silent, and effortless.

At about 20 miles from the airport, we were still over the water and he leveled at 3,000 feet. The sun was brilliant and the clear water was reflecting so brightly that the entire cockpit glowed orange and blue.

"Give me flaps 8 degrees."

He still hadn't touched the power and the airplane decelerated gently back to 210 knots.

The wing on the early model Lear Jets wing was thin and flat, designed for high speed flight. The flaps were designed to increase the curvature giving us more lift at slow speeds. Just like a bird curving its wings coming in for a landing, the landing flaps did the same thing. Otherwise we would be landing at over 200 MPH.

With the power still as idle, the airplane continued to decelerate back to 180 knots and Rags called for more flaps.

"Flaps 20!"

We were 6 miles from touchdown and the needle giving us vertical guidance dropped down, indicating we had intercepted the glide path

"Gear down!"

The increased drag from our landing gear slowed us significantly and the speed dropped back even more. As the airplane neared our final approach speed, Rags finally fed in some extra power.

Passing through 1,000 feet, Nassau control had cleared us to land. The runway, all 14,000 feet of it, was ours.

"Flaps 40!"

He slowed to 130 knots and he added more power to hold that speed. Some other jets with leading edge flaps could approach at even slower speeds but in the interest of simplicity Bill Lear only installed trailing edge flaps. It saved an awful lot of grandmothers.

We passed 500 feet and with Ragsdale focused on the outside, I made one final check of the cockpit. The landing gear was down with three green lights. Flaps were set at 40 and we were cleared to land.

We continued inexorably towards the runway end. And as we got closer to the ground I began to sense how much faster we were going than I was used to. I squirmed in my seat. I felt like we were too fast and I pulled up my feet off the floor.

As we passed over the runway threshold we were about 50 feet high and I reared back in my seat.

Still at 130 knots. We were too fast!

40 feet, 30 feet, 20 feet. Then just a couple of feet above the runway, Rags chopped the power to idle. The Lear 24 was very fussy at low speeds and had a tendency to roll over if flown too slow.

Hence, you didn't flare the Learjet. You basically just flew it on. Rags only pitched the nose up imperceptibly, maybe one degree, just enough to shallow the descent. And I heard the gentle chirp of rubber against the hot concrete. It was a perfect landing.

With the thumb of his right hand, he toggled the spoiler switch and large panels on each wing extended up to dump lift, which transferred the airplane's weight from the wings onto the wheels. This made the wheel brakes more effective and he applied some gentle braking. Halfway down the runway we turned off one of the high speed exits.

We carried enough fuel to make the round trip so all we had to do is clear customs but we added some gas anyway to show some goodwill to the airport businesses. Not by coincidence, this seemed to make the whole customs process go much more smoothly.

The owner of the airplane showed up on time and the return trip to Fort Lauderdale was equally uneventful although I was still badly behind the airplane.

After landing back home, we taxied up to our large blue hangar and Rags brought the airplane to a firm but smooth stop. The nose strut compressed slightly and the airplane rocked forward gently and then back before settling to a stop.

Rags lifted the throttles slightly over the stop detent and then pulled them all the way back, which closed the fuel flow to the engines. Their job was done and starved of fuel, the engines gave up with a descending whoosh.

Rags was quickly out of the left seat and left me to the shutdown checklist. He opened the cabin door with a swift and graceful two step motion. The owner was out of the airplane just as swiftly and into his waiting car with only the briefest of goodbyes. Once he drove away, Rags lit his first cigarette since we left two hours ago.

I climbed out of the airplane.

"Good job, tiger. The linemen will wash the airplane later but in the meantime, just give the leading edges of the wings and engine nacelles a quick wipe to get the oil and bug splatter off."

Just then, a woman hurried out from her office towards Ragsdale. It was Chloe. She ran the charter department and the scheduling of airplanes. She had a worried look on her face and she held up her hand to stop us.

Chapter 11

Right Back Out Again

'Ron, we just got a pop-up trip."

She was the only person to call him by his first name.

"The customer will be here in just 30 minutes. It's a drop off to Martinique, and return empty. John Coe will be the captain. He is on his way but he won't get here until about the same time as the customer. We still need a copilot. It's Benny's turn to fly but I can't get a hold of him. Greg is already here so I'm sending him right back out with John."

Chloe was about the same age as Ragsdale and she too had a face lined with years of tobacco and bourbon.

She looked to Rags for approval. They both knew the implication of assigning two trips in a row to the same copilot. He shrugged his shoulders, and turned to me, "Looks like you're up again tiger. I'll file the flight plan for John but you'll need to get the airplane set up."

He knew the route by heart.

"Plan on Upper Amber 555 all the way down. Destination Fort de France International. The airport identifier is TFFF. It's a long trip so you need all the gas you can squeeze in. Top it off all the way. Start filling the center tank now, that's going to take 15 minutes, and have the fueler pack a tip tank."

Chloe was still concerned. She leaned into Rags. "This is a good trip; Benny will be furious he missed it."

He glanced at Chloe. "He'll get over it."

He then turned back to me. "Get started tiger."

Delighted with my good fortune, I leapt back towards the airplane.

"Martinique," Chloe had said. I loved the way she paused at each syllable when pronouncing it. Mar-tin-ique, with the accent on the last syllable.

It sounded so exotic. I knew nothing about this place, other than it was an island in the lower Caribbean and it had something to do with France. The economy in the US was a little depressed so charter business was slow at the time. Oftentimes, days, even weeks, would go by between trips. So to be assigned to two trips in one day was a special gift. I was invigorated with the adrenaline rush of making a second trip on the same day. I was eager to go to a new place, and my preflight duties now came more quickly.

Customers paid a lot of money for a Learjet charter and the most important thing to them was the convenience and speed. It doesn't matter if they themselves were late; once they arrived at the airport, they expected us to be ready so they could just step on board the plane and go. Some customers even liked us to start the first engine as they stepped aboard. It only saved a few seconds, but more important to them, the visceral sound of a groaning jet engine being started upon their appearance was an intangible thrill of private jet travel.

The Lear 24 was a simple airplane and it was designed for quick turnarounds but there was one exception. The fifth fuel tank was located not in the wings but in the rear of the fuselage just behind the aft pressure bulkhead. The fuselage tank had a capacity of 840 pounds of fuel. It only gave us an extra 45 minutes of fuel but because the Lear was a thirsty airplane, it was an important 45 minutes. The only way to fill it was by pumping fuel from the wing tanks using the onboard fuel pumps. It was a simple but time consuming process and I began on it right away.

I entered the airplane but instead of climbing in the cockpit, I slid into the cabin, knees first, and reached into the cockpit. I turned on the battery switch, which powered up the fuel panel. I checked the wing tanks by toggling the same knob that had kept Rags so preoccupied on our first leg. I did this to ensure we had enough to start the transfer and not run the pumps dry. I quickly flipped the fuselage transfer switch to "Fill." The ramp was quiet and I heard the electrical servos behind me cycling valves and activating pumps to begin the fuel transfer. I checked my watch and got back into the cockpit to set up for the flight.

One of my duties included calculating our takeoff speeds. This was going to be a long flight, right at the extreme edge of the airplane's capability. With all the extra gas, and people, we would be at our maximum allowable takeoff weight. And our takeoff speeds were always different depending on our weight. The heavier we were the faster we would need to accelerate to gain flying speed.

The faster the airplane flew, the more lift the wing produced. That was really no different than any other airplane but the Lear had an especially thin wing, designed to optimize high speed flight. That type of wing didn't produce a lot of lift at low speeds, and just after lift off most of our performance would still be relying on the sheer thrust of the engines.

Once the airplane accelerated, we would transition from the mechanical energy of the engines over to kinetic energy where the wings were doing a lot of the work; but that wouldn't happen until we were well in the air and passing 250 knots.

You didn't just yank a Learjet off the ground and get it on the wing. You had to rotate smoothly and transition to kinetic energy slowly.

If we rotated too soon, the sudden increase in our angle of attack would sharply increase our drag and slow down our acceleration significantly. There had been accidents in other jet airplanes when the airplane would just continue down the runway, nose high. That was a high drag situation and the airplane simply wouldn't fly as it headed down towards the end of the runway.

Rotating too late wasn't good either. It used too much runway accelerating and made your initial climb angle too flat. No, the airplane had to be rotated at the exact right speed.

At heavy weights, there was less margin for error and the airplane had to be flown as precisely as possible. Therefore, my most important calculation was our Vr or rotation speed. With that in mind, I gave the takeoff calculations some extra attention to ensure I got the runway data and takeoff speeds exactly right.

A fuel truck pulled up and parked behind the airplane. It looked brand new and had a white cab with a polished aluminum fuel tank. In the midday sun, the truck sparkled like the airplane. Emblazoned on the side of the tank was the logo "Phillips 66."

A teenager jumped out and I got out of the cockpit myself to meet the driver. He was of medium height and had thin blond hair framing his pink face. He was wearing the same white shirt with the vertical blue and red vertical stripes as Benny. His name patch read "Scott."

He trotted over to me and his clear blue eyes glowed in a friendly way. Like many of the other ramp workers at the airport, Scott was a light airplane pilot aspiring to make it to the airlines someday. It was a common way for civilian pilots to get started in the industry. Hell, pumping gas at the airport in Pompano Beach was my first job in aviation, as well.

He stopped right in front of me. "Top it off, right?

"Yeah, Rags said to pack a tip."

"Yeah, that's what I figured." And he turned back to the truck.

Packing a tip was a fueling procedure peculiar to the Learjet to ensure there were no air bubbles in the fuel tanks, so we could fill every possible space in the tank with fuel.

The problem with the Lear — and there seemed to always be some problem that needed a workaround — was that it had exceptionally high wing loading. What this meant in layman's terms was that the Lear had short and thin wings. Everything in aircraft design is a tradeoff. This high wing loading made the airplane very fast but also more difficult to maneuver. It also meant there wasn't a lot of space for fuel in the wings, hence the addition of the tip tanks.

So for long trips, where we wanted every bit of space in the tanks filled with fuel, crews had developed an arcane process of packing a tip to get rid of any air bubbles in the fuel tanks. And I was told to supervise this process.

Of course, supervise was a strong word since Scott had done this procedure many times and this was my first.

I followed him over to the truck and he talked me through it. "The Lear 24 is a short range airplane. It was designed for one or two hour hops around the Midwest and California." He paused to give me a geography quiz. "What's the bad part about being in Fort Lauderdale?"

He didn't wait for my answer.

"We are at the bottom of a 400 mile long peninsula. Most of the places our customers want to go are cities up north like New York or Chicago. They are within the range of the Lear but only barely. On paper you can make it but you're always sucking fumes when you get there. And in the winter when the weather is shitty up there, you won't have enough gas to divert to an alternate."

I then played my own geography game.

"OK, but being on the bottom of Florida then we're closer to the Caribbean destinations, right?"

"Well, same deal. On paper, yes, we're closer but they're still pretty far away. The Caribbean is a big place. And you don't have a lot of good alternates. You'll see soon enough."

Scott was not yet 20 years old but he knew who he was.

Getting back to the task at hand, I was given a lesson in the tradeoffs involved in airplane design. Bill Lear's obsession with simplicity made for a fuel system that was both plain and light in weight, thereby saving several grandmothers. However, counterintuitively, this simplicity in design caused some complexity for the people working on the airplane. Unlike larger jets that had a single point fueling receptacle that allowed all the fuel tanks to be filled simultaneously, the Lear had only traditional fuel caps on the top of each tip tank.

The fuel truck had two hoses. Scott pulled one hose from its reel. It was heavy and cumbersome and he dragged it across the ground with a mighty effort to the left tip tank and lay it on the ground. He then went back to the truck and dragged the second hose to the right tip tank.

"Fueling the Lear looks simple but if you fill one side first, all that weight in the tip tank will make the whole plane lean over like a drunken sailor. If I was alone, I'd have to go back and forth about a hundred times adding just a little bit so the airplane doesn't tip over. Not only is that more work it takes too long. That's where you come in.

"How's that?"

"Grab a hose and start pumping."

With my new promotion to copilot, I had thought I wouldn't have to do dirty work anymore but as it would turn out in the world of Florida Learjet charter it was, indeed, the copilot that did most of the dirty work. Copilots were paid for flying but we were also a source of free labor for anything else that needed doing. And right then, my labor was needed to help with the fueling.

I reluctantly picked up the dirty hose and placed the nozzle in the tank receptacle as Scott went back over to the other tip tank. I waited for his signal. Once he started pumping on his side I squeezed the handle of the fuel nozzle and a gush of straw colored jet fuel rushed into the tank. The tank was empty and I was greeted by the sound of fluid splashing against hollow aluminum. As the tank filled, waves of the oily stench rose into my face. Unlike gasoline, jet fuel is a close cousin of diesel fuel and it has the same greasy makeup, which began to cling to my already sweaty clothing.

Jet fuel weighs almost seven pound per gallon and as the tanks filled, the airplane settled slowly and evenly on her landing gear struts. Even with two hoses, the process was slow and prone to having air trapped in the various baffles. I had to pause several times to allow the fuel to gurgle its way deeper into the tanks. After standing in the hot sun for about 15 minutes the fuel was right up to the lip of the tank opening and the airplane was sitting about one foot lower than before. Laden with full tanks, the Lear 24 was now carrying a burden of almost 6,000 pounds of fuel.

The tank looked to be full but our job wasn't over.

Scott came over to my side of the airplane.

"Now we have to get all the air bubbles out."

He jumped on the tip tank, straddling the tank like a bronco. He then jumped up and down, jostling the fuel to break any air bubbles. After a minute of this strenuous and somewhat embarrassing activity, the tank gurgled indicating the tank had made more room. The fuel level dropped enough so we were then able to add another 30 gallons. But he still wasn't done.

"The fuel cap is on the side of the tank, not on the top. Even after we filled it up as much as we can, there's still empty space at the very top of the tank. Now, we'll pack the tip tank. Just latch the cap tight and we'll transfer fuel from the other side to fill the very top of the tank."

"That's about 400 extra pounds," he announced. My pilot brain translated that into about an extra 20 minutes of gas.

Once we had packed the tip, Scott walked back to the fuel truck, pressed an electrical button and each hose retracted into their respective reels, coiling and slithering like two monster black pythons obediently returning to their lairs. While I waited for him to prepare the paperwork, I noticed a dog eared paperback in the cab of the truck. It was in French and even with my pitiful high school French, I was able to make out the title, *Terre des Hommes* by Antoine de Saint-Exupéry.

He quickly finished the fuel slip, which I signed, verifying I had accepted exactly 541 gallons of aviation turbine fuel, Type Jet-A, from the Phillips Petroleum corporation.

I returned to the cockpit to complete the last of my preflight duties when a yellow Cadillac Eldorado screeched around the corner of the hangar and entered onto the ramp area. Without breaking its momentum, the driver continued his swift turn and jerked to a stop in a parking spot labeled "Chief Pilot." It was John Coe.

The driver got out and yelled across the ramp in my general direction. "I'll be right over!"

As opposed to Rags, Coe was dressed in the fashion of the day. He was wearing a red polo shirt, and Gucci loafers peeking out from underneath the flare of perfectly hemmed Calvin Klein jeans. His wavy chestnut brown hair was brushing his collar. It was a bit too long and shaggy for a pilot. His hairstyle was in sharp contrast to the close cut precision of Ragsdale's thin gray hair. Coe also looked like he was dressed for the local yacht club. However, unlike Andrews and me, Coe had some wealth and was, in fact, a member of the local yacht club. Coe was also tall, about the same height as Rags. I made a mental note that as small as the Lear Jet was, most of her pilots were large men.

I glanced at my watch and figured the customer should be here soon so I quickly finished up my preflight. I called for our ATC clearance but at this time of day the frequency was much busier with airliners calling for their own clearances. I had to fight to get my request in the queue. Most of the airliners were heading to the north. Air Traffic Control was busy because they were all getting extensive re-routes different from their intended routes. Conversely, we were heading to a much more remote stretch of airpace and just as Rags predicted, we were cleared all the way to Fort de France airport just as we requested.

A great advantage enjoyed by Learjet pilots was that the airplane flew much higher than airliners. Our usual operating altitude was between 41,000 and 45,000 feet. At those altitudes, we had most of the airpace to ourselves and hence, we could fly wherever we wanted, unimpeded by the congested airspace in the mid 30,000 foot range, which was heavily populated by airliners. We always got the routing we wanted and, even better, after takeoff, ATC frequently granted us direct clearances to our destinations. Given that we always seemed to be tight on fuel, the ability to go direct was always a welcome event.

Coe had disappeared in the flight office and was likely taking care of some last minute dispatch issues. While I waited, I reached for the navigation charts. There were several thick leather binders jammed tightly between the two pilot seats. Each binder contained detailed information on hundreds of airports. The airports were listed alphabetically by city name. I flipped through the tissue thin pages and found that even though I was told we were going to the island of Martinque, we were actually going to the airport serving the city of Fort de France. It had one runway, 9800 feet long, with an elevation above sea level of 16 feet and a cautionary note about high terrain to the north of the airport. The island only had one airport and that airport had only one runway. If for some reason we couldn't make it in, the next closest diversion airport was Guadeloupe, about 100 miles to the north of Martinique.

I then opened the Pilot's Guide to the Caribbean, an almanac listing in exhaustive detail anything a pilot would need to know about operating an airplane in the Caribbean. I saw that Martinique was not a colony but legally, a part of France. As I read, I was further instructed that there were several resorts located on the island and nude sunbathing was popular. Martinique offered some of the best cuisine in the Caribbean. Gauguin painted there in 1887. It sounded great but unfortunately the trip was just a drop off. We were just refueling and heading right back home.

While I was preoccupied with fueling, the rest of the ground crew had already given the airplane a quick wipe down and vacuumed the interior. I still had a minute and it was my job to give the cabin a last minute check. I squirmed out of the hot cockpit to wipe some dust off the passenger window-sill. I was pleased to see the cabin could now pass a military inspection. At that point in my career, I was graded more on my general affability and house-keeping skills rather than my actual flying abilities so little gestures like this counted for a lot. I climbed back in the cockpit and waited.

Chapter 12

....

Flying the Beautiful People

A burgundy Mercedes sedan passed through the gate and drove up to the airplane. The car was driven by a chauffeur. A handsome couple got out of the rear seat and they were dressed as though they were heading to a photo shoot for a fashion magazine. They were both in their mid 40s. The man was wearing white pants, a yellow cashmere blazer, and a well-pressed open collar blue shirt. The woman was wearing an orange halter neck jumpsuit. Even in the midday heat, they looked crisp and I felt self conscious about my own disheveled appearance. After preparing for my second flight of the day in the noontime heat, I was soaking wet from the humidity; and after wrestling with the fuel hose, grimy and smelled of Jet-A kerosene.

As they walked to the airplane door, Coe came out of the flight office lobby. He had changed into the standard pilot uniform of black pants, white shirt and epaulets. However, the Gucci loafers remained. He intercepted the beautiful couple by the nose of the airplane and greeted them with a wide grin. It seemed like they knew each other and they exchanged small talk with no indication that only a minute or two ago, both Coe and I had been rushing like maniacs in preparation for their arrival. They had only one leather satchel. Many of our customers never traveled with luggage. They often had an entire separate wardrobe waiting for them at their getaway vacation homes. Cumbersome luggage was for the middle class.

The passengers boarded and took their place side by side in the rear most row. It was a small settee facing forward. It was a small space but they were leaning against each other. They clearly liked each other and didn't seem to mind the intimacy.

Coe followed the passengers and closed the cabin door. He had his own satchel, which he tossed up into the cockpit. It was made of a rich brown leather and was about the size of a school textbook. It was a standard issue for every Lear captain. It contained cash, credit cards, and all the required documentation for each flight. He then slid into the left seat as gracefully as Rags did just a few hours ago. Compared to my own clumsy performance, I saw that I still had some learning to do.

With the door closed, the heat was rising in the cockpit. Coe smelled faintly of cologne and I smelled of sweat and jet fuel. He took a quick survey of the instrument panel and immediately saw something he didn't like.

We hadn't even exchanged introductions.

"Why isn't the air conditioning on?"

He reached over in front of me, and snapped the cabin air switch to "cool." A fan in the back of the passenger compartment came to life and cold air immediately poured into the cabin.

"I thought you had to have an engine running to run the air conditioner."

Or, at least, I thought that's what Rags said.

And then it occurred to me: "Did Rags keep the air conditioning off intentionally as a power trip, when he was giving me his drawing a line down the cockpit briefing?"

Coe seemed uninterested in my musing. Before I could give it a second thought, he started his own preflight ritual. He reached for the fuel selector gauge switch and rotated it through each position. The same ritual repeated by thousands of Lear pilots, millions of times. Left tip tank…left main tank… fuselage tank…right main tank…right tip tank. When selected to the right tip tank, the needle was noticeable higher than the other four tanks. Scott's handiwork packing the tip tank has given us a few extra minutes of fuel.

Coe grunted his approval, "Before start checklist."

Rags was there to monitor our engine start and give us the salute. And just as we did earlier in the morning we started the left engine only. I got a taxi clearance and Coe advanced the power. It was over 90 degrees and the black asphalt ramp by now was much softer. We were heavy and only operating on one engine to save fuel. In order to break free of the sticky asphalt Coe had to advance the power much more than usual. The shriek of our single engine straining against the asphalt was noticeable even inside the cabin. Outside, the noise must have been painful as everyone was holding their ears waiting for us to pass. The airplane broke free and Coe began his turn immediately by swinging the nose hard to the right towards the taxiway.

Just as we turned away I saw Benny run through the airport gate. Unlike his typical sharp dressed demeanor, he was disheveled. He ran up to Rags and began gesturing wildly but Rags turned away to shield his body against our impending jet blast. Conversely, Benny seemed unaware he was about to be hit with a flood of scorching air from our tailpipe. We continued our turn and they disappeared out of my field of vision. My attention turned to my duties at hand.

Fort Lauderdale was still using Runway 9 Left for departures. The same as this morning, right into the prevailing winds. Taking off to the east was going to point us in the direction of Martinique immediately after takeoff, which will save us some fuel. But we still had to taxi about a mile and a half to get to the end of the runway and with this long flight ahead of us, there was an increased sense of urgency to get airborne. Coe was taxiing out much faster than Rags this morning but this was an entirely sensible way of managing our endurance. The less fuel we burned out the tailpipe here on the ground meant that much more would be available to us in the tanks three hours from now.

As we approached the end of the runway, Coe again repeated the same habit of every Lear Jet pilot. He toggled through the fuel gauges three more times checking and re-checking the fuel. As we approached the end of the runway, there was a Braniff Airways 727 on final approach. It was painted solid orange, one of Braniff's iconic paint schemes developed in the 1970s. In 1982, Braniff was probably the most glamorous airline in the United States and they were near the top of everyone's list as a dream job. However, at the time, neither of us realized that Braniff was just one month away from shutting down and placing another couple thousand pilots in the unemployment line.

Coe slowed down his taxi speed just enough so the Braniff jet would pass over the threshold just as we ourselves approach the end of the runway. It is a truism that a pilot will always stop what they are doing to watch an airplane go by; and we both scrutinized that pilot's landing technique as the glistening airliner swept past us with a muffled roar.

Satisfied we would be able to takeoff without any delay, Coe started the second engine while we were rolling and he then called for the before take-off checklist.

He swung the airplane around to face the runway hold line and slowed to a crawl.

And it turned out, Coe was an even more efficient steward of fuel than Rags. We were number one for takeoff and we had only burned 200 pounds.

Chapter 13

Into a New World

Coe had timed our taxi perfectly. As we rolled up to the runway hold line there was another airliner about seven miles out on final approach but the gap was big enough for us to squeeze through. The control tower saw the gap and cleared us for an immediate takeoff. Without having to stop short of the runway, Coe used our momentum on the airplane to swing the airplane onto the runway and lined up on the centerline of Runway 9 Left. Just before applying full power, Coe adjusted the heading bug on his compass indicator to 115 degrees, a heading of southeast. It was a visual reminder to turn to that heading immediately after takeoff. That course would take us over Bimini, just like this morning's trip to Nassau. But now we would continue for another two and a half hours, along the spine of the Bahamian archipelago. With only one slight course correction after passing Nassau, we would maintain this heading to the southeast for the next 1300 nautical miles.

As Coe applied power, things on this takeoff moved much more slowly. Perhaps, because we were heavier than the earlier takeoff to Nassau trip or maybe I was more used to the acceleration. No matter. Once we rotated and lifted off, I was again behind the airplane. I made the same bumbling radio calls and I had to be reminded by Coe to keep an eye on the cabin temperature or else the cabin would have become cold soaked as we climbed into -40 degree temperatures.

Air Traffic Control cleared us to climb unrestricted up to Flight Level 410. And once we leveled off, I checked the clock. Even at our maximum takeoff weight, we had leveled off in just 12 minutes from brake release. I did the math. That was more than 3,000 feet per minute, even at our maximum allowable takeoff weight.

Coe was still hand flying and, like Rags, he flew the airplane smooth and straight. I began to think Andrews was wrong and the airplane was much more stable to fly than its reputation. Pilots like to do that: exaggerate the complexity of their job to make themselves look better. So, yes, I was sure that once my turn came at the controls I would have no trouble with it.

Once we leveled off, he kept the throttles at full power and allowed the airplane to accelerate. As the airplane accelerated, he then reached for the windshield heat switch. The switch controlled a flow of hot air from the engines to a vent at the base of the outer windshield. He tapped it lightly and I felt a slight bump in cabin pressure as air was diverted to heat the windshield.

Unlike Rags, who was mostly silent, Coe talked as he flew. As the airspeed needle crept higher, he started.

"This airplane has a pitch response different from what you are used to.

"The engines are placed higher than the center of gravity so a thrust increase causes a pitch down and a thrust decrease causes a pitch up. It's the opposite of propeller driven airplanes. The opposite of what you were trained to do."

By now, the mach indicator was nudging up against the red line of 0.82, meaning we were flying at 82% of the speed of sound.

"Watch what happens when I reduce to cruise power."

To demonstrate, he reduced power to 90% and took his hands off the yoke. I found this disconcerting. I wasn't comfortable flying at such a high altitude anyway and given the airplane's reputation, I waited for the airplane to roll over out of control. Instead, the airplane was docile. It wobbled a little but the airplane's natural stability kept us level. However, he was right about the pitch. With the power reduction, the nose did pitch up. The opposite of what I would have expected but the airplane wasn't as fearsome as I thought. I would just have to learn its quirks.

He reached back to the yoke and gently squeezed in a little forward pressure to maintain altitude. He continued to hand fly rather than engage the autopilot.

"Keep your eye on the cabin temperature. It's starting to get a little chilly. Crack the heater valve a little more. If the cabin gets cold soaked, you'll never catch up with it."

On the far right side of the instrument panel was the cabin heat valve, which modulated the amount of hot engine air into our heat exchangers. It was one of the few switches out of the captain's reach. Meaning it was one of the few controls the designers entrusted solely to the copilot.

I toggled the switch. It controlled the amount of bleed air heating the cabin and with a flick of my finger a soothing flow of warmth crossed my ankles.

Coe continued, "Once the power is stable then the control inputs are normal. You just have to figure out the right touch to finesse it. It is a high workload airplane. No doubt about that. You always have to fly it, and at altitude you have to be extra careful. Not only do you have to baby the flight controls, you have to do the same with the engines. The turbines themselves can take a lot of abuse, but the problem is that they are fast to respond. If you push in too much power to correct your speed then they'll come on too strong and then you'll get a nasty oscillation. At altitude, just fly the airplane as gently as you can. There's not much air at this altitude so there isn't much margin for error. Flying it can be like balancing a broomstick on your fingertip. It's a balancing act. Just think light pressure. Just squeeze in your control inputs."

I tried to take it all in and was able to ask one semi-cogent question.

"Why did you start the windshield heat so soon? Rags didn't open it until we started our descent."

"We do most of our flying in hot and humid areas. On a long leg like this, if you don't preheat the windshield it will get cold soaked. Just like everything else with the Lear, you have to stay way ahead of the airplane. Unless you keep the windshield warm the entire flight, once you descend into the humidity the windshield will completely fog over. Even if you do preheat the windshield for several hours ahead of time, you'll be lucky to have just a four inch hole to see through."

Coe continued with his tutorial but after about an hour and a half, he tired of talking. We had reached that point in every flight when the workload had lightened, the conversation had run its course, and each pilot was left with their own thoughts.

Still traveling at 420 knots, almost 500 miles per hour, we were now over the southern Bahamas. This airspace was under the control of Miami Center's deep ocean sector. I had never been this far south before and while we were still under Miami's control, we were about to leave their area of radar coverage. Once they handed us off, we would leave the modern infrastructure of the United States behind us. Ahead of us was a place more similar to what early aviation pioneers experienced. It was not just a different world but a different time.

The air traffic controllers through most of the region south of Miami were using technology from the 1950s. For aviators, it was a place without any guidance from the ground. A place with no radar facilities and limited navigational aids.

We now needed to make position reports at designated fixes along the way so the ground controllers could track our progress. However, in this remote part of the world, position reports were only a formality because the airspace was mostly empty and oftentimes, the air traffic controllers only had a limited interest in what we were doing. As we continued south, we would be on our own.

I looked down again at the ocean below us. The Bahamian archipelago sits on a shallow limestone platform perched on the edge of the Atlantic Ocean. The aquamarine water there averaged only 20 feet deep and the white sandy ocean bottom was clearly visible from our altitude. Just like earlier in the day when passing Bimini, each island was a green and white gem and the Bahamian chain created a necklace floating in the placid waters. Each color sparkled from the reflection of the tropical sun creating a rainbow of blue, green, and aquamarine below us. The sun was directly overhead, brilliantly orange, and it dominated the cloudless blue sky.

Many of the ancient cultures considered the sun a masculine god due to its brilliance and potency. However, before the rise of patriarchy, cultures even more archaic considered the sun a feminine god, the giver of warmth and life. Today, the sun's rays were pouring through our large cockpit windows, and as I leaned my forehead against the windshield, I was of both minds. It was minus 40 degrees outside but in our small cocoon, we were bathed in a warm kaleidoscope of color, all a product of the sun's power and benefice.

I looked to the back of the cabin. Our passengers had finished their bottle of champagne and were asleep. The husband had taken off his jacket and was curled up with his head on his wife's lap. Her hand was draped gently on his shoulder.

The radio crackled to life and called my attention. It was Miami Center.

"Lear 55 Whiskey. I show you approaching Guana intersection. Radar service terminated. At Harde intersection, call San Juan Center on frequency 124.35."

I dutifully responded and checked in with San Juan Center, who, in turn, cleared us to continue on our filed flight plan.

Coe was still hand flying as we continued on our southeast heading. The air was smooth and the airplane was tracking straight as we passed Grand Turk. It was here where the seafloor dropped off sharply and the nature of the sea itself changed. We had left behind the inviting waters of the Bahama Banks. Instead, the deep waters of the Puerto Rico Trench lay ahead. In those waters, the ocean floor dropped 28,000 feet and the ocean became cobalt dark. Not only did the nature of the ocean change but as we progressed south I would find that the nature of the people changed also. And it would be near this patch of dark ocean, where I would someday make a harrowing escape.

Ahead of us, the nature of the land mass changed as well. The Bahamas were a chain of flat sandy shoals that barely rose above the ocean surface, and were not, geologically speaking, part of the Caribbean The Caribbean region itself was made up of two major archipelagos, The Greater and Lesser Antilles. The Bahamas resided in a placid geologic zone but the Antilles sat atop the Caribbean Plate. It was a region where several tectonic plates clashed and was home to intense seismic activity, volcanoes and frequent earthquakes. The Antilles were a sharp and jagged ring of volcanic islands thrusting above the deep ocean floor.

Over the millennia they had been home to several cultures, First were the Taino, who migrated from South America. Then there were the Carib people, also from South America, who migrated a few centuries later and mostly displaced the Taino. The Spanish were the first Europeans to land in the Caribbean and themselves, quickly displaced the Carib people and the few remaining Taino. The Taino were more peaceful and willing to cooperate with the Spanish; the Carib were more warlike and less inclined for cooperation. No matter, the end result for both was the same.

Once the rest of Europe found out about the Antilles, a mad land grab followed. Expeditions and settlements followed quickly, first by the English and French, then the Dutch and Danish. And each of those European groups brought in African slaves to repopulate the plantations. Of course, like in every era, there were the pirates who bore no national allegiance, but fed off of the wealth generated in the region. And like the tectonic plates, these opposing cultural forces had clashed over the centuries.

It was what is up ahead, in the area we call the Deep South, that I would find that many of the rules I learned would no longer apply. As a pilot, there were many airports nestled against high mountains in the region forcing me to learn a different set of survival tactics. It would require a careful threading between the established rules of the road and the stark realities of the topography. As a man, cultural differences would also require a careful balancing between my old standards of behavior and the stark realities of surviving in the region.

Chapter 14

Deep South

We passed over Puerto Rico quickly and they handed us off to Piarco Control leaving the United States far behind us.

Piarco Control was located in Trinidad and they were responsible for all the air traffic over the Lesser Antilles. This was airspace with no radar coverage. It meant that the ATC controllers couldn't see where we were and that we had to give them regular position reports advising them of our progress. It meant we were no longer under the watchful eye of a fellow airman who could look out for us. And for some pilots so inclined, it also meant they could pretty much do whatever they wanted without anyone knowing the wiser.

I made the first position report to Piarco and compared the chart to what I saw outside. We were over St. Kitts, with Guadalupe coming over the horizon. We still had almost 400 flying miles to Martinique, about an hour away, and all of it was over water. We had less than an hour to landing but we had a decision to make before we could continue. We had to be certain we had enough fuel to make it to Martinique.

Coe cycled through the fuel indicator switch again checking the status of each tank.

I wasn't sure why he was checking fuel again because he had to have checked it a dozen times in the last hour alone. Rags had done the same thing. We emptied the fuselage tank immediately after takeoff so it was empty. The tip tanks had also long since been drained dry. Nonetheless, he checked all five tanks. I watched his progress and I saw our wing tanks were still full, about 2500 pounds of fuel. I checked the fuel flow meter. At this altitude, we were only burning about 1200 pounds per hour so I figured we still had about two hours of gas. But I was wrong.

Coe then reached over to tune in to a new frequency on the number two radio. He closed his eyes and cocked his head as though he was listening intently. After a couple minutes he snapped the radio switch off.

"That was the Martinique weather advisory. It's visual flight conditions down there. There's a scattered layer of clouds at 3,000 feet and the visibility is seven miles. We'll be able to get in OK."

I respond as a neophyte would. "Well, we still have 2500 pounds. That gives us plenty to head back to St. Croix if we can't get in."

Coe grunted a laugh.

"That's what you think. This isn't anything like you are used to. The Lear is all about speed and altitude."

He then repeated the same mantra as Ragsdale.

"You need to spend as much time as possible as high as possible; and as fast as possible. We burn so much gas all the time you always need to be going fast to make the fuel burn worth it. We're in our element in the thin air at altitude. Once we start down, our fuel flow goes through the roof. Down low, that 2500 pounds will go fast. That's why you never descend unless you know you can get into your destination. Remember that. Always know you can safely land at your destination before you start down. Because once you are down low, you run out of options real fast."

He then explained his logic as he committed us to landing in Martinique.

"We've got 2500 pounds. I figure we'll burn another 1000 before landing, maybe a bit less. There is only one runway there so if an airplane ahead of us crashes and blocks the runway we're screwed, but that's pretty low odds. We should land with 1500 pounds. That's not enough gas to divert but it's still legal. The weather is good there, so let's press on."

With no other traffic in the area, Piarco gave us clearance direct to Fort de France and a descent to 3,000 feet. Coe retarded the throttle back to idle and he pitched down to accelerate to maximum descent speed. Like earlier in the day descending into Nassau, we came down like a speeding bullet.

We approached Fort de France uneventfully but as we descended into the hot and humid air, as predicted, the windshield began fogging over. Despite Coe's best attempt over the last three hours at keeping the windshield warm, the windshield had become cold soaked and in the humid air, the windshield defrosters just couldn't keep up. Coe reached towards a compartment by his left elbow and pulled out a large cotton towel. While flying with one hand he used his free hand to mop up the condensation on the windshield. Once the windshield was cleared he kept the towel on his lap.

"There's a towel under your seat. Start wiping your windshield dry. Otherwise, it's going to start dripping all over the cockpit."

I dutifully complied as instructed.

Passing through 10,000 feet we were deep into the thick tropical air and we were both doing our flying duties one handed. The other hand being occupied almost continuously mopping and re-mopping a continuous flow of dripping condensation. Once we wiped, the windshield fogged again in less than a minute. The only part of the windshield that remained clear was a small 8 inch diameter spot immediately in front of the defroster vent. Other than that, the windshield was essentially opaque despite our continuous efforts to wipe it clean.

Thirty miles from Fort de France, Piarco handed us off to Martinique Approach Control who then cleared us for the approach and landing to the east. Outside the verdant green island beckoned but inside we only had a glimpse of the airport through our little periscope holes so we continued mostly flying the airplane on instruments. We lowered our gear and flaps to begin our final descent and Coe alternated even more frantically between flying and wiping.

However, for the very last minute or two before landing, he needed two hands to land the plane, one for the control yoke and the other to modulate the throttles. As a result, he couldn't keep his windshield clear during the last critical miles before touchdown. I had two hands free but the angle was awkward so I couldn't reach over to clean his side for him..

With less than 30 seconds to touchdown he gave the windshield one last vigorous wipe, creating just enough visibility to make the landing. He timed it so his last wipe would still give him enough visibility while still having both hands free to fly the airplane. I quickly realized that the ability to wipe the windshield clean and fly accurately at the same time was one of the more important skills required to be an expert Lear Jet pilot.

Even with all that wiping, Coe had to crane his neck down and to the right to direct his vision through the peephole he so diligently created. Despite the challenge, he made a perfect landing and he taxied in with one hand still dedicated to wiping the windshield clean.

We arrived at the passenger terminal and opened the door into the steamy midday air of Martinique. Coe and I went inside the terminal to escort our passengers through the byzantine customs and immigration process. Once they were on their way, he disappeared down a long hallway to attend to a different government bureaucracy. That of filing a flight plan for the trip home, leaving me again to preflight the airplane.

I turned back to the ramp to ready the airplane for our return flight and I found it covered in a thick layer of dew. Much the same as a thoroughbred lathered after a strenuous run, the humid tropical air had the entire cold soaked airplane dripping with condensation.

Chapter 15

An Amateur Once Again

Coe was eager to return home so we quickly refueled and with the same sense of urgency as earlier in the day, As we found ourselves poised for takeoff I thought I would soon find myself again at FL 450 enjoying the view but Coe had other plans.

Coe made the takeoff himself and he handed me the controls of the airplane passing through 18,000 feet. I was both eager and anxious to take the controls. At first, I did a passable job. Since we were climbing, I only had to keep the wings level in order to maintain the proper heading. We were heading northwest, back to Florida. The airplane seemed a bit unstable but still easily controlled.

But things became more difficult as we climbed. With every thousand feet the air became noticeably thinner. And with less air, we lost aerodynamic damping. In other words, the higher we climbed, the less stable the airplane became.

High altitude was both our friend and our enemy.. The thin air meant we had less aerodynamic drag and we burned less fuel. But with every foot of altitude, the thin air offered less support and I struggled to fly the airplane.

I climbed initially at 290 knots but as we got higher I then transitioned to Mach speed. We climbed at .70 Mach, 70% of the speed of sound. As we approached level off at 410, I accelerated to Mach .80. We were flying just below the redline of Mach. 82. Coe coached me on high speed flight in the Lear.

"You have to remember, this airplane is way overpowered. The engines can push the airplane much faster than the wings can handle. But if you go past the redline, the shock wave shifts suddenly and you'll get Mach tuck."

I was unaccustomed to the sensitivity in the controls and as he talked I was trying to listen and concentrate on flying. I didn't have enough capacity to do both.

I made a clownish attempt to level off. First, leveling off too soon, descending, then climbing again, overshooting the altitude, then overshooting it on the down side again.

Coe coached me through it.

"Don't over control!"

"Hold what you got!"

"Fingertip pressure only!"

His coaching, while well meaning and accurate, was ineffective due to my own clumsiness. And the oscillations got worse. I continued to abuse the controls and the airplane porpoised wildly. There was a warning bell on the airplane that sounded whenever the airplane deviated more than 300 feet from assigned altitude. I continued to fight the airplane through each oscillation, out of sync with each phugoid. Up and down, then up again. During the ensuing hours, a long succession of altitude warning chimes reminded me of my incompetence.

Once we had passed San Juan, Coe called Miami Center with our call sign and position.

The controller responded with a friendly acknowledgement.

"Roger. This is Miami Center. I have you in radar contact."

With those soothing words, my whole outlook changed. Although I had been enjoying the adventure of unknown airspace, it was reassuring to know we were heading back home. Even this far south, we were under the powerful umbrella of Miami's radar coverage.

But that was only a momentary comfort. I was drenched in sweat despite the cool conditioned cabin air, and I was still fighting the airplane. I had been told that the engineers made stability on the Lear a secondary concern. I was told that to fly the Lear, a pilot had to be on his game. I was told a lot of things about the airplane but I ignored them. I thought it was all just some clever bar room bravado. Here in the real airplane, at altitude and flying up against the redline, I was in way over my head.

Even when I had a bare inkling of what I should do, it was hard just to keep my sweaty grip on the hard plastic yoke. Every now and then when I was at risk of completely losing control of the airplane, Coe would grab the yoke and the airplane immediately settled down into stable flight. This gave me just enough time to wipe my hands dry on the front of my pants. Then he would hand me back the airplane before we repeated the wild process all over again.

I went on like that for hours until, just before descent, Coe mercifully took over the airplane and made the landing in Fort Lauderdale. After we parked the airplane, he choked out a reluctant "nice job" and left me alone to clean up the airplane. It was only about 6PM and the hangar was quiet as I looked around for some rags to wipe down the airplane. Cleaning the jet was my final duty of the day and I was eager to finish it up. I was drained from the day's adventure and ready for bed.

However, Andrews was also inside the hangar after finishing another flight of his own and he had other plans for me.

"Hey, when you get cleaned up, meet us at the office."

Chapter 16

Bahia Cabana

I walked into Bahia Cabana. It was a tiki bar on the Intracoastal Waterway and it was a favorite haunt for local charter pilots that was nicknamed the office. Therefore, when asked where a pilot had disappeared for several hours, the answer given, with only a modest amount of deceit, was always the same, "I was at the office."

Of course, Bahia Cabana wasn't an office at all. It wasn't even a building. It consisted of just a few wooden benches underneath a thatched roof hut, open on all four sides with a commanding view of the New River. It was across the street from the beach and naturally cooled by the tradewinds coming off of the Atlantic Ocean. The only decor were a few tattered beer signs and a collection of rusted automobile license plates that had been nailed to the ceiling by several generations of patrons. It smelled of hot thatched grass and warm ocean air. It was a crummy dive bar but that's what made it so great. Its best attribute, though, was that the bartenders poured the strongest drinks in town. Sitting under its shade was a welcome retreat from the world

Andrews was sitting at a table by the water. The yellow paint on the bench seat was badly chipped and he was shaded by a tattered green umbrella. One of the barmaids was leaning happily against his broad shoulders waiting for the next flash of his megawatt smile.

I sat across from Andrews on the bench and ordered a strawberry margarita.

The smile left his face and he took a deep breath.

"Bad news today."

"Oh yeah, what's that?"

This month's aviation magazine came out. There was an article about a Lear 24 that crashed out in Oklahoma a few months ago.

"What happened?"

"It said they were flying from Wyoming down to Texas. The captain had only 28 hours in type. The investigation board said the captain operated the airplane beyond his experience level."

"OK, I'd say so, but what happened exactly?"

"It said they had an overspeed, and then got into Mach tuck."

"You mentioned Mach tuck yesterday."

"Yeah, but I didn't think it'd come up so soon. It affects every airplane, not just the Lear. As you approach the speed of sound, a shock wave builds up on the wing. No big deal really. It's like a bow wave on a boat. But if you go faster than the engineers designed the airplane to go, you then get an abrupt shift in the shock wave. When that happens, you get a sharp pitch down. Like I said, all airplanes do it, it's just that some have a more severe reaction than others. And depending on the airplane, recovery can be uncontrollable. The higher you go, the less margin for error you have. The pilots really screwed up. They were probably doing something they shouldn't have been doing and then on top of weren't even careful about it."

"What do you mean?"

"If you're doing something wrong, then don't do anything wrong."

 His riddle left me with no additional insight.

"What do you mean by that?"

"Well, accidents don't happen because of just one thing. It's a chain of errors. One thing leads to another, and then another, until you have an accident. I hate to admit it, but there are a lot of guys out there who do shit they aren't supposed to. They push the airplane beyond its limits. I'm not recommending it but if you find yourself in that kind of situation, doing something you aren't supposed to be doing, just make sure you do everything else right. If you're flying at the redline, then make certain the air ahead is absolutely smooth. You don't want to have to juggle too many balls at the same time. And, watch it like a hawk. If things start going bad, you have to act immediately to recover. And stop doing the wrong shit. "

That did not sound like good news and I still wasn't sure what Andrews was trying to tell me. So I spent some time thinking about the implication of what he just said.

The sun was low on the horizon flooding everything around us with its golden rays. I peered straight into the setting sun as I nursed a sip from my frozen drink. The afternoon heat and the alcohol melted me into the chair.

I had been wracked with self doubt since my adolescence and I had desperately wanted to be good at something, and to be a part of something. Unlike what my mother had taught me, it was not enough just to be smart and a nice guy. I was coming to the realization that you had to work hard at being successful. And I was having a hard time with it.

Flying airplanes was easy enough and it offered the adventure I yearned for. It was a magical and alluring combination. And I thought I was good at it. That was, up until this afternoon. But I was all over the sky today. I knew jets were unstable at high altitude but after today's performance, I was wondering if I could perform at this level. And now, it sounded like I was being told that you had to break the rules to survive.

Andrews was facing the entrance and he waved to someone entering. It was Frank Sutton, and Andrews beckoned him over. Sutton was a former Lear captain who made it to the big leagues. I had never met him but knew him by reputation. He had graduated to become a 727 captain for Air Florida, a new airline operating out of Miami. It was the most glamorous and desirable pilot jobs in the area. And they were hiring. Everyone had an application on file with them.

Sutton wore his lofty status casually. He was still in his uniform of black polyester pants and a rumpled white pilot shirt but he had taken off his tie and captain stripes. The cloth epaulet flaps lay loosely to the side hanging down over each sleeve. He was in his mid 30s, medium height with blond hair and blue eyes. He smelled of sweat and stale cigarette smoke, and he seemed tired. Without asking, the barmaid brought him a beer.

I was eager to be introduced to Sutton but none came.

He took a sip and asked Andrews, "I haven't seen you in a while. Still flying the Lear?

"Yeah, still. We were just talking about an accident that happened a couple months ago. The article said for some reason they had an overspeed."

Sutton chortled, "For some reason? Come on, you know exactly what happened."

Andrews was defensive, "We don't know anything yet about the exact cause."

Sutton continued unabated, "Remember a couple years ago? Those guys in a Lear 25 over the Gulf of Mexico? They had an overspeed, too. But it didn't happen by accident. The investigation board said they had a go fast switch installed."

Andrews remained silent.

He looked at me for the first time. "You're new?"

"Yeah, I just started today."

He seemed unimpressed. So, I guessed that was to be the extent of our introduction.

Andrews jumped back in the conversation. "But the go fast switch wasn't the problem. They were up at 450 and got into some turbulence. Then got into a bad pitch oscillation, and lost control. They used spoilers to slow down. Stupid move. That only aggravated the pitch down. They went in almost straight down. It was the pilot's fault."

Sutton ignored Andrews and looked to me again. "Your first day? Who did you fly with?"

"Mr. Ragsdale."

He laughed. "You flew with Rags…on your first trip? I guess they must've been desperate. What did you think of him?"

"He's fine," I demurred.

He filled in the blank for me. "He's a cranky old bastard but there is no better pilot in South Florida. He's a modern day Odysseus."

How's that?

"He ran away from home when he was a teenager and never went back. He's been flying around South America for over thirty years. No one really knows for sure because he never talks about it, and he's been here longer than anyone else. He lives in a crummy apartment on the New River and basically has no life other than flying.

He grew up in Indiana, some little town near Coal City. That much we know.

His dad had a farm supply business or something like that. He wanted Rags to take over the business. But he ran away from home to join the Air Corps. After the war he migrated down here, flying Lockheed Lodestars all around the Andes. I guess he got hooked on the mountain flying. Going back to sell tractors to farmer Jones held no appeal."

I only vaguely remembered my Greek classics. "Yeah, but Odysseus got back home. Right?"

"A lot of pilots are like that down here. They are running from something but once they leave it behind, they just keep on running. They don't know when to stop. Or they can't."

I braved a retort. "What's a go fast switch?

Sutton reached into his shirt pocket and pulled out a fresh pack of Marlboro Red cigarettes. Hard pack with the flip top.

Every Lear pilot who smoked preferred Marlboros Reds and bought the hard pack with the flip top, not the soft pack. It was important to be seen using the hard pack. The only exception to the rule was Rags who smoked Pall Malls.

He tapped the top of the pack against the palm of his hand. It supposedly packed the tobacco tighter but mostly it just looked cool. He then unwrapped the cellophane.

He pulled one out for himself and placed it between the two fingers of his left hand.

With his right hand, he pointed the pack towards us. "Want a Red?"

Andrews waved it away.

I was not a smoker but I accepted one anyway. I figured it would make me part of the club.

Like Rags, Sutton took a long draw, collected his thoughts and began.

"The go fast switch is an illegal installation some people put on their airplane. It does two things, it disables the overspeed warning horn and it also disconnects the stick puller, the computer that automatically slows you down. It's usually hidden under the captain's seat. In any airplane, you never, ever exceed redline. In a propeller driven plane, if you overspeed you may only get a little tail buffet, or worst case, stress the airframe a little. In jets, it's a lot worse because you get Mach tuck. The airplane pitches down suddenly. It's almost uncontrollable and then you fall out of the sky like a trimmed up Coke machine. In a jet, at altitude, it's pure insanity to exceed your max Mach limit..."

He stopped to think about what he just said.

"Jesus... I can't believe anyone would be stupid enough to exceed redline and then be even more stupid to disable the warning system. Especially after so many accidents."

Andrews still defended the airplane, "Test pilots at the factory have had the airplane way over the red line, all the way up to Mach .86."

"Sure, and they knew it was coming, and it was probably perfect daytime conditions....and they were test pilots with PhDs in engineering...and they had perfectly calibrated airspeed indicators... and they probably practiced the recovery several times. It's hardly the same.

What's worse, the old Lear manual had the wrong recovery procedure.

You said they put out the speed brakes? That was the old procedure. It just made the pitch down even worse. Those guys didn't have a chance."

Sutton paused to take another drag on his cigarette and Andrews filled the silence.

"That's not the airplane's fault. Sure, if you push the airplane beyond her limits then it'll bite back but that's true of any airplane. And like you said, extending the speed brakes was the old procedure. It was bad training. You're only as good as your training, and if you haven't had any training, then you're no good. Everyone else has been flying the airplane for years with no problems."

I listened intently. I puffed from my cigarette trying to act nonchalant. But after the third puff, I drew in too deeply.

I tried to tamp down a cough but I couldn't and my convulsion broke the standoff.

Sutton was willing to end the conversation. "Look, the problem is that most charter operators are working on a very low budget. There's not enough business to go around for everyone. Only trust fund babies and the boys can afford to fly right now. Everyone is pushing the airplane, and the regulations, right up to the legal limit to make a buck. And sometimes, they go over the limit. There's minimal training and no room for error. I'll give you that. But the Lear flies like it looks... fast. It is not forgiving of inattention. It must be constantly flown... and flown well. Engineers back in the 1960s didn't really know or care about ergonomics or gentle handling. As far as they were concerned, that was the pilot's problem. They just built the fastest airplane they could. But everyone thinks like they can fly it like their old propeller transports, the airplanes with fat wings and gentle dispositions. That's why they get in trouble."

I chimed in, trying to sound worldly. "Well, life's not fair."

Sutton looked at me. "You're right. Life isn't fair. You know how I know that? Because if life was fair, we should all either be dead or in jail."

He paused and continued to stare at me.

"Congratulations on getting hired kid... I think... Just be careful. Follow the flight manual like it's your bible and don't let your guard down. You're entering the most dangerous phase of your career. You are in way over your head... in more ways than one. And what's worse, you don't even realize it.

You're going to be asked to do a lot of shit you shouldn't be doing. Don't be stupid and you'll be fine."

I had never received much mentoring in my life. In my past, I had mostly just figured out things on my own. As harsh as it was, I found this conversation full of the kind of insight I thought I craved. Charter flying, especially in the Lear, opened up a whole new world for me. Some of my fellow pilots coming out of flight school went to work for the local, small commuter airlines.They had a steady schedule plodding between Miami and Key West. It was more regimented than Lear Jet flying and a lot safer but that kind of flying held no appeal for me. The promise of charter flying in the Lear was that each time the phone rang, I could be going anywhere. To far off and unknown places. It was an irresistible siren call. And now that I was getting a tutorial in the dangers involved, I had a mixed response. I craved the coaching but I mostly ignored it. All this talk of danger was just a show of weakness.

Andrews stood to leave. He said goodbye to Sutton and turned to me,

"Anyway, I talked with Chloe, she said Coe gave you the OK and you were cleared to fly with all the captains. You're going right back out tomorrow. Stop by early. They'll give you a beeper and get your info for payroll. The pay isn't much but you're building jet time. That's what counts. You're flying a trip for Garrett Construction with Walpole. A two day trip, up to Charlotte, then Springfield, Missouri, for an overnight, then home. It's a decent trip and you'll like Walpole. His first name is Ken but everyone calls him Kenny. Don't forget to try the barbecue ribs at the hotel in Missouri."

Andrews paused then laughed heartily. "Oh yeah, by the way, Benny is really pissed off at you. He thinks you stole his Martinique trip today. Good luck with that."

Chapter 17

Validation

I drove home along the beach, breathing the sweet sandy air. It had been a long day. I had been up for about 20 hours but I didn't want it to end. Once I did get home I was tired and eager for bed but I still had one important task left. I went to the top drawer of the battered desk in my small bedroom to take out my most prized possessions. It was my pilot logbook. Like every pilot, it was a detailed diary of all my flying experience. It was a document that I one day hoped to show to an airline interview panel that I had the experience they sought. I sat down in my dirty and smelly uniform and opened it to a blank page and neatly recorded the following.

"Learjet, Model 24B.

Fort Lauderdale-Nassau-Fort Lauderdale-Martinique-Fort Lauderdale.

Turbojet, second in command, 7.8 hours."

And with that entry, it was official. I was a Learjet pilot.

I liked flying the airplane but more importantly this was a new home with my fellow pilots. I had just joined a new fraternity and it felt right. For the first time in my life I felt as though I belonged.

Chapter 18

Apprenticeship

The next few months found me in the regular rotation of flying. However, in the hectic and unpredictable world of charter flying we had no set schedules. This was mainly due to the reality that many of our trips came up on short notice due to some businessman who had a crisis, a poor unfortunate with a medical problem who needed an air ambulance evacuation, or a moneyed playboy who wanted a spur of the moment change of scenery.

Unlike the airlines where the pilots knew their schedules weeks in advance, we always wore a beeper, and oftentimes found ourselves departing for some unknown destination only 30 minutes after a phone call. We flew the trips assigned to us and waited for our turn to fly again. The next trip could be in the same afternoon or it could be a week away. As a result, we never ventured more than a few miles from the airport. To miss a trip, or more importantly, to miss logging precious jet time was inexcusable.

In this world we also never knew who we were flying with until we showed up at the airport. This tumbling world of mixed up schedules allowed me to meet several different captains to whom I would serve in my apprenticeship.

And it was on my second day of Lear flying I was introduced to Walpole, who was to take over the next phase of my initiation. He was 40 years old, tall and slender. He showed up at the airport dressed in conservative business attire.

You see, we had two different uniforms in South Florida aviation. When flying south of the border, we wore the vestments of a traditional airline pilot. In those countries, they still viewed pilots with a high degree of respect, even awe. Wearing a traditional pilot uniform allowed us to walk around the secure areas of the airport with relative impunity; and when negotiating with other uniformed government representatives, our own uniform placed us on a more equal footing However, when flying around the United States, we wore business garb.

For that morning's flight, Walpole wore gray slacks, a starched white shirt with a navy blue tie, and a cashmere navy blazer with brass buttons. He was impeccably tailored and also looked like he was on his way to the yacht club. I was seeing a trend. And unusually for a pilot, he also had a beard, albeit closely trimmed. Walpole was prematurely gray, and the salt and pepper on his head and chin contrasted nicely against his deeply tanned features. If he were twenty years older and wearing tweed, he could have been a retired university professor. His appearance, though, was in contrast to his alter ego. He spent most of his free time at a dive bar on Ravenswood Road and when the charter flying was slow he would supplement his income with stints as a long distance trucker.

On this trip we were assigned a Lear 25. It was essentially the same airplane as the Lear 24, although the fuselage had been stretched four feet to accommodate three extra passengers. This airplane, like so many other 25s, had been modified with the Mark II wing, which made the airplane's handling characteristics much more gentle. Although, the extra fuselage length and associated weight came at a price. The airplane used an ungodly amount of fuel, even by Learjet standards.

Our passengers arrived at 7 AM, exactly on time. Five middle aged men. They were typical of half of our customers. Tired and busy business men who were willing to bear the expense of a private chartered jet because their time was more valuable than the cost. Chartering a Learjet for them was not a way to show off. For them it was a business tool, plain and simple.

They were in the construction business and they looked like construction men. If you took away their coats and ties, they would have been just as comfortable in steel tipped boots and hard hats.

I was already in the right seat and Walpole followed them in and closed the door behind us. Unlike Ragsdale, Walpole kept his jacket on and tightly buttoned around his slender frame even after he settled into his seat.

We were heading to Charlotte, North Carolina where our passengers were to check on one of their projects. It was a short flight but the weather in Charlotte was marginal so we had a full load of fuel. On taxi out, Walpole toggled through the fuel gauges. He was the third captain I had now flown with and all three shared the same nervous tic fiddling with the fuel indicator switch.

Walpole was from Akron, Ohio. And like many Floridians, he moved here as a young man. In his case, he came to attend the College of Aeronautics at Florida Tech. He was formally trained and took a slow and methodical approach to the airplane. He exuded a relaxed confidence, which I found comforting.

As we preflighted the cockpit, he started with my tutorial.

"Do you know what this fuel gauge measures?"

I figure it's a rhetorical question so I just shook my head and grunted a "No."

"This fuel gauge doesn't measure fuel. It measures minutes left to live. The less fuel in the tanks, the fewer minutes you have to live. But there are lots of variables. You can't just say 100 pounds equals ten minutes or whatever. Your fuel burn depends on altitude, throttle movement, power setting, airplane weight. You have to continuously check your fuel flow to see how much you're burning and compare it against fuel remaining. The fuel gauge is like an alarm clock. Once the fuel is gone then the alarm rings. An alarm you never want to hear. So before that happens, you have to get the airplane on the ground."

Then he adds with a chuckle, "Preferably on a runway."

And he repeated the wisdom mentioned by Coe.

"The 25 is a nice flying airplane but even more than the 24, you have to watch your fuel burn. The idea in the Lear... any Lear... is to get high as fast as you can and stay high for as long as you can. Don't start down unless you know you can get into your airport. We usually don't have enough gas for an alternate airport. Once you're down low, you're committed to landing at your destination airport. If you don't think you can get to your destination and might need to go to your alternate, then you should make an enroute stop to get gas. Fuel is life."

It was another early morning departure and we taxied to the end of Runway 9 Left without any delay. I had finished the checklists but Walpole was not done with his own checks.

As he turned on the runway, he recited a litany.

"Spoilers, flaps and trim."

As he recited this short prayer, he looked at and touched the control switch for each of those things.

"Those are the three things that will kill you if they're not set correctly before takeoff. Make sure your spoilers are retracted, and the flaps and trim are set properly. It doesn't matter if you did the checklist. Always check those three things for a second time before each takeoff. The airplane will forgive some other mistakes but just not those."

It was a ritual that, I myself, would learn and use before every takeoff as well.

After takeoff, we climbed quickly to Flight Level 410 uneventfully. Since I was an unknown to him, Walpole elected to fly the leg to Charlotte and I returned to my usual administrative duties talking to air traffic control and monitoring the flight plan.

Just like Rags and Coe, he continued hand flying during cruise flight. The autopilot control panel was in the center of the lower console but it was unused.

"Don't you want to use the autopilot?" I asked.

Walpole threw me the briefest of glances as he chuckled.

"Everybody that believes in using the autopilot, stand on their heads."

"What do you mean?"

"A good pilot tries to reduce the number of unknowns. And that's what we do, we avoid the unknowns. The problem with these early autopilots is you never know how they'll react. They're notoriously unreliable. Not just unreliable, but dangerous."

He paused to stroke his beard with his one free hand.

"There have been at least three fatal crashes recently where the autopilot was suspected to have pitched the airplane down unexpectedly. In each case, the result was a catastrophic loss of control before the pilots could react."

And that was the end of the discussion.

Walpole was unfazed by the lack of an autopilot. He flew the airplane gently at 410 and his altitude never deviated by more than 20 feet, unlike my own erratic display of airmanship the day before. His flying was as precise as Rags and Coe. I didn't think it was possible but he was even more smooth than those two.

After one hour, we had burned 2500 pounds of fuel. And Walpole was right. The airplane did use an enormous amount of fuel. In our first hour of flight, we had already used about 1,000 pounds more than the 24 would have burned. At this point, we were light enough to climb to 450 but instead it was almost time to start down. By now I had a tiny bit of comfort while flying at these high flight levels but since I had never flown north of the Florida state line this was unfamiliar ground to me.

I dialed the frequency for the Charlotte Airport terminal weather advisory, which I dutifully reported to Walpole.

"Charlotte is reporting a low cloud deck at only 200 feet above the surface, and visibility is only 1/2 mile in heavy fog. They say there is patchy ice on the runway."

He seemed unfazed and never responded. We did have enough fuel for an alternate but he made no mention of where it might be.

As we descended, I felt a bit of chill in the cockpit. I reached for the cabin temperature control switch to toggle in some extra heat.

Walpole chuckled again, "That won't do you any good. At low power settings and with freezing temperatures outside, the heater can't keep up." He rolled up the collar lapel of his cashmere coat while I froze in my thin short sleeve cotton shirt.

Thus situated, we proceeded to Charlotte where Walpole made a masterful approach down to minimums, with the anti-skid system cycling us to a stop on the icy runway. The whole experience was another first for me with many lessons learned but I mainly resolved to dress more warmly in the future.

Chapter 19

Seasoning

I did most of my early flying with Coe and Walpole. It turned out, they were not so different. They were both polite to me but I barely registered on their radar. Rather than being an integral member of the crew I was more like a manservant waiting for their instructions. If they were in the mood they might drop a bit of wisdom to quench my thirst for knowledge but often not. Part of their job was to teach me how to effectively fly the Learjet but it was slow going. I continued to be heavy handed on the controls and was too obtuse to pick up the nuances of charter flying. Mostly I learned through osmosis. The Lear was not an easy airplane to fly and her attendants shared their secrets begrudgingly.

Over the following months, I did gain a greater awareness of the world around me and some of its dangers but my sense of adventure was still strong. Every trip was a new adventure. I was exposed to the vast plains of the American Midwest, all of the Caribbean, the congested northeast corridor of the United States, and the Rocky Mountains.

In the congested airspace of the New York metropolitan area I was initiated to the tricky approaches into La Guardia airport. With its short runways and sinuous approach paths it was routinely named the most challenging airport in the United States. The airspace in the northeast United States was congested and the air traffic controllers were much too busy to help novice aviators. The weather in that region was storm prone, but there were always many other alternate airports to choose from if necessary.

We also flew frequently to California and Nevada. The Lear 24 was a short range airplane so on our coast to coast trips we had to make a fuel stop, sometimes two, in the middle of the country. As a result, I learned which airports could fuel us the fastest and get us on our way. In the vast American interior, there were many airports from which to choose. In order to gain our business, each airport had a different gimmick to entice pilots. Of course, each airport promised quick turns of 15 minutes or less. Some airports also offered free steaks and bottles of wine for the pilots. As an even more tantalizing enticement, some companies employed attractive young women who fueled the airplane while wearing hot pants and bikini tops. This was, of course, an irresistible draw. I was surprised to find that Salina in the remotest part of central Kansas was one of the busiest airports in the country. The so-called Salina Flower Girls served dozens of private jets a day, like a truck stop on the old Lincoln Highway. And air traffic controllers in this isolated space often had landing airplanes lined up for miles like at a New York rush hour. Notably, the lowest fuel price was never a consideration when choosing an enroute stop.

The Great Plains of North American stretched for a thousand miles and even at our speed it took hours to cross the midsection of the United States. At 45,000 feet and without mountains or urban smog to obstruct our visibility their flat monotony stretched from horizon to horizon. But on deeper inspection, they revealed their true character.

In 1862, Abraham Lincoln signed the Homestead Act. The law awarded 160 acres of land for settlers willing to work it for five years. It was designed to fill the unoccupied land west of the Mississppi and to, also, thwart the expansion of plantation style slavery.

What was once raw wilderness had been tamed by settlers only a century earlier, with orderly section lines defining property boundaries. Inside the squares defined by those lines were tidy white farm houses nestled in their 160 acre blocks that had been painstakingly tended by the great-grandparents of the current owners. The property lines were straight and honest, just like the people who lived there. And I continued to slowly learn.

About this time, a new captain was added to the rotation.

Farmer had been professionally trained in the Air Force and was a decorated Vietnam War veteran. In short, he was the sort of pilot I idolized in my earlier boyhood dreams. He was a careful and diligent professional, but with his blond hair, blue eyes, and carefree demeanor, he could have just as easily been a lifeguard on the beaches of Fort Lauderdale, which is exactly what he had been before leaving for the Air Force.

Farmer was a furloughed pilot from United Airlines and had found himself flying the Lear to support his young family. On our first trip, we flew to Winfield, Kansas, home to the General Electric facility that overhauled our engines. Once we landed in Winfield, we had a two day wait while the factory technicians changed out our engines. Farmer and I were both of the mindset to explore the region so the local airport operator loaned us a dilapidated station wagon. It had bald tires and a heater that barely worked but it gave us freedom to reconnoitre the local area.

On the ground, the Great Plains were different. It was mid-winter and fresh snow had fallen, covering the land in a dreary sameness. Under a canopy of low-lying monochromatic gray clouds, the immense flatness in each direction was suffocating. Or so it seemed. On closer inspection, the region revealed a diversity that continued to draw us forward.

While wandering aimlessly around the back roads along the Oklahoma border, we stopped at a Mexican restaurant on the side of a lonely dirt road. It was housed in a shabby concrete building nestled in a gravel parking lot. Outside, the landscape was gray and bleak but once we walked inside the smell of salty hot tortillas enveloped us. The menu cover had a drawing of a guitarist serenading a Spanish lady and the bottom was titled "Welcome Amigos!"

It was, indeed, a sincere welcome with the owner offering us heaping portions of warm hospitality, recorded mariachi music, and inexpensive margaritas. Despite the isolation and lack of glamour, it remains one of my fondest memories of flying the Lear.

During this time, I also flew around the entire Caribbean where I learned each island had its own unique culture. Because of the Lear 24's short range we always kept an eye on the distance to each little island we passed. In the Caribbean, it was important to kee

p in mind the location of each safe harbor for our little airplane.

From a performance standpoint, the Lear could do one thing better than any other. Because the Lear was originally designed as a rapid response interceptor against Soviet bombers, it could climb to 41,000 feet in a matter of minutes. Oftentimes, when we were light enough, we would have contests to see who could climb to altitude fastest. My personal record was from sea level to 41,000 feet in 12 minutes using 600 pounds of fuel. For a civilian pilot, the Lear 24 was the closest we could come to flying a jet fighter.

Flying again with Walpole, I experienced my first real go around. It was in Beckley, West Virginia. The airport was shrouded in low clouds and fog. We tried twice to get in and we had to miss the approach twice. We still had enough gas, so we could have lingered a while longer waiting for the weather to improve. However, with so many mountains around and the weather still questionable, we decided twice was enough. Our best course of action was a retreat to Pittsburgh.

We frequently flew trips to New York. It was popular with both the jet setters and the finance people. On back to back trips to New York, we had an airplane with a recalcitrant pressure controller. With Spruance as my captain, we flew the three hours to New York with me working the pressure controller manually. Maintenance thought they fixed it and we departed on a subsequent flight. Climbing out of Teterboro airport, it finally gave up completely and we diverted into Atlantic City. It was my childhood home but it held no attraction for me and I was glad to leave it behind. Once the pressure controller was fixed we continued home at FL 450, sliding serenely over a line of thunderstorms while the airliners below were screaming at ATC for deviations. As I recorded more precious jet time in my logbook, the flying began to blur together.

Each region held its own rewards and each had its own challenges. The economy continued to improve and business got better. Along the way, I learned more about high performance aerodynamics. I learned about ram effect, boundary layer energizers, and vortex generators. I experienced first hand the effects of aileron buzz, the drag curve and Dutch Roll. As part of my studies, I was taught the lessons learned from each airplane accident. I learned why a Lear 24 crashed into the water, just short of the runway, while attempting a night approach into St. Thomas from the west. As a result of that lesson, I overcame the dangers of empty field myopia and black hole approaches.

Speaking of St.Thomas, its airport loomed large in the minds of all jet pilots flying the Caribbean. It had the reputation of being one of the more challenging airports in the region and it had that reputation for several reasons. It did have a short runway with a hill at the eastern end but this alone was not much different than many other airports in the region. Its real notoriety came from a 727 crash a few years prior when the crew botched the approach. They came in fast and landed long. Once they realized their mistake, they attempted a go around but it was too late. There wasn't enough runway remaining to accelerate back to flying speed and they half slid, half flew into a Shell gas station. As you might imagine, the ignition of jet fuel along with automobile gas lit the sky for hours and the smoldering wreckage took weeks to clean up. 37 people died because of that mistake. A black scar was left on the hillside. And for many years, that scar was a stark reminder to all airmen passing by. Both of those incidents in St. Thomas taught me the importance of scrupulous speed control on approach. And that wasn't the only crash site we saw. The entire Caribbean and South American region was littered with the wrecks of all kinds of different airplanes and each crash held a cautionary tale.

I also learned some things not directly related to stick and rudder skills. I learned how to flight plan a trip in my head and to calculate quickly how many fuel stops would be required on a transcontinental flight. I learned that a chain of islands off the coast of Honduras, named Islas del Cisne, translated into Swan Island; and that Charleston, West Virginia, was nicknamed "Charlie West." I learned which control tower operators actually enjoyed it when we did a high speed fly by. I learned that Santa Cruz, Bolivia, had the most avaricious bureaucrats and they were not to be denied. Adding to the malicious reputation of Santa Cruz, it was reported that the Bolivian Air Force had shot down an airplane that did not pay the appropriate bribes before smuggling cigarettes and whiskey into Santa Cruz. And I also learned how to avoid overzealous government inspectors. As I mastered each region my sense of accomplishment increased accordingly.

My fellow pilots and I, we became automatons just following the orders of the dispatcher. Our lives were a constant cycle of answering the beeper, rush to the airport, fly a long day, return home to sleep. Then we would repeat it again the next day, beeper… fly… sleep. It was that way for many months without any break and without any social life. It mattered less and less where we went. With each trip, we made a few extra dollars and we were building up precious jet time for an airline job. That was what we wanted and that is what we did.

I will say, though, there were peaceful moments. We had flown to St. Thomas to drop off a celebrity and we were to pick them up the following week. Normally, we would have flown back to Florida but the customer insisted we keep the airplane close by. I was flying with Allen on that trip. He had grown up sailing on Long Island Sound and was an accomplished sailor. After the first day, trapped in a charmless resort hotel, Allen decided it would be better and cheaper to charter a local sailboat. And after a few phone calls, we found ourselves sailing the Virgin Islands for a week. As it turned out, Allen was not just not an accomplished sailor but an avid diver and an even more ardent drinker. We spent the entire week aimlessly sailing in the daytime and then spending the nights attending impromptu parties, gorging on freshly caught lobster, and going through too many bottles of local rum.

I gained more control and more finesse over the jet. We began to understand each other, the airplane and I. The Lear didn't suffer fools, that was for certain. But I found out she was lovely to fly for those she respected. Because of all that, I came to the mistaken belief that I was growing up.

Chapter 20

First Thunderstorm

Walpole and I were heading home and he was at the controls. We had taken off from St. Louis and had just leveled off at 430, southeast bound. The sun had set behind our tail some time ago and ahead was black, broken only by the lights of Memphis sliding underneath the nose.

Autumn had returned to the Northern Hemisphere and it was during this time of year the earliest of the frigid polar air masses clashed mightily with the warm and moist air oozing up from the Gulf of Mexico. It was these when these two titans met that weather was at its most volatile. These weather fronts were so named because the violence in the air was so intense that meteorologists were reminded of a battleground.

Looking ahead, I peered into the darkness and the night sky seemed flat. The weather briefing we received in St Louis said we could expect to pass through a cold front stalled out north of the Florida panhandle. But so far, the sky was undisturbed.

I turned down my cockpit lights to better adjust my night vision and I placed my forehead against the windshield to scout for any storms.

Nothing.

I waited even longer to let my eyes acclimate and squinted into the blank sky.

On the horizon I saw a flash. It was a faint strobe light in the distance and it was the very top of a squall line peeking over the horizon.

At our cruise speed, we were flying towards a squall line at seven miles a minute.

Walpole saw it as well.

"Looks like a line of weather ahead."

As we drew inexorably closer, reports from other airplanes ahead of us gave us a grim realization of what we faced. The squall line towered well over 50,000 feet and ran along a diagonal line for several hundred miles perpendicular to our course.

Walpole made a dispassionate statement of our predicament.

"We can't fly over it and it's too wide to go around. We are going to have to pick our way through it."

Walpole reached over and turned on the onboard weather radar. At his command, an antenna located in the nose of the airplane woke up and began to swing back and forth probing the night sky with high frequency pulses. The cathode ray tube on the instrument panel took a minute to warm up and after a few sweeps of the antenna, it illuminated the ugly truth ahead of us. The screen glowed a ghostly green with a nebulous image of the storm.

I had little experience in turbulence and even less navigating at night around thunderstorms. I saw only a solid impenetrable mass of terror and I wanted to flee. The more I studied the radar, the more it increased my unease. The frontal boundary was a living thing. As I watched it on the radar, I could see the various cells rising and falling and wrapping around each other like a nest of snakes.

Walpole made a simple statement but his voice was still cold and offered no comfort.

"It looks like there are a few soft spots in the line."

We continued our course towards the squall line. As we approached the lightning flared with increased intensity. First, a single flash, then several flashes in rapid succession. A pause then more flashes. Each flash raised another hair on my scalp. I tried to time the flashes but there didn't seem to be any consistency. It was probably a meaningless gesture but it made me feel better being proactive.

With each flash, the squall line was illuminated and we got a better look at the sinister storm ahead. For a brief moment we could see the cloud formations before they went invisible in the dark. Until now we had been resolutely holding our course but we had reached the time for a decision.

Walpole had used those brief visual sightings along with the ghostly green blobs on the radar screen to piece together a picture in his mind. Walpole pulled his fingers straight back across his steel gray hair. He made no other show of emotion.

"Well, it looks like we have no choice. We're going to have to penetrate the line."

He turned up his cockpit lights on his side all the way to full bright.

"Turn up your cockpit lights on your side all the way. In a few more minutes, you won't need your night vision."

The closer we got, the more the monster seemed to reach out for us but Walpole was unflinching. He only adjusted the antenna tilt to peruse the storm up and down.

With each adjustment, he peered at the radar screen like a seer divining the future with a crystal ball, able to ferret out its hidden secrets. The line looked impenetrable to me but to his trained eye, he was able to think through a plan of action. After a couple more minutes of inspecting the storm with the radar beam, he made a declaration.

"Tell Memphis we want to deviate 20 degrees right of course."

He was still hand flying and once we got permission, he gently banked the airplane to the right.

We flew on for another few minutes and the lightning increased both in frequency and intensity. Each firebolt illuminated the whole cloud like a field of neon gas and each flash brightened the cockpit noticeably.

Walpole turned back to the passengers, those rough edged construction men.

"Hey guys, strap in tight. It's going to be rough for a few minutes."

I stole a look back into the cabin myself.

Four men. Their faces were visible in the dim cabin lighting. Their good natured jocularity had evaporated. Plumes of cigarette smoke streamed through the stabs of light made by the overhead spotlights.Their faces were somber and ashen. In the small Learjet cabin, there was no divider between the cockpit and the passengers. There was no hiding them from the reality we saw. They saw the same light show as us. The difference is that we had been trained for this and we had some control of our fate. It was our job to face the danger. They were just innocents along for the ride.

There was also no hiding our own reactions from them. To keep them calm, we had to remain calm ourselves.

Walpole turned forward again. He peered into his crystal ball radar. "Tell them we want another ten degrees to the right."

"This heading should be though the thinnest part of the line."

We were just a few miles from entering the squall line itself.

Walpole checked his watch and took a deep breath. It was his first show of emotion.

"Storm lights coming on," he said. And as he flipped the switch, a fluorescent light flickered to life and filled the cockpit with a harsh white light.

At this point, there was no need to save our night vision. Just the opposite; the lightning could cause temporary blindness. The storm lights flooded the cockpit with a steady light, brighter than the lightning itself so we didn't have to adjust and readjust our eyes between lightning strikes.

He chuckled. However, I didn't think it was a real show of humor so it didn't do anything to inspire confidence.

"The line is about 30 miles wide here. If we lose the radar, we'll just hold this heading for 5 minutes. We should be out of it by then. At this altitude, we don't have a lot of margin between high and low speed buffet. If we get in a downdraft, I'm not going to chase the airspeed. I'll just hold attitude and heading."

One of my duties as the non flying pilot was to talk on the radio and he reiterated my job.

"If we're off by more than 300 feet of assigned altitude, just let ATC know we can't control altitude."

Walpole repeated an axiom that even I knew. Once inside a storm, especially with severe turbulence, the airplane would already be under a lot of stress. And banking the wing increased the G-load on the airframe even more. Turning around in a severe storm to retreat was a death sentence. A death sentence that sadly, too many pilots placed themselves under by panicking and trying to turn back once inside a storm. You just had to ride it out straight ahead and let the airplane's natural stability even out the ride. Over-controlling the airplane would only overstress the airframe. However, in his tutorial he left unmentioned that if we started climbing in an updraft it would reduce our already narrow margin between low and high speed buffet and place us right in the apex of coffin corner.

That ominous sounding place was a region at very high altitudes where our stall speed increased but, at the same time, our critical Mach speed decreased. Critical Mach being the speed at which the flow of air over the wing increased to exceed the speed of sound. In short, when we were in coffin corner there were no good options for recovery. Flying too fast to avoid a stall would risk Mach tuck; slowing down to avoid Mach tuck would stall the wing. Either was fatal and the margin between the two was only a few knots of airspeed.

The airplane had drifted low by two hundred feet. Walpole coaxed the airplane back up but he did so very gently. There wasn't a big concern to get back to our assigned altitude. I would have done the same thing. Right then, our greater concern was to fly the airplane gently rather than the one in a million chance of hitting another airplane. At this point, we had committed ourselves and we had to ride it through no matter what would come.

We flew through a ripple, which rocked the airplane slightly. Walpole just let the airplane's natural stability return us to level flight. He squeezed the throttles back a hair just to reduce the speed to Mach .73. It was the speed for turbulent air penetration and it further reduced stress on the airframe.

My stomach hurt.

We entered the first cloud in the line and the windshield turned blue with rivulets of charged plasma streaming off the airplane. It was St. Elmo's Fire caused by a buildup of static electricity around the airplane. Old time sailors found it comforting as a sign their patron saint was watching over them in times of danger. However, I found myself less convinced.

The plasma buildup also made its presence known by a buildup of static in our radios. The noise of the static rose in our headsets covering up the normal chatter on the frequency.

Practically blind and now deaf, we were alone in the storm.

Another jolt, and then another; each slightly more harsh. Each time, the airplane rocked gently and righted itself.

We got into a shallow updraft and the altitude crept up a few hundred feet. Walpole wasn't flying the airplane now as much as he was just guiding it. Rather than forcing his will on the airplane he was letting the airplane's natural stability do most of the work, only nudging it slightly when necessary.

We progressed deeper into the storm.

Rain began to splatter on the windshield. At this altitude, the heaviest rain was below us but our biggest threat was hail. It was known to shatter windshields, crush wing leading edges, and had even caused engine flameouts. What was even more concerning was that hail didn't show up on radar. Given the state of our technology at the time, it was an invisible threat.

Yes, hail was definitely our biggest threat. That was, if we didn't get into a high altitude upset first, which of course, the Lears had a propensity to do.

A burst of lightning appeared and I went blind for a second. Even with the storm lights on full bright, the lighting intensity was so great it overpowered our little world. Before my eyes could fully adjust there was a deep rumble of thunder and it reverberated across the airplane's aluminum body and into the seat of my pants.

The airflow around us changed and we were then in a downdraft. There weren't many other planes around so again Walpole let the airplane drift away from our assigned altitude. Doing so risked the possibility of blundering in another airplane's block of airspace. But it was another risk we were willing to take. I focused almost exclusively on the airspeed indicator. At this altitude, the air was so thin, the wing was precariously balanced. We had to maintain an exact airspeed. In the turbulence our margins in the coffin corner were even more diminished.

Speed was the most crucial parameter.

The St. Elmo's subsided briefly and I heard the many airliners around us calling for deviations as well. Air Traffic Control was overwhelmed. Other airplanes were no longer asking for permission to deviate; they were just stating their intentions and letting ATC sort it out after the fact. The static increased and we were again alone in our little bubble.

This line of weather had caught everyone by surprise with its intensity. We were not yet halfway through and the turbulence now jolted us every few seconds. It was uncomfortable but not yet dangerous. My greatest concern was we would fly unexpectedly into extreme turbulence that would overwhelm even Walpole's ability to keep the airplane stable.

He was now flying with both hands. Not because he needed the strength. Flying the Lear at this altitude required extreme finesse not force. He also had both of his hands resting on his knees. Flying in that fashion gave him more precise control over the airplane.

The five minutes that Walpole predicted to pass through the storm had passed but we didn't break out. The radar had originally shown this to be a thin spot in the line but it had lied to us. Instead, the rain got heavier. It began a drum beat against the nose of the airplane and I felt the percussion against my legs. There were only a few inches of thin aluminum skin separating me from the raging tempest outside. Walpole had his head cocked to the side, as though he was trying to sense his way through the storm cell. I felt the urge to relieve myself but I tightened my bladder.

We were approaching the wall of the storm, the sharp delineation between the storm itself and clear air. We were almost out but we still had to pass this last impediment. And it was the area of the worst intensity. Another jolt, worse than anything yet, and I was thrown against my seatbelt. I tightened my seatbelt expecting worse. The static in the radios rose to a crescendo and stopped.

Then, in an instant, we were spit out of the storm and into the clear air.

In less than three seconds, we traversed from the worst turbulence I had experienced, to normal flying in smooth black air.

Walpole broke the tension with a shaky laugh.

"Report clear of the weather. Tell him, we want direct Tallahassee."

He seemed nonplussed about the whole event but I was enormously grateful to Walpole. He had guided us through the dangerous straits without much fuss. I picked up the microphone and felt a sudden lightness as the tension left my body.

He squeezed the throttle back up to cruise power. "And tell him, we're going back to normal speed."

Memphis Center cleared us as requested but we were an afterthought for them now. There were still a few dozen airplanes feeling their way through the weather who deserved more of their attention.

As we proceeded further east, we left the squall in our exhaust and we returned to some degree of normalcy. We changed ATC frequencies silencing the cries of those still in the storm. We loosened our seatbelts and dimmed the cockpit lights, There was no moon but once my eyes adjusted, the Constellation Pisces materialized slightly to our left.

In the back, our passengers had regained their composure and began joking with each other again. There was a compelling observation. Men who face danger become sober and focused in the moment of peril, even if they have nothing to do but ride along. However, once the menace passed and their manhood was tested successfully, they returned again to their carefree ways.

Eventually, our passengers quieted down and fell asleep. As for Walpole and me, we faced an unexpected challenge and came through it OK but we didn't talk about it. We were left alone with our thoughts as we pressed on to home.

Chapter 21

....

Mountain Flying

I was flying with Coe again and we were at FL 410, just about 200 miles east of Aspen, Colorado, preparing for our descent. Autumn had turned into winter and with the change of seasons all the migratory animals began their treks across the continent. Included in that assembly were the wealthy who were beginning their annual march to their ski resorts in the Rocky Mountains. And it was our job to carry them there.

In the back were two couples heading for a week of skiing and glamorous apres-ski parties in Aspen. They were all in the 40s. Two men and two women. Unusually for a Lear charter, the lead customer wasn't a man but one of the women. Her name was Colleen. She had made her money running a modeling agency and she herself looked like she could have been one of her own models. She had copper red hair and was wearing a white leather jumpsuit, white boots, and a white fur cape. And although she was dressed for the frigid alpine weather, she was still showing plenty of cleavage. The rest of the group was just as beautiful and striking, each in the latest designer couture. They also brought along an extra passenger as part of their entourage. He was a Great Pyrenees dog and his massive shaggy white frame was sprawled across the cabin floor. He was sleeping peacefully and adding to the Jack Frost charm, every available space in the cabin was filled with Christmas presents. Our passengers had money and they were comfortable spending it extravagantly. Further crowding the cabin were champagne bottles and fur coats piled to the ceiling but our passengers didn't seem to mind. They started their party before they boarded and they had been laughing and singing Christmas carols ever since we left Fort Lauderdale. The festive air was contagious and it had been hard for Coe and me to maintain our usual stoic composure.

The thing about charter flying was that each customer and each trip had its own personality. And much the same, each of the Lears I flew had their own temperament. Today we were flying a 24 A Model, registration number 100VQ. It was a variant converted from the original Lear 23. The cockpit was equipped with the very oldest instrumentations of the era but the wing had been upgraded to the Mark 2 conversion making her much more gentle to fly. In stark contrast to the decrepit cockpit, the passenger cabin had been upgraded to rival that of a royal barge from antiquity. The seats were swathed in a soft lambskin leather. The side panels were suede and the floor was covered in a cashmere carpet. All of it in a light cream color.

100VQ was much different from the other airplanes in our fleet. We also flew the 24 B and D models and they were the muscle cars of aviation. The owners of those airplanes had decided to spend money on performance upgrades. They still had the original straight wing and had been upgraded with the larger engines and were the most demanding to fly. They had very little in the way of creature comforts with interiors of plain cloth and vinyl better suited to air ambulance trips or cargo runs. But each airplane had its own charms, and its own frailties; and each was loved equally by their pilots.

The 24s didn't have the range to fly from Fort Lauderdale to Aspen non stop so we had made a fuel stop in Amarillo, Texas. As a result, approaching Aspen the fuel gauges read much more than we needed. Extra gas was like having extra money in a bank account. It was a luxury that made everything else so much better. It was a beautiful day for flying and every one of my mundane tasks was a delight.

Despite having the extra gas, Coe cycled through the fuel indicator switch, checking each tank and then checking again. Like any good pilot, he was always suspicious and didn't allow seeming good fortune to lull him into complacency.

"In the mountains you always want plenty of gas. There are fewer options in the mountains and less room for error. The extra gas gives us plenty of escape hatches. Aspen is nestled in a narrow valley. The airport itself is at 8,000 feet surrounded by mountains at 18,000. There are no instrument approaches and the weather is unpredictable. You need to make sure you can get in before you even start your descent; but more importantly, once you descend into the valley, and you realize you can't actually land, then you have to make sure you can get out again."

Since we were flying a domestic trip, Coe was wearing clothing appropriate for the region. He was still wearing his favorite designer jeans along with an expensive dress shirt and ostrich skin cowboy boots.. Coe, like Walpole, didn't like being cold in the airplane so he was also wearing a shearling coat. Dressed as such, he could have attended any party in Aspen along with our passengers.

I looked ahead. In the western United States the air was drier and on cold winter days, compared to the more murky east coast, the sky would sparkle. The Rocky Mountains ahead were covered with a shield of fresh snow and they stood sharply against the crystal blue sky. 200 miles away every topographical feature of the front range stood out in exquisite detail and beckoned us.

Coe continued. "There are two ways to enter a mountain valley."

As we approached the inhospitable terrain below, he had my attention.

"Low flying prop airplanes have to snake their way through the canyons. But since we cruise so high we can enter the valley from directly overhead."

I had the chart out for the Colorado low altitude route structure and I was trying to make sense of the topography depicted. The terrain below was beautiful but it looked like a venus fly trap. Easy to get into, hard to get out.

Coe was reading my mind.

"There's not a lot of room to maneuver in Aspen Valley. Some guys go screaming into the valley at 300 knots but at that speed your turning radius is way too big. And at those speeds you have a lot less room for error."

The best way to enter the valley is to fly over the valley at altitude. Here, Denver Center will give a clearance to the Red Table VOR. We'll use that as the point to start our initial approach. We'll descend to 18,000 feet until we get to Red Table. Then we'll get the flaps out and slow down to approach speed, about 180 knots. Once we're over Red Table, we should see the airport, we'll just chop the power and descend down gently like a butterfly. No drama and it works great every time.

Just make sure you have a visual on the airport. If you descend blindly, you may end up flying down into a dead end canyon. The Lear has enough power to climb yourself out of almost any trouble but don't let you get yourself there in the first place. Don't get overconfident or complacent and don't rely on the airplane to get you out of trouble."

I then betrayed my simple mindedness.

"I thought you always wanted to stay fast in the Lear?"

"Except for in the mountains. It's the one exception. In the mountains, you slow down, then get down. That bears repeating. In the mountains, you slow down, then get down."

Just as Coe briefed, Denver Center cleared us to 18,000 feet and from that altitude, we peered down into the valley. Below was the Aspen airport tucked into the rumpled continental divide. The entire valley was blanketed in snow and it reflected the brilliant midday sunshine. Even with my dark sunglasses the light was painful.

"Look for the Roaring Fork River. It will line you up on the runway."

I quickly picked it up. The river rapids cut a dull gray line through the stark white snow-covered banks. I followed the line and called a visual on the Aspen airport.

Denver Center then cleared us to proceed visually and once Coe saw the runway himself he pulled the throttles back to idle to begin a quick but controlled descent. Coe was a master Learjet pilot and was completely at ease in this environment. At 180 knots everything was in slow motion as we maneuvered gently and landed. There was some patchy ice on the runway but the brakes on the Lear were powerful, and along with the anti-skid system cycling the brakes over the slippery patches, we came to a gentle stop with plenty of runway to spare.

Once we said goodbye to the passengers, we ordered some fuel and I expected we'd head back to Fort Lauderdale right away.

Instead, Coe had a chore for me to perform.

"I need you to run into town and get some beer."

"We already have some on the airplane and we're going home empty. Why do we need extra beer?"

"It's not for this leg. It's for us to drink at home. We need some Coors."

"What's Coors?"

"It's a local Colorado beer. It's really smooth. It's like honey going down."

"Can't you get it back in Florida?"

"No, it's only available west of the Mississippi. Whenever we fly out here we always load up. Truthfully, it is a pretty good beer, but hardly worth dragging halfway across the country. But in Florida it's like forbidden fruit and everyone goes crazy for it. Here's 300 bucks. The fueler will lend you a crew car and give you directions."

Coe began to do some math in his head. But instead of calculating our maximum passenger load, he was calculating the weight of a case of beer.

"Buy as much as they have but no more than 25 cases. That's about as much as we can carry back."

I did as instructed and we were back in the air quickly with our load of amber brew. I was heartened by my easy experience in the Rockies and I was confident I understood the complexities of mountain flying. Although, as I was to find out, one entry into a danger zone did not make one an experienced hand. I was unaware that in my future there was another valley waiting for me. A valley that could trick even the most wary of prey to enter its wily trap. And despite all my precautions, on that day, I would do everything wrong.

Chapter 22

....

Night Flight

We had taken off from Aspen with the sun already low in the sky and had gotten out of there just before their sunset curfew. Aspen was behind us and we were over the great plains at Flight Level 450. Coe and I were in an empty airplane with a load of Rocky Mountain beer in the back. As we proceeded east, we rapidly flew into the face of the night sky, with about three hours of flying ahead of us.

A cold front had swept the air clean in front of us and the entire eastern half of the United States lay under a dome of high pressure air. That same polar energy that had pushed an Arctic air mass deep into lower latitudes was also forecast to give us extraordinarily strong tailwinds.

It was my turn to fly and I had matured enough to do a passable job. I also had enough mental reserves that I could think about other things as I flew and I calculated our ground speed in my head, which gave me a number of just over 600 knots. I thought about commenting to Coe that if this kept up, we should be able to make the flight from Aspen to Fort Lauderdale non stop. That was an extraordinary feat for a Lear 24. And that would have given us bragging rights with our buddies back home. But I was alone for the moment.

Coe was in the back readjusting our precious cargo of Colorado beer leaving me in the dark cockpit alone to hand fly the airplane. At high altitude, the Lear did not react well to any mishandling, and if something were to go awry, there was little time to correct. Therefore, whenever a captain left a copilot in the cockpit alone, in any airplane, it was a major vote of confidence. But in the Learjet, it was an especially prized honor.

As we sped along, a crescent moon appeared and hung low on the eastern horizon. To me, the most evocative moons were the full moon and the crescent moon. They were reminiscent of the moons in the tales of the One Thousand and One Arabian Nights, the stories I read as a boy. Those stories provided a break from the banality of long winter nights.

In those legends, Aladdin had his wish for wealth and power granted by a genie.

As for me, I never had a magical genie and I never yearned for power, only adventure. However, if a genie had granted me a wish, I would have wished that words could describe the silky and mystical nature of night flight.

As I flew alone, the air was soft and the airplane trimmed straight and true as we streaked under God's great firmament. Despite our speed, the sensation was one of being suspended in infinite space. The prairie lands of Kansas lay below us and the flat earth was visible horizon to horizon. There was a new fallen snow and a blanket of white glistened in the moonlight like a Christmas card. It was late and the air traffic control frequency was quiet. It was peaceful as I flew along in solitude, accompanied only by the reassuring hum of our engines and the rush of air along the windshield. On long distance flights in quiet airspace, the drone of the engines created a meditative state. The airplane then became a chapel and it somehow became transcendent. At altitude, especially at night, we became part of the infinite. The possibilities seemed endless and, only when we had to, did we reluctantly descend to earth.

This type of night flying was a new and pleasant experience for me. In single engine airplanes night flight was something that put me on edge. If the engine failed and there were no emergency landing fields visible, then the pilot had to glide down to an emergency landing onto an unknown and foreboding land. Robbed of light, an unpowered airplane gliding towards the ground could only hope to blindly steer towards some type of flat surface, and then hope find a suitable crash site visually in the last moments of flight. The wags in the hangar would say that if you were to make a forced landing at night, you should turn on your landing light just before impact. If you liked what you saw, then you would land. If you didn't like what you saw, then you just turned off the light and accepted your fate. It was a disconcerting proposition and even in an era of more reliable piston engines that uncertainty had always left me uneasy in single engine airplanes.

Coe had returned to the cockpit but we remained immersed in silence as we sped along with the jetstream at our back. We approached New Orleans in short order and prepared to cross the Gulf of Mexico. But before we crossed this large expanse of water, with no diversion airports underneath us, I had an important navigational task to perform.

I had to ensure we could make the crossing even if the tailwind died down. I calculated our groundspeed again. Still over 600 knots. I checked the fuel remaining and I then checked that number against our fuel burn and our estimated time to Tampa on the far side of the Gulf. I did the math twice and was rewarded with the same answer. We had plenty of gas to continue.

But, to account for any contingencies, I did the math again, this time assuming no tailwind at all. Both calculations told me that we would have plenty of gas to make it across the Gulf of Mexico. Satisfied that we had enough fuel, I reported to Coe we could continue.

Just past New Orleans, we flew over the Leeville VOR and I prepared to fly outbound Jet Airway, Quebec 100, on a course of 100 degrees. The VOR navigation radios were accurate and reliable navigation aids but they had a limitation. They had a range of only 200 miles. Flying over a land mass, this wasn't a problem for there was always another VOR waiting ahead of us when we flew out of the range of the last one.

Thirty minutes out of Leeville we flew out of range from its VOR. Ahead of us was several hundred miles of dark water. The next VOR, located in St. Petersburg, Florida, was still long out of range. As a result, we then had to revert to more antiquated methods of navigation.

I tuned our direction finder to an NDB radio on the Florida west coast. The NDB radio was an acronym for a Non Directional Beacon. It was a throwback to the 1920s and it was essentially an AM radio station that we could home in on. It was powerful and long ranged but its weakness was that it was less accurate than the VHF navigation radios. However, an even bigger problem with the NDB was that its signal was subject to all sorts of vagaries in the atmosphere. Tonight, however, the sky was clear of any sort of atmospheric disturbance for thousands of miles around us. We were in a stable bubble of air and the NDB needle pointed straight ahead to home.

I glanced at the clock. It was 11 PM. I clicked my way through all five fuel tanks and I recalculated our fuel burn. In the Lear, we were always calculating and recalculating our fuel burn. We would land with about 45 minutes of fuel. That was a little tight but still legal. I calculated the odds ahead of us. The sky was clear all the way to Fort Lauderdale and would remain so for several hours. Late at night there will be no congestion and we would be number one for landing. Even in a worst case scenario, Florida had many airfields scattered around the peninsula offering us safe haven if we needed a diversion. We had lots of escape hatches if needed.

Far ahead, Orion the Hunter rose silently above the horizon to escort us home. I decided to follow his lead and press on.

I was learning not just to fly the airplane, but to think strategically.

But more than that, I was beginning to understand that the Lear was not an inanimate object. No, she was a unique being with a unique personality. It was our job as pilots to build a relationship with our airplane, to know when to be gentle and when to be firm. When to give and when to take. It was then, I began to fall in love with my airplane.

And like any love affair, it had been an uncertain road.

As a teenager, I dreamed of flying for the military, flying the most glamorous of all airplanes. While I was in university, I talked with the recruiters and they dutifully sent me to the medical officers for screening. I was poked by the flight surgeons and spent time with the psychiatrists until I was pronounced fit for the high standard of flight qualification and offered a training slot, but with one exception. Because I was nearsighted I was told I could not be a pilot but instead, a navigator. It was an important job, the person whose job it was to lead the pilot to a target and make sure the weapons were ready for their lethal chore. But he was not the pilot.

And I decided that job wasn't for me. I had to be the one flying the airplane. Maybe it was because I had read too many cheap novels about courageous wartime pilots leading missions against all odds and nursing damaged airplanes back home, or maybe it was my ego speaking but that was just how it was. I thanked the local commandant profusely but instead I went to the local civilian airport and began flying lessons on my own. Many of my fellow Learjet pilots had similar stories. There were a few charter pilots who had military pedigrees but mostly we came up through the grinding path of civil aviation.

Military aviation, of course, has its dangers but there were many pitfalls in civil aviation as well. In the short time I had been flying, I had several friends killed in airplane accidents. First there was Tom Demitus age 19, one of the kindest people I knew, killed in a Cessna 172 trying to race a thunderstorm to the Daytona Beach airport. Then there was Marsha White, a radiant 20 year old woman with a beautiful smile. She was killed near Orlando in a Piper Cherokee while penetrating a cold front. I was the last person to see Marsha alive as we waved goodbye on her taxi out of Pompano Beach airport. About a year later there was Diana Leonard, age 25. She was copilot on a DC-3 lost on a dark night over the Gulf Stream, on the way to Freeport. The investigators attributed the crash to a faulty airspeed sensor. Diana's loss was especially close to home. We were both vying for that same job on the DC-3 so her death could have been mine instead. Shortly after that, there was Sue Hartigan, age 27, an enormously capable pilot. She was piloting a Cessna 310 that crashed just after takeoff from Fort Lauderdale Executive Airport, cause still unknown. And there would be more lost friends yet to come. Somehow, though, I had survived that most dangerous part of my career and had made it this far. Perhaps, I was just more lucky than they were. Or perhaps, I really was a better pilot. I wasn't sure but I deceived myself to think the latter.

Even flying the Lear in charter operations, we took great risks. But that was all right with us. Like military aviation, we just had a duty to perform and we did it. But somehow it was different. It seemed less noble. And even though we certainly filled an important social function when flying air ambulance or relief missions, no one ever thanked us for our service. We just got paid and went on to the next job.

Speaking of jobs, I had to turn back to the main matter at hand, that of my current flight. I knew we had enough fuel to make it home and I was fairly certain the weather was good all the way to Fort Lauderdale but I had to conduct one last formality. I had to check the weather before committing us to our destination. I tuned our number two communications radio to call the New Orleans Flight Service Station. "Flight Service" as it was called and it was another throwback to more quaint times with meteorologists located at airports around the country.

In the case of New Orleans Flight Service, there was a World War Two era Quonset hut located by the side of Moissant airport. Inside was a lone meteorologist surrounded by teletype machines and banks of telephones. He probably had a pencil wedged against his ear and he responded to my radio call on the first try.

Once I called him, he tore a long sheet of paper from the teletype and pulled the pencil from his ear and underlined the airports ahead of us. He then radioed me the reports for all the Florida airports ahead of us. He read them aloud in aeronautical code and I translated the reports in my mind as he read them to me.

"Tampa is clear, visibility unlimited, temperature 45 degrees, winds calm. Fort Myers, the same. Fort Lauderdale and Miami, sky clear, temperature 50 degrees, winds light and variable."

That was all good news for a tired pilot nearing the end of a long flight. The weather would be one less thing to worry about. I thanked the meteorologist and hung the microphone on its hook and returned to my silent flight.

It was near midnight and we sat silently bathed in the red instrument lights and the moonglow. The lights of Tampa became visible on the horizon indicating home was within easy reach. It had been a long day. We were both tired and eager to finish the last hour of the flight.

I basked in the silence but I also need some human engagement. I turned to Coe. I wanted to say something profound but I was still only the student and he, the master. I was certain any words I could muster would be inadequate.

Coe sensed the moment and he simply said:

"Merry Christmas."

I smiled and nodded for that was all there was to say.

We crossed over Fort Myers and I knew our magic carpet ride had come to an end. I reluctantly reduced the power to begin our descent back to earth and we landed gracefully back in Fort Lauderdale.

It was after midnight when we parked the airplane. The hangar doors were locked tight for the night and the ramp was deserted with only the white "Graf Jets" sign illuminating the ramp. Coe was impatient to get home and quickly unloaded a few cases of beer into his Cadillac and was gone.

I was left behind to accomplish the usual copilot's chores of cleaning up the airplane.

I found a bucket of red shop rags that were left outside and a can of household cleaner. The air was cool but still heavy with humidity and the cold surfaces of the airplane had beaded with condensation. The heat inside the engines smoldered and they vented off smoke from both the intake and exhaust ducts. Each engine tinkled as the hot turbine blades cooled. It had been a long day for the airplane too and she was coming down off of her own high and settling in for the night.

It was late and there was not another person around for a mile. I worked silently around the curved shape of the airplane. I was tired and ready to head home myself but, yet, I lingered.

I never really had a definitive plan anyway so I had no expectations. Although, it was a bit of a surprise: Standing on a dark airport ramp on Christmas Eve. But I had fallen in love. I loved the airplane. The strength of it, the sheer beauty and how it responded when I was at the controls. I loved feeling the throb of the engines transmitted through to the throttles, and I loved how the thrum of the airflow would transmit through the flight controls into my hands. I loved how just through feel, the airplane told me what it wanted. Sometimes, it would surge ahead, sometimes draw back. And I loved the power that the airplane granted me. I guess that is something that non aviators don't understand. An airplane is not an inanimate collection of parts. Rather, it is a living, breathing creature that becomes one with the pilot once we strap in. I suppose mariners say the same thing about their ships and drivers say about their race cars.

Like every relationship, we had ups and downs. There were times when she scared me, and there were times when I almost destroyed the both of us. But no matter what, when the chips were down we both did our job and we would bring each other home.

Yes, I had fallen in love, not just with the Learjet but with flying itself. It had become my purpose in life. I loved being at altitude, far above the world's problems. Humans had stared at the sky since the dawn of time but now I was completely immersed in it. The sunrises, the sunsets, the sky in all its variations, the untold variety of clouds, the constellations.

I also loved my fellow humans who created something so lovely. Especially, when you realized that every component on the airplane was just something that we scratched out of the dirt and then molded into a work of art. I loved that the human mind was finally able to master a form of wizardry that could take us anywhere on the planet within hours.

It wasn't just the airplane but I also felt at home with my fellow pilots. Most of us shared that same emotional bond to airplanes and to each other. We had stared through the same windshields, fought our way through the same squall lines and ice storms; and nursed the same broken airplanes back to the ground. We shared the same history and we had become brothers. They were my family.

Chapter 23

Springfield

From our perch at FL 450, the upper midwest of the United States sprawled for hundreds of miles in each direction. Above us, the sky was cobalt blue and the sun glared hot white through the windshield.

The weather above was to be expected but I was surprised to see so much white below me as well. With no real understanding of winter weather, I had expected the sky below to be grey and gloomy. Instead, the cloud deck below reflected the brilliant sun and it was solid for a thousand miles around. Having flown mostly in the tropics I was about to get my first lesson on weather in the northern latitudes.

Walpole was the captain and while I flew, he had been listening to the weather report at Springfield, Illinois.

"The weather is bad there. It went below forecast. It's 200 overcast and just a half mile visibility."

It was news I wasn't prepared for.

"Are you sure?"

"I'm sure. And that's not all. The winds are gusting to 35 knots. The reception is scratchy as hell. I listened to the weather tape three times to make sure I had it right. They blew the forecast. It was supposed to be fine for our arrival."

"Do we have enough gas?"

"Just barely."

Government regulations required that we land with 45 minutes of fuel, however that minimum was for when the weather is good and we could expect to land with no delays. When the weather was forecast to be poor, we had to add enough fuel to divert to an alternate airport; and at that alternate, the weather had to be better. When we left Fort Lauderdale, the forecast for Springfield was good. We added St. Louis as an alternate only as a formality. In the ensuing three hours, a massive cold front had moved in much more quickly than expected.

We were just 30 minutes from landing at Springfield and I glanced quickly at the fuel gauge. We had just over an hour of fuel left, probably less.

I ask, "Should we divert to St. Louis now?"

"I don't think so. The weather is bad there too and all the airliners are diverting there from Chicago. We can get there but we'd probably have to hold and we don't have gas for that."

"Terre Haute is off to the side? We could duck in there?"

"No. it's going down also and the glide slope is out of service."

I looked at the distance measuring indicator tuned into Nashville (DME). Nashville weather was good but it was by then much too far behind us now. We couldn't turn back.

Walpole rolled through the various diversion options in his head.

"Peoria weather is better but it's a little too far ahead. We really shouldn't overfly Springfield if we have a chance of getting in there."

At altitude, we were in a bubble of polar air and the sky around us was dry and crisp. Visibility was unlimited and we could see the gentle curvature of the earth. The sky was clear all around us but I felt trapped. There was a vast continental expanse below but most of it was an inhospitable shoreline, smothered in a blanket of low clouds. I felt my own heartbeat pounding and I forced myself to control my breathing. We had only a limited amount of fuel with even more limited options for landing.

I rubbed my sweaty palms on the front of my pants, switching my hands as I flew with the other.

In the very early days of aviation, when faced with bad weather, the air mail pilots flying biplanes could just drop into any farmer's field as a safe haven. Since that ancient time, airplanes had become much more capable but our superior capabilities also came with a vulnerability. There were only a certain number of airports that could accommodate us. And those airports had to have runways that were concrete and long. Grass fields weren't an option.

And on days like today, there was an extra complication. There were even fewer airports with all weather approach systems that could guide us down through the thick cloud layers. We were mariners trapped offshore with only a few harbors available for refuge. Time began to slow down. We had no good answers. I couldn't think clearly and stared at the blank sky for an answer but none came. Nature was impassive to our dilemma and I felt the fear rising in my throat. Walpole was the captain and this was his decision to make. I looked to him for an answer.

He stroked his jaw and announced the final decision. "We're committed to Springfield. Let's just press on. We'll be able to get in. Or, at least, we'll have to. We don't have a choice."

We had already delayed our descent as long as possible to conserve fuel, and it was now time to start down without any further delay. I prepared to hand over the controls to Walpole.

Although I had gained a modest amount of capability, it was times like this when I knew to defer the landing to the captain. It was not that I was without competency. It was just that when the chips were down and when there was no room for error, it was best for the most experienced man to make the landing. Walpole was obviously the most experienced of the two of us and it was, by all rights, his landing. But I had another motivation to hand over the controls. I was nervous and my muscles were tight. I just wanted to hide. I was ready to relinquish responsibility and let my surrogate parent keep me safe.

However, Walpole had other ideas.

"This is going to be your first real approach down to minimums. Let's see how you do."

I blinked and wanted to voice an objection but nothing came out of my open mouth. I was torn. I desperately wanted to prove myself, but I was afraid.

"You're going to eventually have to do this on your own. Someday, you are even going to have to do it when the stakes are even higher. Now is a good time to see how you do."

It was flights like these which caused Lear pilots to live in a constant state of anxiety. The flight from Fort Lauderdale to Springfield was at the extreme ragged edge of the range of the airplane. We knew when we left that we were only barely carrying enough fuel to get to our destination and then to a safe harbor. Unlike Beckley, we didn't have the luxury of trying it again.

We were in a Lear 25, the thirstiest of all the Lears. Our airplane was equipped with early generation jet engines. The lower we descended the more fuel the engines would burn and at slower speeds down low, they would devour fuel even more greedily. Walpole was a scrupulous aviator and was not given to emotion but we both knew we were in trouble. He rotated the fuel indicator selector switch through all five positions again, doing the math in his head to calculate our total remaining fuel load. I followed his motion and I came up with 1800 pounds. Just over one hour. We had enough to shoot the approach and barely make it to an alternate. However, that was just a guess. I knew the fuel was getting tight but up until now, I had always trusted my captain would keep me safe. Now I was being told I was responsible for my own safety and it gave me a sour taste in my mouth.

We descended towards Springfield at idle power the whole way down in order to conserve fuel. We leveled off momentarily, just above the clouds at 5,000 feet, and we skimmed the tops. At 250 knots, we had the illusion of surfing along a flat white ocean. We enjoyed this brief interlude like otters frolicking in the surf but we still had a serious matter to attend to. It was now time to fly the final approach into Springfield.

The air traffic controller instructed us to descend. I pulled back the throttles again and we descended in the gray mist. Inside the clouds, the cockpit darkened and my spirits fell accordingly.

I reached over to the navigational control panel and selected the flight director to engage. The flight director was a rudimentary analog computer that took data from the navigational radios. It then provided a bright orange chevron shaped indicator overlaid on my attitude indicator and was the primary indication for me to follow on approach. The flight director was not an autopilot. It only provided guidance. After it dropped into view, I focused on its command bars intently. It was to be my lifeline to the ground.

Walpole craned his head around to the left to check the left tip tank.

On the very front of the tank was a back plastic disc. In addition to looking really cool it served an important purpose. It was an icing indicator. The leading edges of our wings were out of our field of vision from the cockpit. We had to look at the tip tanks to see if we were picking up ice. However, because the airplane was painted white, the white ice wasn't easily visible. Instead, the ice showed up readily on the black disc.

Walpole turned back to the front. "We're picking up ice. And a lot of it."

And with that announcement, he turned on the anti-ice for our engine intakes and wing leading edges.

The anti-ice was a critical piece of protection. If the ice were allowed to build up, it would deform the perfectly shaped wing and we would lose lift. And the engines were especially vulnerable, for any ice build up on the intake could break off and destroy the turbine blades.

However, the anti-ice protection, as necessary as it was, came at a high price. Because it used engine bleed air as its heat source, our fuel consumption increased accordingly.

As we approached Springfield airport, the approach controller lined us up on Runway 31 and gave us the latest weather.

"Springfield current observation: 200 feet overcast. 1/2 mile visibility in mixed snow and ice pellets. Winds are from 270 degrees at 25 knots, gusts to 35 knots."

That was just as bad as expected but I was heartened that it hadn't gotten any worse. The weather was still at landing minimums and assuming I did everything right, we would be able to get in.

However, my relief was short lived when the controller added this extra bit of unpleasant news.

"Braking action is poor, as reported ten minutes ago by a Beechcraft King Air."

"Damnit!"

This was unexpected. Despite the cold, my palms were sweaty against the hard plastic yoke. I wiped my hands again on my pants. My right hand was cramping from holding the yoke too tight and I flexed my fingers to relieve some stress.

We were two thousand feet above the airport and I had slowed to our approach speed of 150 knots. This speed was much faster than usual due to the gusty weather. A strong crosswind when landing was difficult enough but when the winds were gusty, the airflow over the wing became variable and unpredictable. That extra speed gave us an additional margin of safety if we lost airspeed suddenly. However, just like everything else, it came at a cost. The added speed would make it harder to stop the airplane.

Walpole, sensed my anxiety and interjected, "OK. The runway is 7400 feet long. If the runway was dry we could stop in about 3500 feet, so you have almost 4,000 more than you need. Just continue just like you are and hold your target speed as close as you can."

It was a small consolation. Not only did I have to fly an approach to minimums but I also had to bring the airplane to a stop on an icy and slippery runway. Neither of which I had ever done before. Despite the added stress, I was relieved to hear Walpole's calm instruction and I resolved to loosen my grip on the yoke.

Approach control gave us the final turn onto course and cleared us for the approach.

I checked the fuel again. We had enough…to at least make the approach… and probably try again a second time. We had burned so much maneuvering down low especially with anti-ice on that we were committed to landing here in Springfield. Diversion was out of the question. We had to get in.

All I had to do is fly the needles of the ILS down. The ILS had two separate guidance needles. One lined us up on the runway centerline and the other provided a glideslope to touchdown. Once I got the course and glideslope needles centered they would lead us unfailingly to the runway. Together with the flight director guidance it was a very easy exercise. I had done it a hundred times before. But it was only practice… on a good weather day… and with plenty of fuel.

Five miles from the airport, the ILS needles centered and the flight director engaged commanding a descent. I dutifully followed both down to the ground.

Walpole continued to coach me.

"Doing good. Just stay focused on the flight director. Keep it tucked tight against the command bars and you'll be good."

I had all my attention on the flight director and as I struggled with the airplane I willed myself that this was going to be a textbook perfect approach.

As we descended, we entered the area where the blowing winds met with the friction of the earth's surface creating even more turmoil. With each gust of wind the airplane became more agitated.

Walpole continued his coaching.

"Normally, you have to be gentle with the airplane but now you can't rely on the airplane's natural stability. It's too slow to recover. Use as much control input as you need to stay locked on the command bars. And use every bit of what you need. Don't be timid and don't worry about finesse. Make the airplane do what you want. Not what it wants."

Descending through 1000 feet, I stole a glance outside.

Nothing.

It was still solid thick cloud. I went back inside to the flight director. It was my lifeline and I flew it like my life depended on it. Before beginning the approach I was uneasy. But now, in this moment of action, my fear had dissipated. Instead, it had been replaced with grim determination.

Walpole announced, "500 feet."

We were then just 500 feet above the ground or about a half a mile from the end of the runway. I stole another glance outside. Sometimes, if the ceiling was ragged you could pick up the runway visually a little earlier than you might expect. But today, there was nothing but solid clouds. I was a few knots fast and I squeezed the power back ever so slightly.

I tightened my grip slightly on the yoke. This extra firmness was acceptable. I was making the airplane do what I wanted. Plus, our weight was so light that in case we did have to go around, the airplane was going to leap back in the sky once I added full power. And I didn't want to lose control.

From the corner of my eye I sensed a dull pulsing light illuminating the clouds. We were by then, so close to the end of the runway that we were actually over the approach lights. The flashing strobe lights were there to guide us in visually like a lighthouse and they were penetrating the gloom. But that wasn't good enough to land. I needed to see something more definitive.

Walpole warned me we were approaching our decision altitude.

"300 feet above the ground. Approaching minimums. Nothing in sight yet."

I tensed up on the controls. This was it. We were almost at decision altitude and traveling forward at 230 feet per second. Things were happening fast.

I waited for his command. Even though I was flying, it was still his decision to land or to go around. Once we arrived at decision height, we had to see the runway to continue visually. There was to be no debate this close to the ground. Going below minimums without the runway in sight was a cardinal sin of the highest order. "Ducking under" it was called. And whether a pilot did it intentionally or due to sloppy flying, the result was almost always fatal. Without the runway in sight, we had to go around. And once the command from Walpole came to go around my response had to be instantaneous.

We were now at 200 feet above the ground, right at minimums. I sensed the approach lights getting brighter and they flooded our cockpit with their pulsing light. But I waited for Walpole's command. I began to squeeze the throttles up a fraction in anticipation of going around. We had waited until the very last second. We had maybe even passed the time for decision. It was now time for action. We didn't really have the fuel but I had to jam the power full forward and go around.

Then, I heard from Walpole.

"Minimums!"

"Approach lights in sight!"

With that exclamation, I knew that he saw the runway ahead of us. We could continue. I looked up. I was expecting to see a runway but the view was still murky. I could only just see the white sequence flashers. Those were the strobe lead-in lights. The runway itself was still hidden in the mist. But following the strict interpretation of the rules, what little we did see was good enough. I was able to continue and each strobe light sparked an explosion of white through the mist to guide me in.

I was off the gauges and tried to focus on outside references but the heavy snow was streaming towards me at 150 knots.

At our speed the snow was coming at us horizontally and the glare of our powerful landing lights reflected the snow back at us. It was a phantasm that created an optical illusion that had caused many airplanes to undershoot and crash just short of the runway. In these conditions, the visibility wasn't good enough to proceed solely on visual references. I glanced back inside to check the glideslope needle to ensure I didn't get too low.

I waited a half a second and took another peek outside. The red approach lights were now in view. They marked the undershoot zone. Instinctively, I just breathed a fraction of back stick to stay above the red danger zone. With just a few seconds until landing, I toggled my focus back and forth between the gauges and the runway.

I was too fast at 150 knots but I needed the extra speed for the gusty conditions. I wasn't used to the extra speed and I was slightly disoriented as the ground was coming up faster than usual. The green runway end markers then became visible. They marked the runway threshold. Beyond that was my safety zone and that's what I targeted. Everything around me was a blur but I was finally able to see the runway itself. It was just a nebulous patch of grey covered in patchy white ice. A snow squall swirled across the runway and the edges of the concrete were outlined with white runway lights. As I got even closer, our own strobe lights began reflecting off the ground. All around us now was an explosion of various color lights. Each light was designed to impart some important information to guide me in. But at this point, each light was meaningless to me. We were immersed in a cauldron of visual distraction but I stubbornly focused on the gray touchdown zone.

We passed over the threshold of the runway and by now the runway had taken on a more definitive shape. The sound of our engines bounced off of the concrete runway and there was a perceptible rise in background noise. Two seconds until touchdown. We were now getting into ground effect, a cushion of air that builds up between the wings and the ground. That cushion of air created some extra lift. I was already too fast so that was exactly what I didn't want. I squeezed back on the throttles slightly, reducing power just enough to compensate for the extra lift.

The paint of the white runway touchdown markers were barely visible under the carpet of ice and they flashed under the airplane's nose. To my left, I could see Walpole. He was sitting in what appeared to me to be a state of tranquility. He was just as focused as I was but enormously calm with the palms of each of his hands resting on his knees.

But then, I saw it.

In the corner of my eyes, there was a twitch of his right hand. He had been cool and silent up to now, but this inconspicuous bit of body language was an important non verbal command. It was time. I had to get the airplane on the ground.

I then watched my own hand quickly pull the throttles all the way back to the idle stops. The roar of the engines went quiet, replaced by the sound of the slipstream over the windshield. It was times like this when the pitch peculiarity of the Lear would get pilots into trouble. In most airplanes, when the power comes off the nose pitches down so you have to have a bit more back pressure to hold it off. Instead, the nose of the Learjet wanted to pitch up. I squeezed in a little extra forward pressure on the control yoke to compensate for the loss of thrust. It was counter intuitive but that's one of the peculiarities of the airplane

With that power reduction we were gliding. Just a foot above the runway. Nose high, slowly bleeding off airspeed. Down to the last foot to the runway… waiting, waiting… More runway passed behind us. I was still too fast and I was wasting time. Worst of all, I was squandering the runway I had available. I needed to get the airplane on the runway.

However, the runway was wet and had built up a thin sheen of slick fluid onto which the tires could slide gently. But that wasn't good. The tires needed to break through the surface friction and get a good bite on the pavement. I bled off a little more airspeed but not too much. Just like at high altitude, there was only a narrow margin for the aerodynamics to work properly. Too fast, and we would waste runway. Too slow, and we could lose roll control and drag a tip tank on the ground.

I needed to get the airplane on the runway. On a slippery runway, there were no style points. You just want to get it on the ground; and I had long passed that point. The saying among pilots for operating in these kinds of conditions was succinct and accurate.

"Chop it and plop it."

I relaxed the back pressure on the yoke, just a fraction and the airplane settled.

The airplane gave up flight and we met the earth with a satisfying thud.

Assured the main wheels were firmly on the ground, I still had more work to do and it was the more delicate part. I had to stop 10,000 pounds of metal and humans straight ahead on a runway glazed with ice. There was a 70 foot margin of runway on either side and 5,000 feet of concrete remaining ahead. I had to thread that needle at 130 knots.

I slid my left hand away from the throttles to the spoiler extension switch just to the left side of the throttle quadrant and with a flick of one finger, moved it to the "Extend" position. At that same instant, two large panels, one on the top of each wing extended with the force of 3000 pounds of hydraulic pressure. The spoilers were designed to instantaneously destroy any remaining lift produced by the wings. Simultaneously, I saw the red "Spoiler Extend" light flash on the forward warning panel and heard Walpole report "Spoilers out!"

With no more lift, the full weight of the airplane settled on the wheels. With that perceptible drop in the seat of my pants I graded myself with an A minus landing.

But only momentarily. My job was still not done.

Walpole reported "3,000 feet remaining!" At our speed we would run out of runway in just 15 seconds. The nose was still high in the air so I relaxed some of the back pressure on the control yoke and allowed the nose wheel to gently kiss the gray concrete.

I had dallied for too long and there was no more time to waste; I had to begin decelerating in earnest. I squeezed on the toe brakes.

Nothing.

I pressed harder and the anti skid system began cycling and pulsing feedback into my toes. The anti-skid system was controlled by a small unit in the brake lines. It was designed to release brake pressure to prevent skidding. But we had a problem that the anti-skid couldn't overcome. Even with the full weight of the airplane on the wheels there wasn't enough surface friction for the tires to bite into the pavement. The Lear had powerful brakes but on this slippery surface they were worthless and I was asking the tires to do more than they could.

We needed more. I moved my left hand back on the throttles and reached slightly forward for the thrust reverser sub-throttles. I pulled them back slightly and heard the gratifying click of the thrust reversers engaging. The sound of that click meant that 20 feet behind us 3000 pounds of hydraulic pressure slammed the reverser doors open. And in that instant, the thrust from the engines was deflected forward. I squeezed the sub-throttles back-wards even more. The engines roared in protest but they had a critical job to perform. We had to slow the airplane and without wheel brakes we had only the thrust reversers to slow us down.

Walpole called "110 knots!"

I pulled back harder on the thrust reversers.

We were still fast but I knew everything was working as it should, and the airspeed was now decaying rapidly.

At this lower speed, the tires had a better grip on the runway so I reapplied the wheel brakes. The anti skid system again kicked back in protest but this time between pulses, I could feel the brakes catching on the concrete and we continued slowing.

Walpole again made a call out, "80 knots! 2,000 feet remaining!"

The 80 knots call was my signal to stow the thrust reversers. We were then slow enough that I knew I could stop safely with just wheel brakes. So with a forward motion I stowed the reversers back to the idle position. The engine roar receded, replaced by the sound of rain pellets tapping the windshield. The Lear had no windshield wipers (too many grandmothers). At our slower speed the slipstream no longer blew the precipitation away from the windshield. And with that, the world around us blurred into an abstract painting with a palette of white, green and blue runway lights as we searched for the runway turnoff.

As I turned off the runway I glanced at the fuel gauges, not really wanting to know.

The last ten minutes had me totally focused on flying the airplane. I had checked the fuel before the approach and thought we had enough to fly the approach. All of my attention was focused on flying the airplane so I had not paid attention to our rapidly deteriorating fuel state. And what I had failed to calculate was the shocking increase in fuel consumption when using both engine and wing anti-ice.

The gauge read about 800 pounds of fuel. Maybe 20 minutes of gas. Maybe enough for a second try to land, but maybe not, and certainly not enough to have gone to an alternate airport.

Shortly after we landed, a Sabreliner tried the same approach and the icing conditions had overwhelmed their anti-icing capability. Both of their engines were severely damaged from ice ingestion and they were just barely able to limp into Springfield on reduced power.

We spent the evening in Springfield to rest before our return home. Over dinner there, I saw that we had faced the same challenge as those other pilots and succeeded. It had been the greatest flying challenge thus far in my career, and in the worst possible conditions. The experience was both dangerous and exciting. I was ashamed of my fear but proud of my accomplishment. My heart was soaring from meeting the challenge but at the same time, I was exhausted.

What we did was so wrong, so on the edge, but it felt so right. And I wanted more.

However, I was soon to find out that excitement and danger did not always come in equal doses. Sometimes, the danger was far greater. And sometimes the excitement could just as easily mutate into terror.

Chapter 24

Death Sometimes Comes Quickly

I looked to the north. A storm front was approaching and I was eager to get out of town.

I had finished my preflight duties and was waiting for our customer to show up for a trip to Merida, Mexico. I was standing on the ramp at the executive airport in Fort Lauderdale. The sky was grey and foreboding with the imminent arrival of the season's first cold front, but for the time being the airport was running normal operations. It was busy mid afternoon and I was killing time watching the parade of planes taking off and landing on Runway 31.

The mix of airplanes was a challenge for the air traffic controllers but they always handled the flow of traffic without any fuss. I was familiar with the airport because this was my old home where I spent time as a flight instructor.

As I leaned against the tip tank of the airplane I admired myself in my newly purchased uniform. I had advanced far enough that I no longer had to suffer hand-me down uniform items. I sported sharply creased trousers, a starched white shirt, and three shiny, new stripes on my epaulets. For special effect, I had also added a new leather jacket to my wardrobe. Although at 80 degrees, the jacket was superfluous. No matter, I was pretty certain that my crisp uniform and my cavalier attitude marked me as a pro. I was also certain that any other pilots, especially those not as far advanced in their careers, must surely be envying me; just as I had envied other Learjet pilots not too long ago.

I looked forward to my trip to Merida. It was to be a grand adventure to a new destination and it would add even more precious jet experience in my logbook. Things in my life were progressing well.

Gal-Nur was my captain for this trip and that added to my general sense of contentment. In the world of Learjet charter, much of a copilot's self esteem was directly related to his captain. And captain personalities covered the entire spectrum. The Lear was originally designed to be flown by only one pilot. As a result, most captains saw young copilots as an unnecessary burden imposed on them by government regulation and only begrudgingly accepted our presence.

They were perfectly capable of flying the airplane solo and used their copilots for menial chores. There was also a significant number of captains who took a sadistic pleasure in making the copilot's life miserable. You could tell those afflicted copilots by their scared and nervous demeanors. Nothing they could do was ever right. And at the opposite end of the spectrum were captains like Gal-Nur, who treated their copilots as valued crewmembers.

He was a former Israeli fighter pilot who himself was seeking an airline career. He was a small man, thin and strong, and he had a self-confidence that was unshakable. In one of the innumerable wars his country had fought, he even had a Mig kill to his credit. Gal-Nur had an impish smile and always saw the best side of human nature. Before he was even 26, he had served in two separate wars fighting for the very survival of his homeland. This made him a supreme realist as well. From my lowly position he was aviation royalty, but despite his lofty standing in the pilot hierarchy he treated me as a peer.

I now had 200 hours of flying time in the Lear and after several successful trips where I was able to show off my flying prowess, I was again feeling good about myself as an aviator and had developed a bit of a swagger, maybe even arrogance. Either way, I didn't notice it myself. However, if I had paid more attention in high school literature class, I would have remembered the Greeks taught us that hubris was often followed by a great fall.

While I waited, I noticed that the fuel cap on the left tip tank that hadn't been dogged down properly and I reached over to refasten it when I heard the sound of an engine accelerating sharply.

It is, of course, a universal truth that pilots will stop whatever they are doing to look at an airplane in flight. Just as a cat is hypnotized by a passing bird, pilots will stop in mid stride and stare at an airplane passing by. And it is just not sight that triggers this response but all of our senses are keenly tuned to anything aviation related. And such was the case with this sound. And it caught my attention even more than usual because it was not a normal sound. It was a sour and groaning sound. It was the sound of an engine in distress and a propeller overspeeding.

I instinctively looked up towards the sound and my eyes focused on a sight that pierced my soul. I saw a small piece of sky where something should not have been happening. Just 100 feet in front of me, and 100 feet above the runway were two airplanes occupying the same small piece of air.

A Cessna 172 trainer painted in a lovely two tone blue had just taken off while doing touch and go practice landings. It was clawing itself back into the air. The 172 was a slow and plodding airplane and by itself appeared completely normal. But it was not by itself. Looming behind it, I saw a specter that was not possible, that should not have been possible.

But it was possible and it was actually happening.

Immediately behind it was another Cessna painted with bright red stripes. This airplane was larger, a twin engine 421 model designed to carry eight people. It was a sleek and fast airplane and was a common sight in Fort Lauderdale. Those twin Cessnas were often used by charter companies to transport people to the Bahamas.

The twin was bearing down rapidly on the smaller airplane. It was bigger and heavier, like a shark chasing down its weaker prey. They were in each other's blind spot. Neither was aware of the menace and neither took any kind of evasive action. I hoped that maybe, just maybe, with pure dumb luck, they might just slide past each other.

I stood, frozen in place.

They continued to close in. Another second passed by and they were then just an airplane length apart. I calculated their trajectories and saw there was a sliver of air that would offer an escape.

I silently beseeched the pilot of the faster airplane.

"Push the nose over. He is climbing into you."

"Just level off and slide underneath him"

I continued to stand helpless and I noticed I was not the only one. A small crowd of people around me were also horrified witnesses.

We waited. Mesmerized.

They were passing each other, side by side, with wingtips overlapping. It looked like they might clear, if only by a foot. In another second, it would be over and they would safely pass. I held my breath and silently cheered to myself.

But then, then the unthinkable happened.

I cried out.

"NO!"

The smaller blue trainer came out of the blind spot and the pilot of the red twin made an instinctive but fatal reaction. He was surprised by the sudden appearance of the blue trainer to his left and he rolled his own red airplane sharply to the right. It was a natural reaction, but it was the wrong reaction. As he rolled to the right, his left wing tip rose sharply up.

And then… it was done.

Instead of passing harmlessly, the wing tips of the two airplanes collided with a sound of thunder.

The impact rolled the blue trainer aircraft sharply to the left.

I stood utterly fixated on the trainer as the red twin flew out of my field of vision. It must have been an optical illusion because it looked like the trainer had lost all of its forward momentum. The trainer hung in mid air, motionless, but with its wings now perpendicular to the ground.

At that angle, the wings could no longer provide lift. The airplane was only 100 feet above the ground and the pilot only had an instant to react. I feared that since it was a training airplane, the pilot was probably a novice and doubly startled. First, he had just experienced a violent shove and then, the airplane was sideways. I hoped that maybe a more experienced instructor was also onboard. Perhaps, the more experienced hand could recover.

I fully found my voice and I yelled to the sky, trying to coach the pilot.

"Push the nose over!"

"Roll right!"

"Get some air flowing over the wings!"

"Please!"

A sob rose in my throat but I choked it back down.

"Goddamnit…push!"

The moment demanded an instantaneous reaction by the pilot. But that moment had by then passed. The airplane, itself, didn't know it was only 100 feet in the air. It only knew the laws of aerodynamics and without pilot action, it only could only follow those laws to regain the lift it needed.

The airplane's natural stability then took over and the nose dropped in an attempt to regain airspeed and get life giving lift back over the wings. But the airplane's self righting stability would take too long, and at such a low altitude there was not enough room to recover.

By now, an even larger group had now formed around me and we all watched as the nose of the blue trainer began a sickening pivot towards the ground.

I pictured myself in the cockpit of the Cessna. The pilot never saw it coming. The terror of not knowing what happened, now only seeing the earth rising up and filling your windscreen. The pilot was probably now making a desperate attempt to pull back. It would have been the wrong response but if the pilot was only a student it would have been the natural reaction. He wouldn't have known any better.

No matter. At this point, there would have been no response from the dead flight controls.

Without lift, the airplane was no longer obeying the laws of aerodynamics but instead, it was an 1800 pound block of aluminum dropping to earth.

The airplane was now pointed straight down and it only took another two seconds before it met the ground. The nose hit first, not with a crescendo and an explosion like in the movies but with a sickening thud. What energy that wasn't absorbed by the ground reverberated back along the spine of the airplane and the tail crumpled forward, back over itself like a scorpion's tail. The airplane stood on its nose for a moment and then pirouetted, falling backwards where it finally came to rest on its back on the grassy side of the runway

The whole event took less than ten seconds. Our small group stood in stunned silence. Thirty seconds ago we were all leading our lives consumed by whatever petty little chore was occupying us in the moment. Then, our separate lives were joined by the misfortune of another.

Another second of frozen shock passed by and we all sprang forward simultaneously towards the wreckage.

I ran to the wreckage in a full sprint and I dropped to my knees as I approached the airplane and slid to a stop on the grass. I crouched down and placed my face against the windshield. It was dirty and muddy from the impact but I could still see inside. Hanging upside down from his shoulder straps was the pilot. He was alone.

I looked to another Good Samaritan. We clambered onto the wing with the smell of a gas around us and the engine still smoldering. We had to get the pilot away from the wreckage. We were working inside a cauldron of gasoline and heat, just one spark away from an inferno.

I used to teach in this model airplane so I was familiar enough to open the door latch with one swift motion. There were now six of us gathered around and working as a team, we unbuckled the pilot and pulled him safely away from the wreckage.. His face was red and smashed in. He was young. Just a boy really, but with his injuries, it was hard to tell. We lowered him gently to the ground beside the wreckage. I had him by the shoulders. Two people lifted him by his ankles and I was sickened to see that his legs were broken at the shins and his bones were protruding through his blood soaked trousers.

There were now another dozen or so who had joined us. We all wanted to help but once he was laid on the ground we were helpless to do much more. Mercifully, he was in shock. I was secretly grateful that he wasn't conscious enough to know what was happening to him. I remembered that basic first aid to treat shock said to raise the victim's legs but I looked again at his shin bones and decided against it. I decided to keep him warm, at least; and I stripped off my new leather flight jacket and covered his torso and tucked it around his body.

I knelt beside him and placed my face close to his. I wanted to soothe him like the star in a war movie and whisper heroic things to comfort him. I wanted to say something, anything, that was empathetic, and strong, and wise. But the reality was that I was none of those things. As much as I wanted to say the right things, nothing came out. He was semi-conscious so I was not sure it would have mattered anyway. I was only able to put the palm of my hand on his chest and hoped that maybe the warmth and closeness of another human would soothe him.

I looked to the sky. I am not sure why. Perhaps it was the closest I could come to prayer. In the distance I saw a plume of smoke on the north side of the airport and I instantly knew what had happened. The pilot of the other airplane, despite only suffering a glancing blow, had lost control of his own airplane and crashed just north of the airport. I was later to find out that all five on board were killed on impact.

Our small band of witnesses could only wait and provide company to the young pilot. Some ran for help but that was unnecessary because the control tower had already sounded the crash alarm. Some watched silently, in shock themselves; some prayed out loud, some cried. But mainly we just waited alongside the young pilot still lying in the grass. All of us helpless. All of us bathed in a brew of gasoline, sweat, mud, scorched grass, and vomit as the forlorn chill of the looming storm front whistled through our ears. I looked at the wreckage. What only moments before had been a thing of beauty was now a blackened and grotesque mound of metal.

The paramedics quickly arrived and being experts in this area, I respectfully turned away to give the young pilot his privacy. It was apparent all the bystanders were useless so we all shuffled back to our respective lives.

As for me, I went back to my beautiful and unscathed airplane, the airplane that had been waiting impassively. I sat on the steps of the airplane. My trip hadn't even started yet and I lacked all energy. The leading edge of the front was now upon us and it began to drizzle but I sat motionless in the rain. I couldn't bear to look back at the wreckage. Somehow, I hoped that ignoring it might make it go away. The injured pilot was probably unaware of the impending threat. He was just an innocent kid taking flying lessons. I felt like I should sob but nothing came out. After a lifetime of blocking my emotions, even a trauma like the one I just witnessed did not evoke any emotion. It was too late for me. I had jammed down all feelings a long time ago. And now I wasn't sure if there was even anything to let out. Instead, I drew out a fresh pack of Marlboros.

Flip top, that was important.

I pulled out a pack of matches and paused. The stench of gasoline permeated my shirt and my pants were stained with grass, grease, and blood. But I didn't care. I struck the match and I drew heavily on the hot acrid air, glad to be alive.

Chapter 25

Merida

After a while, a cold rain had settled more deeply over the airport and along with the lingering smoke from the twin Cessna crash a black shroud settled over the airport. The cold front wasn't the type of front that cleared things out. Instead, it had stalled and enveloped us in a gloomy pall as I waited in melancholy for our passenger to show up.

When our lone passenger finally did arrive, it was without any joy that we started the engines and launched for Merida.

Once we leveled off at Flight Level 410, Gal-Nur engaged the autopilot and we both took a moment to relax before he spoke.

"I have a problem."

I turned towards him. "Oh yeah? What's that?"

"I don't have a visa for Mexico."

"You don't need a visa to go to Mexico."

"I'm not being clear. You don't need a visa, because you have an American passport. My passport is Israeli and I need a visa for Mexico."

"Oh yeah? Is that a big problem."

"It depends."

"Depends on what?"

"Depends on the immigration officer."

"Why should it depend on him? Don't they have one set of rules? It shouldn't depend on the officer, right?"

Gal-Nur didn't answer. I was a child who didn't understand and he only indulged me with a smile.

"So what are you going to do?"

"My passport is the same color blue as yours. From a distance it looks the same. I'll just hide mine in the middle of the stack with yours and the passenger. Hopefully, the customs agent will only give them a passing glance. But if he notices and looks more closely, I'll hide a few dollars next to my photo page."

It took me a moment to understand what he just said.

"Isn't that a bribe?"

"Not really, it's just a handling fee to smooth over any discrepancies."

"That sounds like a bribe. What if he takes offense? Won't that get us in trouble?"

"Well whatever you want to call it. It's nothing dirty. It's just the cost of doing business. That's how they do things. 'Mordida' they call it… in English, it translates into 'the bite.' Everyone gets a little bite. It's fair that way. He'll only take offense if it's not enough."

How much?

"Depends. The rest of our paperwork is in order and we have the proper landing clearances. This is just a minor oversight. It's not as though I am trying to sneak into the country. I am heading right out. It's late, so the customs officer will be a junior guy without any real authority. He's not paid well. $10 should do it."

Gal-Nur left it at that as we continued into the sunset enjoying the silence of cruise flight. Although, as we progressed closer to Mexico, I was increasingly uneasy about the idea of bribing a customs official. Back in the United States, I had been taught that rules were to be obeyed and government officials were the impartial arbiters of right and wrong. My own parents were scrupulously honest, even to a fault. Although, looking back on it, I have to say I'm not really sure it gave them any advantage.

The air was smooth so Gal-Nur was flying right at the redline on the Mach meter. Despite our high speed the sun was slowly pulling away from us and by the time we called Merida Control for descent clearance we were fully embraced by the night.

Things were quiet and we landed in Merida without any fuss and taxied over to the area for private airplane customs inspections. After deplaning we escorted our passenger into the main customs office.

We entered the customs office and the starkly bright fluorescent lights assaulted my eyes. Once they adjusted I saw that we were in a room with polished white linoleum floors and wood paneled walls about the same color as honey. Waiting for us was an overweight middle-aged customs officer who was sitting at an old wooden desk. He was wearing a dirty khaki uniform with sergeant stripes pinned to his sleeves. His salt and pepper hair peeked from the sides of his cap. He carried a small caliber revolver holstered to the front of his pants. His face was puffy and his belly stretched over his belt, pushing the barrel of his pistol directly towards his own groin.

Gal-Nur placed the three passports on the desk and we stood patiently. The officer was slouched in his chair and made us wait while he finished picking a piece of dirt from his fingernail. He then reached forward and slid the passports along the desk towards his big belly. He leaned back in his chair with the three passports in his hand. He opened the first one briefly, giving only a cursory check of the photograph and expiration dates. After he inspected the first one, he slid it behind the others like a casino dealer shuffling cards. He then got to the Israeli passport. The passport may have been the same blue as mine, but the gold embossed Menorah on the cover stood out starkly. I held my breath.

The officer paused and looked up over his glasses. Gal-Nur remained silent. I tried to read the officer's name tag but it was too badly scratched. He flicked open the passport deftly to the section where the precious visa was supposed to have been located. However, the visa page was missing the appropriate stamp. In its place was a $10 bill. The officer paused. He leaned forward and placed the passports on his desk. He looked up again at us, then looked down at the money. He then looked over his shoulder and back down to the stack of passports.

In one motion, he slid the ten dollars from the passport, along the desk, and into his front pant pocket. He then stamped the passport with the seal of the State of Mexico and he motioned us away.

I let out a breath.

It worked.

Our passenger departed and I went on to my preflight duties. Gal-Nur had assigned me the task of getting fuel at that late hour while he searched for the flight planning office to prepare for our flight home to Fort Lauderdale. After my own brief search, I found the office of a low level functionary who could release the fuel truck.

He sat behind his desk.

I greeted him with my pidgin Spanish.

"Buenos noches Señor. Necesitamos petróleo por favor."

He was reading a newspaper and chose to ignore me.

I asked a second time.

He then lowered his newspaper and pointed to a white slip of paper on his desk.

I reached for it and turned it over.

It read simply "$100. American."

I had heard about this. It was a way that a bureaucrat could ask for a bribe without actually asking for one. From my earlier lessons with other captains, I knew I had two choices.

I could either pay the fee and get the fuel now; or I could get righteous, and wait until the start of the business day to get fuel without having to pay the mordida.

It was midnight and I didn't feel like sleeping in the back of the airplane till morning so I knew which choice to make.

I pulled out my roll of cash and without any emotion, I peeled off one hundred dollars in twenties and laid them on the desk. Satisfied with our transaction, the anonymous bureaucrat picked up the phone and ordered a fuel truck for us.

I returned to the airplane and lit a cigarette to wait for Gal-Nur while I weighed the pros and cons of what just happened. I had now witnessed one bribe and conducted another of my own. I smiled to myself for becoming worldly with the ways of the south but I didn't like the dark pit in my stomach. Some people just called them normal handling fees, others called them what they really were. Deep down, I knew this was not how my parents raised me, but those rules from middle class America didn't seem to work here. I tried to justify myself by saying that was just how things were done in the real world but that gave me little solace. No matter, I pushed the matter to the back of my mind. It was late and I was eager to crawl into my own bed.

Chapter 26

A Midnight Decision

I had been standing by the airplane on the dark ramp alone for a while. The fueler had never arrived despite the bribe, but I was more worried that Gal-Nur was missing. We, of course, needed two pilots to fly the airplane but it was more than that. Gal-Nur was my lifeline. I was a stranger here and not really able to survive on my own.

I heard some steps coming from the shadows and I saw two people approach the airplane. The first person was a police officer. He had a lot of braid and I thought he must be a high-ranking officer. The second was a man dressed in an expensive business suit. The uniformed officer came right up to me and without an introduction, stated,

"Señor, I am sorry but you will not be allowed to leave. There is a problem and we have some questions for you."

My knees then went a little weak and I had to steady myself.

Was it not having a visa, or was it the bribe?

"Your passenger has been arrested and we need to interview you. Your fellow pilot is already in a car. You must join us and come into the city."

After a short car ride, Gal-Nur and I found ourselves in a waiting room in the police station sitting on hard orange molded plastic chairs. The room, actually it was more of a long hallway, had the same polished white linoleum floor and stark fluorescent lights as the customs office but it smelled strongly of cleaning chemicals. The area was open and brightly lit. Once we entered the waiting room, our host in the business suit locked the exit door.

He then turned to us.

"Wait here. We have to ask your passenger some questions."

I checked my watch. It was 1 AM.

And so we sat, with no option but to wait while they interviewed our passenger in the next room. Although judging by the sound of crashing chairs and shrieks, the interview sounded like more of a beating.

As a teenager, I had been stopped by the law occasionally but I was always able to work things out. The police back home were willing to make an exception for some local kids just having some fun and we were always let go. But this was different. These were people who didn't mind inflicting physical abuse and we were just strangers to them. Being a feckless and privileged kid wasn't an excuse anymore. Just the opposite; we were targets just because we were the privileged outsiders. I looked up and down the hallway looking to escape but the view only reminded me that the one door was barred shut. I wanted to push back into my chair hoping to become invisible but my muscles were slack. I was a thousand miles from home and no one knew where I was. This was not an adventure anymore. I looked to Gal-Nur for reassurance. He sat in his chair and only nodded to me.

After a while, the plainclothes policeman came out from the room. He looked to Gal-Nur and reached out his hand.

"Captain?"

Gal-Nur stood and shook his hand.

I thought calling him "Captain" was a bit odd. It seemed that if we were in trouble, they wouldn't be using a title of respect. Maybe that was a good sign.

"We must continue the investigation so we will be keeping your passenger here. We do have some questions for you but first I have a request. My brother works in the mayor's office and he needs to go to Houston on an important trip."

Gal-Nur remained silent but nodded.

"How much is it to charter your airplane to Houston?"

I then saw immediately how this game was played and I felt a sudden lightness.

I knew how I would have answered but Gal-Nur was the captain so I looked to him to respond.

Gal-Nur paused only a second.

"Señor, It would be a great honor to transport your brother. We are going there anyway so we can carry him free." As an extra motion of goodwill and fraternity, Gal-Nur then repeated the promise in Spanish.

"All we need is to buy fuel and file a flight plan."

With that small addition, Gal-Nur made it clear we were willing to buy our own fuel; and not willing to horse trade our freedom.

Gal-Nur continued.

"If one of your men returns us to the airport, we can be ready to go in one hour."

I suppose the police negotiator got what he wanted because he smiled.

"Very good, my friend. We will have a car take you back to your airplane. My brother will be there soon."

And he turned to unlock the door.

Once we were back at the airport, all our needs to prepare the airplane for its flight to Houston were magically and swiftly accomplished by a large group of airport workers who were waiting for us. No mordida required. One hour later, it was with great relief we broke ground from Mexico and pointed our nose north to the United States where we dropped off our new Mexican friend.

Chapter 27

Crossing the Gulf

A fter a brief rest in Houston, we returned to Fort Lauderdale empty and it was quiet as we glided across the Gulf of Mexico. It was my leg to fly and I reflected on what had happened. Or, I thought I knew what had happened but I needed a more experienced hand to make it more clear.

"So, what's up with that cop back in Merida? Do you think they really would have arrested us or was it just a ploy to scare us to take them to Houston?"

"It's hard to say exactly. They can do pretty much what they want. Even though we were just a charter flight they can still hold us and impound the airplane if they suspect our customer of something. They really don't care if you only met the passenger a few hours earlier. They can make as much trouble for us as they think they can get away with. There are no rules. Remember, out of the United States, you have no rights."

"How often does that happen?"

"How often does 'what' happen?"

"Them making trouble for us?"

Gal-Nur answered with a riddle.

"There are four types of officials you are going to run across down south."

He used the expression "down south" for any flying that was not in the United States.

"The first type is the guy who stamped my passport. They're low ranking, modest guys who know they are lucky to have an easy government job. They aren't high ranking enough to cause real trouble and get any big money. But if they can make a few extra bucks when no one is looking so they can help feed their family, well, they'll just look the other way. They're the easiest and you see that all the time.

"The second type is the self-important type, the petty officials. They will bully and bluster and try to intimidate you. They like the ego trip, but once you pay the bite, they will eventually let you go.

"The third guy was the guy in the suit at the police station. They usually have important family connections and they are pretty self-assured in their position. They can be bullies and they can make our lives really miserable. But they're mostly interested in political power and money. They can eventually be bought off also, just for a much higher price."

At that point, Houston Center interrupted him and instructed us to switch over to Miami. Gal-Nur picked up the microphone and answered the call. He paused, changed frequencies on the number one VHF radio, and checked in with Miami.

His train of thought was broken and he just looked straight ahead. The sun was directly overhead and the cockpit was filled with orange light as we were suspended above the glistening blue Gulf below us. I looked at him and waited for him to finish. While I waited, I took a moment to marvel at Gal-Nur's life as a young man. Here was a guy that fought for the very survival of his home in two separate wars. His own father was killed in the Israeli fight for independence. These were brave men who had faced ruthless enemies, so I suppose facing some corrupt official in Latin America was hardly a concern. I was humbled to share a cockpit with him. He stared ahead with a faint smile on his face.

"And the fourth?"

"The fourth what?"

"The fourth type of customs official?

"Oh, yes. The fourth. You don't find them very often but they're the most dangerous.

"They're harder to explain but you'll find out soon enough. And if you do run into one, just be very careful."

And he left it at that.

We then continued on in silence where I was left with my own thoughts. My initial repulsion over the whole event disappeared. Instead, I was filled with an odd satisfaction. We were faced with an authority figure who didn't play by the rules I had grown up with, and we survived. This was a different game with a different set of rules. It appealed to my rebellious streak and my sense of adventure. I became intent on playing this new game well.

Upon landing in Fort Lauderdale, it had been a day since the crash I had witnessed and things were back to normal at the airport. Once I was home, I read in the local paper that the young man we had pulled out of the wrecked airplane the day before had died of his injuries. They said he was an aspiring airline pilot. He was 17 years old and had a total of 21 hours of flying time.

I read the story again… and then again.

He was just a baby, doing what he loved and he had done nothing wrong. But now he was dead.

Just a few years ago, that was me…

It could have been me.

But it wasn't me… It was him… I had survived and he had not.

Chapter 28

Clashing with the Modern Mayan Empire

We made a normal landing at La Aurora airport in Guatemala City. Although the airport serving Guatemala's capital could hardly be described as normal. That's because the area around Guatemala City was originally home to the Mayan Empire. Shortly after their empire collapsed under its own weight, the Spanish conquistadors appeared and started building their own empire. The Spanish found the same area so much to their liking that they made it the capital of their Viceroyalty.

What does all that have to do with airplanes? Well, the needs of jet airplanes were not much on the minds of those ancient empire builders. And as a result, both the Native American emperors and the Spanish developed a propensity to build their capital cities nestled deep in mountain valleys. And La Aurora airport was among the most challenging to modern aviators. It was situated at 5,000 feet above sea level and was tucked in a narrow valley surrounded by 12,000-foot peaks. Because of that challenging topography, the airport required a circling step down approach that was not only complicated but demanded precision flying as the pilot threaded around the volcanoes and their ash plumes. But that wasn't all of the story. Flat land in the valley was in scarce supply, so the single runway was short and sloped downwards with a steep drop at the end. The whole operation required precise lateral navigation during the circuitous descent; as well as exact speed control on landing, followed by hard braking immediately after touchdown. An overrun at La Aurora was certain to be fatal.

I was flying this trip with Zimmer. He was not only my captain on that day but he owned his own charter company with a fleet of extravagantly appointed Learjets. I was flying with Zimmer because in the world of South Florida charter flying, copilots were a low value commodity. Therefore, we were frequently loaned out to wherever the need happened to be. And on that day the need happened to be with Zimmer.

I was flying with him for the first time. When we met in the flight planning room he was pacing around the room searching for nothing in particular. He avoided eye contact with me and only gave me the most cursory of greetings. Once he decided to acknowledge my presence more formally, his briefing consisted only of this one abrupt question:

"Do you know what two things each mountain valley in South America has in common?"

I wasn't sure if it was a real question, so I remained silent and he answered it himself.

"A cross overlooking the city and an airplane crash site."

And with that admonition, we headed to Guatemala.

Back to the airplane: As we descended, I viewed vast stretches of verdant plantations growing coffee and bananas. The city was located in a canyon named the Valley of the Hermit and from the air, the overall sense was, indeed, one of seclusion and tranquility.

Moreover, the appellation "hermit" was an apt one. Guatemala City was different from other capital cities that embraced different cultures and viewpoints. Instead, the masters of Guatemala were hermits and renounced reform. Their primitive views caused much suffering for the people of Guatemala.

Our single passenger on this trip was a businessman with extensive interests throughout the region. He was directly descended from the Spanish aristocrats who had been in Guatemala for centuries and this small group still held a tight grip on most of the country, simply replacing the previous Mayan overlords. Educated and urbane, he was at the top of the socio-economic pyramid, certainly several levels above Zimmer and me. To this day, I am still not sure why, but he invited both of us to stay at his home and join him for dinner that evening.

We were quickly processed through customs with much groveling by the local commander, likely due to the high status of our passenger. Once outside the gate we were met by a motorcade of limousines and trucks. Zimmer and I were offered the best seats in the newest car while our host rode in the rearmost car. We had a driver in the front and two escorts who sat across from us. Our escorts were polite to us but their focus was outside the car.

As we rolled away, I knocked on the side glass.

"This window doesn't roll down and it seems pretty thick."

Zimmer was next to me. At this altitude, the air was chilly, about 50 degrees, but his brow beaded with sweat.

He grunted a half-hearted laugh.

"It's bullet proof glass. There is a civil war raging here and it's pretty ugly. Lots of people in the country just disappear. Some of it is political, people run down by the death squads, some of it street crime. It's a free for all...you've got Argentines and Cubans here playing both sides, plus the CIA...everybody is here. Most of the killing happens in the northern provinces but sometimes they do revenge killings here in the capital. And sometimes, it's just plain criminal abductions. Either way, the streets aren't safe here."

"What's going on exactly?"

"The government here is obsessed with the communst insurgency. Can't blame them actually. Look at what happened in Cuba and Cambodia.

"That's not all...our friend... He didn't give us the nice car because he is a gracious host. We are in the decoy car. If there is an attack, we get sacrificed first, which gives him time to make his getaway."

With this somber admonition, I stared at the glass and tried to sound brave.

"Well, I hope the glass manufacturer was good at his job."

I again looked to our two escorts and realized for the first time that the large bulges under their jackets were firearms.

As we sped through the slums of the city, my muscles tensed waiting for an attack but after a while, I resigned myself to my potential fate and glumly took in the sights. The buildings in this section of town were two story struc-tures made of concrete block. Some of them had corrugated metal roofs but most were only covered with tarps. Many years ago, in happier times, they were painted in gay shades of pastel but at the time of our visit, they were faded and chipped.

We progressed from one neighborhood to the next and the general sul-lenness of the area decreased until we entered an area with larger and more elegant homes shielded by tall hedges.

It was twilight when we finally slowed and stopped in front of an ornate black wrought iron gate. Adjacent to the gate was a guard shack. A lone guard came out and exchanged some agitated Spanish with our driver. He peered into the back seat to look at us. He then made a lengthy check of each car in our retinue, and satisfied we were who the driver said we were, the guard opened the gate.

Our driver pulled ahead slowly onto a circular gravel driveway and the tires made a crunching sound until we came to a halt in front of our host's grand home. One of our guards opened the car door and I stepped out onto the gravel. The main house was silhouetted by the last rays of the orange sunset. We were in front of a two story white stucco building in the colonial style. It had a red barrel tile roof and a massive carved teak front door. Carved on the face of the door was the national bird of Guatemala, the quetzal. The bird was revered by the Mayans and it was believed that the quetzal valued its freedom so much, they would die once caged. Next to the door was a brass plaque inscribed with the words "Casa de Gracia."

A butler greeted us and escorted us through the main door, where we were carried back in time to a 17th century colonial hacienda. Inside the main door was a large foyer covered in terra cotta tiles and the foyer overlooked a large grass cloister with a fountain in the middle.

The cloister was two stories high and lined with teak posts and railings. Each post had a gas light that was flickering just barely brighter than the setting sun. The fountain in the middle tinkled gently.

Our host excused himself to dress for dinner and the butler led us to the dining room to wait. Once we entered the dining room, a steward dressed in a white dinner jacket, who had been setting the table, scurried away leaving us alone in the empty room. Although, I didn't feel alone.

I looked to Zimmer for some guidance. We were still dressed in our flying clothes of brown polyester slacks and wrinkled pilot shirts. It was my first trip with him so I hardly knew the man. He was 41 years old, of medium height with a potbelly. His graying hair was folded over to cover his bald head. Beyond his appearance, what I did know was that he didn't share his thoughts when making a decision and once he did make a decision, he didn't say very much about it. He was a former navy pilot having flown anti submarine patrols. Those were 16 hour missions tracking shadowy Soviet submarines over vast tracts of empty ocean. Sub hunting was a chess game with the endgame of cornering the enemy sub in an inescapable position. It was an operation that allowed the mission commander to think deliberately and strategically. I guessed Zimmer's navy experience trained him to come to conclusions slowly.

The room was quiet except for Zimmer's breathing. It was slow and labored. I wasn't sure if his straining breathe was from the tension or the extra weight he carried around his stomach. He started to speak. Then paused by placing his index finger against his lips. He looked away from me, and then turned back to me to say something, but again paused a second time. He held up his index finger to signal me he was still formulating a thought.

His round face had a perplexed look and after about another minute of thought, he broke into a grin, "I'm a long way from home for a poor farm kid from Minnesota."

I returned the laugh but I had a feeling that we were out of our element and I was unable to relax. What little I did know for certain about Zimmer was that he came across as absent minded but behind that facade, he was a shrewd thinker so it was reassuring to be with him.

While we waited, I took an inventory of the dining room. It was about thirty feet long and twenty feet wide with white plaster walls and terracotta floor. The room was dominated by a heavy oak dining table set for ten people and I wondered who else was joining us.

The room had no electrical lights; instead, two large black wrought iron candelabras on the table provided dim illumination. The dining table rested on a plush Persian rug. It was colored blood red. The brown terra cotta tile floors contrasted sharply against the white stucco walls and the ceiling was about twenty feet high, supported by heavy teak beams.

Guatemala City is set along the tropical latitudes but, nestled as it is in the highlands, a damp chill usually pervaded the evening. To ward off the cold, another servant had entered the room to start a fire in a large hearth, which occupied a ten foot section of wall.

Once the fire took hold in the fireplace, a satisfying warmth emanated from the fire and light from the flame flickered and played patterns on the high ceiling. On the wall opposite the fireplace was a nook holding a small altar with a statue of the Virgin Mary. In front of the statue burned three votive candles. Behind the head of the table were French doors made from polished teak, overlooking a garden with a riot of red bougainvilleas. I looked out but beyond the cloister but the world was dark; beyond our little oasis, the modern world no longer existed.

After a while, our passenger appeared from a side door in mid conversation with some of his colleagues. They were several men who entered the room, and all were dressed alike in dark bespoke suits with crisp white shirts and rich silk ties. We were briefly introduced to each other and then footmen pulled out the high back wooden chairs signaling for us to sit. Once we were all seated on the plush red velvet upholstery, the conversation turned back to each other as they caught up on family small talk.

A procession of servants appeared and we were served a lavish meal of sumptuous meats, French wine, and sautéed vegetables drenched in Spanish olive oil.

As the Spanish are inclined to do, the dinner stretched into the very late hours and these men talked at length about their various business interests while Zimmer and I mostly listened. From their conversation, I could gather that not only did they have vast business holdings but the country itself was their personal plantation. A plantation they ruled with a heavy hand. These were hard working men, but hard working in the feudal style. That is to say, they didn't do the actual physical labor themselves but they directed the work for intermediaries to carry out. Their lofty status had been determined centuries ago because their lineage could be traced directly to those of the Spanish conquistadores.

In order to maintain the Spanish Crown's power in the colonies, they established an elaborate caste system with the pure blooded Spanish at the top and the indigenous people at the bottom. It seemed a tragedy that the local campesinos only exchanged their Mayan overlords for Spanish ones. Even in modern day Guatemala, one's fate was irreparably fixed for life depending on which caste each person was born into. And any action taken to modernize this system was usually met with death.

After the table had been cleared, the wine continued to flow along with cigars for everyone. The conversation then turned to the more pressing political situation of the Communist insurgency in Guatemala and surrounding countries.

Zimmer and I had said little during the dinner. It had been interesting but fairly mundane and we played the role of polite guests. But now the conversation turned to the darker side of Communist insurgency and our table mates spoke quite openly about the various atrocities visited on the local villagers in order to put down the Communist rebels. Similar to in Vietnam, the rural villagers bore the brunt of the civil war. Whether they were in fact Communist sympathizers, or supporters of the government, or just neutral, it did not matter. The rural people were victimized equally. Left unsaid, but highly likely, was that this barbarity was being perpetrated by the agents of these very men.

The room darkened from the heavy smoke of the cigars and tone of the unfolding conversation. These men were unabashed by the violence visited on their fellow countrymen but as for me, my scalp tingled with indignation. I wanted to interject but I held back as I played the role of respectful guest.

The conversation continued and I found my jaw tightening. I continued to only listen but with each report of villainy I found it harder to hold back my displeasure. Finally, I could be polite no longer. I leaned forward and waited for a gap in the conversation.

When the time came, I pretended to ask an innocent question. Given the elegant setting, I posed the question in an urbane manner although I had every intention of it being provocative.

"Perhaps, if more civil rights and land reform had been given to the peasant class, isn't it likely we would not be in this situation now?"

The room fell silent and all eyes shifted to me. Zimmer let out a grunt. Or maybe it was a cough. I glanced at him and his brow was sweating even more than usual.

The dying fireplace hissed and crackled in the otherwise silent room.

Our host was gracious. "Well, you are right to a certain degree. But things are much worse now to concede anything. We are in a difficult situation from which there is no return. Any concessions made will be seen as a weakness. And the insurgents are supported by the Castros and they are our mortal enemies."

I did not reply and the unpleasant silence was again filled with the hissing fireplace.

One man opposite from me had remained silent for most of the dinner. Earlier in the dinner, I had glanced at him furtively but his dark demeanor didn't encourage eye contact beyond that first glance.

But now he was staring me down.

"Did your university professor teach you that?"

His tone was lethal.

There was a pause and all heads turned towards me. I waited to answer hoping my host would rescue me but it was not to be. I had made a challenge and my dinner mate had accepted.

It was now man to man.

I thought I could hold my own. We had this very discussion back in my international politics class in university so I continued headlong into an abyss without realizing where I was going.

"If the poor are given more civil rights and economic opportunities then the country as a whole will be better off. If that happens, then the Communists will lose the source of their grievance. Will it not?"

My opponent continued on the offensive.

"Young man, ideals are a wonderful thing but they are also an enormous burden. I think you will find your life much easier if you relax your grip on them. The world is not perfect."

He then went straight for my weak spot.

"Didn't your father teach you that?"

"No. I am sorry but he did not. My father died when I was young."

"We'll, I am sorry to hear that young man. We all have a cross to bear."

My body filled with rage and shame. My father was not much of a mentor. He was a good man but he didn't understand the world. At least, not in a way that allowed him to thrive. He died when I was 18, so what little teaching he did was cut short just as I was becoming an adult. Conversely, my mother was a deeply nurturing woman but her love was so unconditional I never learned any hard lessons from her either. As a result, I never learned about life and that actions had consequences. I grew up without any discernment about life. I was both naive and cynical and my head was mostly filled with unrealistic mush, not the cold realities of life.

My antagonist was not yet done with me. He paused as he took up his crystal wine glass and lifted it to his nose. The room's attention was still centered on him. He swirled the ruby liquid and took a sip. He had lingered over his meal and the staff had not cleaned his place. Lying on his plate were the leftover bone and gristle of the animal we had just eaten.

He stared deep into the prismatic red liquid and was lost in thought.

He paused and snorted his disapproval. He put the glass down on the white linen tablecloth. His actions were slow and controlled.

"My dear young man, have you seen the atrocities committed by the Communists?"

He paused for an answer that he knew I did not have but he continued baiting me.

"Have you been to any country where you have seen a humane Communist?"

My cheeks burned and now I just wanted to hide.

"No sir, I have not."

I was floundering. My earlier righteousness had evaporated. I was completely on the defensive with no weapons to protect myself. This was nothing at all like the debates we had back in school. All the debates in the classrooms overlooking a leafy campus were so civil and abstract with the obvious answer in clear sight. Back then, it was easy to gain the approval of a smug professor. All I had to do was repeat verbatim the right things and it was an easy "A." Although now, I was parroting all the correct answers but it wasn't working.

These men seemed like mobsters. They ruthlessly victimized their own citizens and unabashedly relished their position. But they were also real people who had real and lethal enemies. And they were doing what they had to do to survive. Things didn't seem so clear cut anymore. In the United States, they would likely have been jailed by the government on a litany of various charges; and yet, here they were, not only the most successful people in the region; but they were in fact, the government. And they were also being supported by the US government.

He continued and answered his own question.

"No, of course you have not, because there is no such thing as a humane Communist. They are never satisfied and only want our heads. They are a mob and once you show weakness you are dead. Look at what Castro did to the Batista government. Hundreds executed in the street and tens of thousands more exiled to Miami. The same thing in Vietnam, a people who your government, I may add, abandoned. And once the Communists gain power, the population is much worse off than before.

"If our people are not happy here, well, let them emigrate to "del Norte"... to the United States, If they so sincerely desire freedom, then your country can have them."

Everyone in the room was now shifting in their chair and looking down. But my tormentor was not yet finished.

"We know how to manage our society and we do not want anyone telling us how to govern our country. This is my home and I will defend it as I see fit."

He finished and his last words hung in the air.

The fire had died out and the only motion in the room were the smoky plumes from the candelabras flowing straight up to the ceiling.

I was about to choke off an apology when our host broke the silence.

"Gentleman, this is something that we, in our own country, can still not agree on. It is late and we can't resolve the problem now. Let us say our goodbyes."

Thoroughly chastened, Zimmer and I also excused ourselves. As our driver took us to our hotel I had an epiphany.

I thought I was a man. The calendar said so, but, in reality, I was still a boy; a boy that was undisciplined and feckless. I had a lot of book knowledge but that seemed useless in the deep south. My smug view of the world was only a facade... shallow and unsophisticated. I had thought I was smart but it turned out that I was only book smart, and that was meaningless here. I needed street smarts.

I wondered what was considered honorable behavior in this new world and I was uncertain what I needed to do to survive. I did remember a verse from a Guatemalan proverb. "It is not the fault of the parrot but of the one who teaches him to talk."

But beyond that, I was left without an answer.

Chapter 29

Port-au-Prince

I stepped out of the airplane into the inferno that was Port-au-Prince. It was mid August and in the harsh afternoon sun, the temperature and humidity both approached 100, soaking my uniform in sweat. While we waited for the customs officer to clear us in, I looked to the airport perimeter, which abutted the slums of Port-au-Prince. Haiti was not a usual destination for us and it was easy to understand why. It was the poorest country in the Western Hemisphere, as well as home to one of the most corrupt regimes in the world; it held little appeal to corporate interests, and even less attraction to affluent tourists.

Our passenger was a Bahamian attorney who we had been flying around the Caribbean basin for the last few days. Unlike most others who avoided the western side of the island of Hispaniola, he was a frequent traveler to Haiti. He represented clients that were some of the few people that did have business interests here. He was in Haiti for two days of meetings and we were to wait for him.

Haiti was known as the Pearl of the Antilles and a few hundred years earlier was the wealthiest colony in the Caribbean. But that was a long time ago and things were much different now. Of course, I had known about the abject poverty in Haiti. It was another topic in my international studies classes. But my classroom studies on Haiti were similar to my earlier views on Guatemala. It did not prepare me for the stark human suffering.

Not only was I unprepared for the squalor but I was unprepared to personally witness the total despair evident in the eyes of the local population. Nor did I know of the duplicity of the US government which helped bring about their fall. But no matter, after the Guatemalan affair I had resolved to avoid amateurish involvement in international affairs. And I only planned on an enjoyable tropical sojourn. However, the various cultural cross currents in the Caribbean were an irresistible riptide, which sucked in all those nearby.

We pulled away from the airport terminal in the back seat of a local taxi cab. It was a mid 1960s vintage white Ford sedan with a vinyl interior done in a ghastly neon blue. The windows were rolled down and a nice breeze passed through the car as we drove. My sweat dried a bit as I took in the sights.

I was flying with Coe again and we were on our way to a hotel in the cooler highlands of Petion-Ville overlooking the city. But we first had to pass through the city of Port-au-Prince itself.

Like many cities around the Caribbean, it had the same sad dichotomy. The people enjoyed a lively and colorful culture but found themselves suffocating under the burden of oppression and poverty. The streets our driver followed had at one time had been paved but after decades of neglect, they had been rendered into a muddy washboard.

We approached a busy boulevard and we paused for a passing train. There were no crossing signs nor any gates; nor was it a light rail line. In the middle of a busy urban street someone had laid a heavy cargo rail line. The passing train consisted of open hopper cars filled with sugarcane and it was moving slowly.

We waited patiently for the long train to pass. While we waited, the taxi driver shut off his engine, presumably to save gas. With the aged engine no longer pulsating my insides, I relaxed in the heat. The passing train was hypnotic and I watched it roll by absentmindedly. One rail car that passed us had a faulty bearing. Its overheated axle glowed red and fire licked the wheel hub. Workmen who were hanging on the sides of the cars seemed unfazed by the fire. Young children scampered alongside the passing cars to pick up stray cane that had fallen to the ground.

I was curious so I asked Coe a question.

"What do they do with all that cane? Export?"

"No, they mostly keep it all for themselves. They process it into rum. Just the same as the Peruvians peasants use coca to numb the pain of their lives, here they use rum. Very little gets exported."

"That seems like a waste, they could make more money exporting it."

The driver's eyes were visible in the rear view mirror and they met mine. He held the stare for a moment too long before he looked away.

Coe was wise to the ways of the Caribbean. Despite his relatively young age, he had many years flying in the region. He saw the same thing and picked up the cue.

He grunted to get my attention. His right hand was lying on the seat beside him. Not visible to the driver he made a slashing cut motion signaling the conversation was over. I took the clue and continued my sightseeing in silence.

We continued the drive under Coe's order of quiet so I spent my time observing the driver, stealing a glance in his direction every now and then. He was a very dark skinned black man, in his mid 50s, wearing a hand me down shirt that would have been fashionable in the US about ten years earlier. He smelled faintly of body odor. Several times, he caught me looking at him through his own mirror and several times we looked away from each other.

The car labored as it climbed up the foothills away from the steamy city. At each sharp turn the driver had to slow and the worn out engine struggled to accelerate again. Each time we turned, Coe and I slid across the slick vinyl seats holding our balance by hanging on to the seat ahead of us. As we climbed, the streets became more leafy and more narrow. We were leaving the steamy turmoil of Port-au-Prince below us.

The driver made one last turn hugging a switchback overgrown with mango trees and the car jerked to a stop. In a thick patois, he declared "Hotel Olaffson."

We got out of the car and for the first time, I noticed there was a rifle lying on the front seat. The driver also climbed out and opened the trunk but made no move to remove our bags.

Instead, we retrieved our own bags. The fare was only three dollars, which Coe paid with cash and tipped the driver an extra $20; an extraordinarily large tip in Haiti.

The car pulled away and we were left standing in the hot sun. We were at the foot of the steps leading up to the hotel so I turned to climb the stairs but Coe stopped me.

"You were talking too much in the car."

I lifted my eyebrows.

"I didn't think I was talking too much."

"It wasn't that. It was what you were saying."

I tried to read Coe's exact meaning but his eyes were imperceptible behind his dark pair of aviator sunglasses.

"Did you notice the front license plate?"

"No."

"Well, I wouldn't expect you to know anyway. It had the number '22' on it.

"Yeah?"

"That number represents the Tonton Macoute. Haven't you heard of them?"

"Yeah, I know about them and the Duvaliers. It's all over the Miami newspapers."

"Well, then you should know better. Haiti is basically a gulag. The people here are not just dirt poor, but it's the worst kind of dictatorship here. The Duvalier regime is brutal and they control every aspect of Haitian society and they do it with the help of the secret police, the Tonton Macoute. They're named after a vodou demon and the superstitious locals really believe they are demons incarnate in a human body. But, of course, the Tonton are not demons. They are real people with real lives. How do you think they earn a living?"

I had to admit that, once again, I didn't know the difference between my book knowledge and real life.

"What the newspapers don't tell you is one of the major perks they enjoy is that taxi drivers are the only ones who can drive the wealthy white tourists. The taxi drivers here are all Tonton. To a man. It's a nice source of income for them, along with whatever else they can squeeze out of the local population though extortion or outright robbery. They're also the eyes and ears of President Duvalier. So, as they drive around they are always spying for the government."

"Is that why you gave him a big tip?"

He didn't answer my direct question.

"Look, just a friendly warning. They don't like getting exposed as thugs. We're relatively safe as white Americans but we can't push it. They like our money but at the same time, they resent our presence. It's a delicate balance. There is no sense in getting their attention. You have to be careful who you talk to and what you say. So it's just best to say as little as possible. And just pretend you're not interested in anything that you happen to see. And yes, cash helps people look the other way."

Chapter 30

Meeting with Vodou

We then climbed up the steep concrete steps to the hotel main entrance. The Olaffson was once the Presidential mansion and it sat on a hilltop overlooking the steaming city below. It was a white brick Victorian mansion with elaborate wood gingerbread trim and a red tin roof. Dominating the facade were two parapets, one on each front corner. Surrounding the hotel on all four sides was a large veranda lined with wicker rocking chairs and ceiling fans.

It was a long climb to the main entrance. It was two flights up a concrete staircase lined with wrought iron railings and lush yellow crotons. Just like in Guatemala, as we walked into the lobby, I was transported to another colonial time capsule, this one a tropical plantation rather than Spanish colonial. The wooden floor under our feet creaked with each step and the lobby smelled of old teak, moth balls, and jasmine. A grandfather clock in the corner by the front desk ticked gracefully. A rain shower had passed just before our arrival and water was dripping all along the patio perimeter. The receptionist checked us in quickly and handed me a room key. Each room at the Olafsson was not numbered, but instead named after a movie star from the golden age of Hollywood. I was assigned the Marlon Brando.

Once inside my room, I noticed there was a handwritten note on the desk. "Bienvenue! Please join us for cocktails on the patio at 7 PM."

And after a brief shower to cool down I was on the veranda, seated in a white wicker chair enjoying a gin and tonic.

Coe was already seated at a table. And with him was a professor from the University of Haiti. The professor was wearing white linen slacks and a white guayabera shirt. Because of the cooler highland air, he was able to wear a silk ascot. It was red and blue, a splash of colors the same as the colors of the Haitian flag. The fingernail of his little finger was an inch longer than the rest, signifying he was a man who didn't have to do manual labor, or that it doubled as a coke spoon. I wasn't sure which.

He was deep voiced and spoke perfect American English. He introduced himself only by his first name, François.

He asked, "Do you like it here?"

I had to admit to myself that when we were driving through the city I was dismayed by the utter lifelessness in the eyes of the locals. I had seen poverty before but this, in Haiti, was something entirely different. However, I paused and reflected on my experience in Guatemala; and how truthfulness was not always the best policy. Thoughtful of the trouble I had gotten into in Guatemala, I decided to stick to my new policy of non-confrontation.

"It is a beautiful country."

He seemed pleased with my answer but before he could respond to me, a young woman entered the patio. She was mixed race and light skinned. She was barefoot and wore a print dress down to her ankles. Her short cut top was of the peasant style popular among the hippies of the 1960s. Her midriff was visible and she wore a beaded chain across her belly.

She circled around the table, leaned against François and put her arm around his shoulder. He proudly announced, "This is Michelle. She is from New York but she has been studying vodou and the Haitian people for years. He drew a deep breath before each sentence and spoke slowly even warily, measuring his thoughts. He had enough time now to appraise Coe and me, so then decided to make the following pronouncement.

"She is a mambo, a vodou priestess."

I was a bit taken aback by his statement regarding her priestly calling. We didn't have such things when I was growing up in a middle class suburban neighborhood. Priestesses existed only in history books about long dead pagan cultures. I took in the new information and said nothing.

We exchanged a polite hello with Michelle and she then receded to a far corner of the veranda. All of the men stopped their conversation to watch her slide onto a sofa shrouded by mosquito netting.

François returned his attention to me. "Yes, it is a beautiful country and we are fortunate to enjoy the good leadership of President Duvalier."

I knew the Duvalier regime began with the father, Dr. François Duvalier. He was a country doctor turned tyrant. He was known as "Papa Doc" and was widely feared. After Papa Doc's death, his son took over the government and, although not a doctor himself, he was given the moniker "Baby Doc."

However, Baby Doc was an ineffective leader. He never wanted the dynastic endowment and his mother actually ran the day to day affairs of the country while Baby Doc, also nicknamed "the fat child," mostly lived as a playboy. The family was thought to have skimmed billions of dollars from the Haitian economy and sent it to France for safekeeping.

Despite my earlier oath to not discuss politics in the region, I could tell that François welcomed the debate. He was an academic and since he brought up the topic so I thought I was on safe ground. I ventured a question.

"They say vodou is an important tradition here."

He was nonplussed by my question.

"Yes, indeed. When the Africans first came here. Incidentally, the colony was named Saint-Domingue at the time. When they first came here, they were forced to convert to Catholicism but the conversion was only superficial. As slaves, they were brutally oppressed, more so than any other island in the Caribbean. And the Catholic Church, the very people who should have protected the vulnerable, only stood by."

The conversation seemed interesting and pleasant enough. It satisfied my academic curiosity without being threatening, although I had a hard time concentrating. Throughout the conversation I was exchanging furtive glances with Michelle.

The conversation with François continued, although it was not so much a dialogue as it was a chess game and my hair began standing up. Each word, each sentence, was designed to place me into an intellectual corner.

He continued.

"The slaves in Haiti were never allowed to congregate, not even for church services. As a result, the slaves turned back to their common cultural heritage...vodou. Of course, the irony is that the slave owners feared vodou most of all but that is what they drove the slaves towards. Not only did the French think it was demonic but they thought it would become a rallying point for insurrection, which is exactly what happened."

Our chess game was in full play as he had moved a bishop deep onto my side of the board.

It was then my move.

"So, because of the brutal oppression of vodou, the plantation owners ended up getting what they didn't want. The first successful slave insurrection in the Caribbean?"

"Yes," he gloated. "We were the first. And I might add… the only successful slave insurrection in the history of the world."

I countered his move.

"That was an extraordinary accomplishment although the people here still seem oppressed. Some people say that the new government actually encouraged vodou in order to control the people."

François squinted his eyes slightly. At that moment, a waiter came by to replace one of the crystal ashtrays on the table. We waited for him to leave and it gave me a moment to steal another glance towards Michelle.

He continued. "No, that is not true."

"It isn't? Papa Doc was always dressed in a black suit, dark glasses, and a wide brimmed hat. He wanted people to think he was the vodou spirit of the dead, Baron Samedi, come alive again in human form."

He smiled. "No, Papa Doc loved his people and he wanted to be a great redeemer."

"You must understand, the great tragedy is that after our revolution, we became a pariah. The French imposed a crushing debt load for reparations. At the time, we produced most of the world's sugar and coffee but the French convinced the rest of the world to isolate us, although it didn't take much convincing. Other countries, including the United States, feared we would spread our democratic notions to their own slaves so we were not allowed to trade with anyone. As a result, our economy collapsed. You know, Napoleon was planning on using Haiti as a staging area to mount an invasion of the United States. He already had the Louisiana territory along with Montreal in Canada; but he wanted all of North America. And it was within his grasp. Our revolution stopped that plan and even forced the sale of Louisiana to America. After our revolution, Napoleon gave up all ambitions of an American empire. You could say that thanks to the Haitian revolution, America was able to grow unfettered. And isolation and embargo was the thanks we got. Haiti never had a chance and we still haven't recovered."

This was all new to me, proving once again that my college education had only been superficial.

"That is not all. In the early 1900s, Germany was the only country that would trade with us. They were, of course, not truly interested in us. They also had designs on an American Empire. They were mostly interested in taking over the Panama Canal. This was a development that was extremely alarming to the United States so they then aggressively took steps to enforce their Monroe Doctrine. The United States staged a coup here and installed a puppet government more to their liking. Thus, for a second time, usurping our right to have our own foreign policy. As you can see, we have never been allowed to exercise our own sovereignty. Papa Doc was doing his best to undo centuries of harm and to re-establish Haitian sovereignty."

This was all a disturbing piece of news to me. Back home, I had been taught America always did the right thing and the good guys always won. But this was like my education at the hands of the Guatemalan aristocrats. There were several overlapping shades of gray and no clear cut good or bad.

While François was talking another tropical squall had approached the hotel, bringing with it a sudden chill. As he finished his history lesson, the rain began blowing onto the patio and the hotel staff scurried over to close the wooden plantation shutters using an elaborate system of ropes and pulleys.

The rain continued in a torrential downpour and the roar of rain on the tin roof made further conversation impossible. We all paused to reflect but there was nothing more left to be said so François and Coe say their good-nights leaving me alone under the wobbly ceiling fans.

The passing squall finally dissipated and the staff returned to reopen the patio plantation shutters. I could again see the city of Port-au-Prince below and remarked to myself how pretty it seemed under the soft glow of moonlight.

I sipped my gin and tonic and prepared to leave. However, Michelle was still lying on the sofa shrouded by the shadows. We exchanged a glance again, and then a longer look.

She came over to me.

"You know, François was right. Baby Doc really does have the best interest of the Haitian people at heart. So what if they don't have true democracy like America? The system works here. People live their lives the best they can. Besides, what will it matter in another hundred years?"

That question may have been rhetorical but it was too easy not to answer.

"I guess it won't matter to us but it will matter to the people living a hundred years from now, won't it? Don't we always have a responsibility to make the future a better place?"

Despite my challenge her voice remained soft.

"Did you believe what the monsieur said about the vodou? That some people think it is demonic?"

I didn't like this topic of conversation at all but Michelle was a beautiful woman. I didn't want our connection to end so I followed her down yet another rabbit hole.

"It depends on what you mean by demonic?"

"Every religion believes in demons and vodou is no different. We believe that the visible and the invisible worlds are intertwined; and that at death we transition to the invisible world. How is that different from your religion? But for some reason the entire religion of vodou has been labeled as demonic."

She was still standing in front of me, although I was only half following her line of reasoning. My mind was less on theology and instead, on the outline of her body through her gauzy linen clothes.

"We beseech God, and we fear the devil, just as you do… just as everyone does. Don't you pray to God?"

The priestess had cornered me. I didn't want to answer such a question, partly because my own communication channels to God were pretty weak; but mostly because I had very private beliefs about God, which was to say I didn't really believe in God at all.

Instead, I answered her by draining the last bit of gin from my glass and placed it back on the table lip down like a petulant frat boy. She sat down on a chair next to me and crossed her legs under her hips. She smiled but I looked away.

Haitian infrastructure being what it was, the electrical lights flared momentarily and went out. We were momentarily left in the dark and we paused our conversation.

These power outages were nightly affairs in Port-au-Prince. As a result, in anticipation of the power loss, the staff had already lit a hurricane lamp on the table. After a few moments, my eyes adjusted and I watched the flame flicker on her face.

"I must be going. We have an early departure."

I was lying. She was beautiful but I was afraid of her. I really just wanted to get away.

She placed her hand on my shoulder. "You know, there is danger for you here in Haiti. It would be best if you did not return."

Those kind of occult-like predictions freaked me out, but rather than show fear, I tried bravado.

"Is that a threat or a promise?"

I thought that was a clever response remembered from my youth when responding to schoolyard taunts. Although, my retort only fell flat. Despite her own youth, Michelle was a mature and wise woman. And I was still just a boy, way out of my league.

"You are a reckless young man. You think you are skilled but you are not. You have just been lucky so far."

She moved her hand down my arm and held my hand with both of hers.

"You need to be more careful. And don't be so independent. You need to ask other people for help. Just remember that, my love."

She closed her eyes and tilted her head back slightly as if she had a premonition. She squeezed my hand tightly.

Her voice had been caring but then her tone turned grim. She looked directly at me and offered me an admonition.

"I am warning you not to come back to Haiti."

Her eyes looked up again. She took a deep breath through her nostrils and paused…

"Although, I know you will return and it will not be a happy experience. Just remember, if you do get in trouble don't be too proud to ask for help."

I had nothing to say. Instead, we looked in each other's eyes for a moment too long and I said goodbye.

I then found my way back to my stale and dank room using a candle provided to me earlier. The heat had returned after the passing storm but the electricity was still out. The ancient window air conditioner in my room that I had previously cursed because it only wheezed and groaned was now silent. So, I cursed it a second time for not working at all. I showered hoping the evaporation would cool me off but that only offered momentary relief from the heat. I laid on top of the faded bed covers. The candle's shadows danced on the ceiling and I hoped for peace. But it never came. Instead, Michelle's counsel preyed on my mind.

Chapter 31

A New Challenge

I t was shortly after that when I flew with Oswaldo Cordova. And the reason why I mention Oswaldo is that he saved my life.

Now, when I say he saved my life, I don't mean that as a metaphor or in some spiritual way that changed my outlook on life. I mean that he literally saved my life. Without his quick and direct action I would have met my end as a greasy spot in the Venezuelan countryside.

How I almost died in Venezuela was something of an irony. I had become a more trusted member of the flight department. I was no longer a nuisance and was slowly becoming a peer. And, as a result, I was given an increasingly more difficult set of flight assignments. The captains I flew with also took more of their time to mentor me. This tutoring was crucial for the next phase of my career because I was learning that it was not enough to only fly the airplane well.

I was beginning to grasp that flying the Learjet, as challenging as it was, was actually the easiest part of the job. More importantly, a good pilot had to think. He had to think in order to stay ahead of the airplane and to avoid difficult situations. Furthermore, if a difficult situation became unavoidable, a good pilot also had to think their way out of it. The more stressful a situation, the more a good pilot was expected to make satisfactory judgements. Good decision making was a life or death skill. Each decision didn't have to be perfect. Each decision only had to be good enough to survive.

It was during this time of growing confidence, I was first assigned to fly with Cordova on a ten day circuit through South America. Our passenger was a wealthy Venezuelan oil man flying in his own personal airplane. The airplane for this trip was a Lear 36. It was the most modern member of the Learjet family. It was designed with the same stretched fuselage of the Lear 25 but it was also equipped with high bypass, high efficiency engines and extra large fuel capacity in the fuselage tank. Together, they gave the airplane an endurance of over six hours for non stop trips even deeper into South America. This allowed us to avoid unfriendly local bureaucrats on unnecessary fuel stops. Despite the stretched fuselage and longer range, the cockpit was no bigger than the earlier Learjets. What this meant in practical terms, however, was the pilots had to suffer an extra three hours in their cramped cockpit. It was a fair trade off.

The 36 was a pretty decent airplane and it was an interesting concept but the people at Lear who dreamed up the design overlooked one major failing. All that extra fuel had to go somewhere. And the only available solution was to have the fuselage tank intrude on the interior cabin, leaving a passenger space no bigger than the interior of the 24. Therefore, everyone, passengers and crew alike, shared the pain of a cramped cabin for long periods. It was OK for the pilots to be uncomfortable for six hours but not the paying passengers, so Lear never sold more than a few dozen of the Model 36.

There was another thing about all the 30 series Lears worth mentioning. Its wings were again modified, this time with the Century III Soft Flite wing. It made the Lear 30 series airplanes even more gentle to fly, although in one crucial operation their hearts still held a dark secret.

Cordova was in his 50s and a scion of a wealthy family Venezuelan himself. But as a teenager he realized the family business held no interest for him so he joined the Venezuelan Air Force. He had a career as a fighter pilot and retired as a colonel when he eventually became a trusted pilot for his even more wealthy friends.

In the fashion of the day, he wore designer jeans with heavy gold stitching, and a silk shirt unbuttoned to his sternum. With his shirt thus situated, he could show off the layers of gold chains draped around his neck. He had a full head of luxuriant, gray, curly hair. His muscular arms were layered in the same heavy grey hair, and a gold Rolex Presidential peeked out from underneath his cuffs. His jeans were too tight and draped too low on his hips for a man his age, so his belly bulged over his waistband.

Oswaldo's regular copilot was Gonzales, who informed me that Oswaldo suffered from chronic back pain caused by years of aerial manuevering in fighters. It caused him constant torment and made him speak in a halting manner. His English was good, although he had a thick Spanish accent.

We first met outside the hangar in Fort Lauderdale just prior to our departure.

"Hello, my friend." He rolled the letter R in the word friend as he gave me the briefing for the trip.

"We are going to Caracas first. We'll spend two days there. Then we'll go to Lima. Probably two days in Lima and then we'll head back to Caracas. After that, who knows?

"You will like the 36. It has more power than you are used to and it also has modern avionics including long range navigation. It is different from the 24. But Coe said I could trust you. It is different but don't worry, my friend. I will teach you along the way."

We then strapped ourselves in and departed south. Cordova was a slow and methodical pilot and a natural teacher. On the way down, good to his promise, he took the time to teach me each peculiarity of this airplane. The most notable of which was the long range navigation system, known as an Omega. It was a rudimentary inertial navigation system made up of a series of gyros and accelerometers that measured the airplane's movement against the known velocity of the earth's rotation. There were so many moving parts spinning around their respective axes that the system was nicknamed "Carousel."

The short range VOR or NDB navigation to which I was accustomed only required the pilot to tune a frequency and just follow a guidance needle on the instrument panel. Conversely, operating the Carousel was a multi step process. Did I say multi step? I meant multiple, multi steps. And each of the multiple steps had its own set of substeps. The Omega unit was a high workload unit and required much in the way of pilot input and monitoring.

I am probably making it sound more complicated than it was, but it was quite simple really. All the pilot had to do during preflight was to enter the latitude and longitude of the departure airport in the correct 16 digit format. Then he would have to enter the correct coordinates of the destination airport's 16 digit latitude and longitude. Once that was accomplished, the pilot would then enter the coordinates of each waypoint along the way. Again, each in the proper 16 digit format and in the proper linear sequence.

A long trip would include many dozens of waypoints but the computer memory at the time only held eight waypoints. As a result, while in flight, the pilot also had to continuously re-enter new waypoints as the flight progressed. Much of our flying was done at night so the pilot had to read the coordinates that were printed on a paper chart in the tiniest of fonts. The Lear 36 still had the same gooseneck map light as the 24. It was mounted on the cockpit side-wall protruding into the space normally occupied by the pilot's elbow. The light produced more heat than light. And as a result, a pilot had a choice of either seeing properly or burning his arm while trying to read the coordinates. The pilots who needed reading glasses had an even tougher time of it. But that's OK because it was unusual to find a Lear pilot in South Florida over the age of 35. And, of course, every waypoint had to be entered exactly without error. The Omega was only a computer, thus the old adage of garbage in/garbage out ruled the day. Oswaldo warned me that loading the coordinates was a tedious process that was prone to error and required checking and double checking by both pilots. Errors here could have fatal consequences. Airplanes that had made gross navigational errors due to incorrect inputs had been shot down for blundering into prohibited airspace. Others had hit mountains at night due to navigational error. Checking and rechecking your work a third or fourth time was not being overly cautious.

And that wasn't all. The Carousel was subject to drift even if everything was entered properly. After a flight of four hours, the Omega could be many dozens of miles off course. This early technology was clearly just suited to point you in the general direction when you were in the middle of nowhere. Once you got close to your destination, you could then pick up the short range navigation guidance, which was much more accurate. It all sounds complicated but overall, the Omega was quite simple really.

Oh yes, unrelated to the navigation system was the cabin heat. Like the 24, the Lear 36 was prone to being cold soaked while at altitude, but even more so because of its long endurance. Therefore, while on climbout, the pilot had to turn up the cabin heat to near unbearable levels in order to remain comfortable later. But overall, the 36 was a pleasure to fly since the engineers at Learjet had smoothed over some of the more feral aspects of the earlier airplanes.

It was my first trip to Caracas but instead of Caracas proper we were flying into Maiquetia Airport. The airport was located next to the small fishing village of Maiquetia. It was a town would have been doomed to obscurity but for one accident of geography. The reason for our diversion to Maiquetia was that the city of Caracas, like so many other South American cities, was built in the bottom of a steep mountain valley.

Located just 30 miles inland, the city was at 3,000 feet above sea level with 7,000 foot mountains all around. The site was selected by the early Spanish settlers because the narrow passes leading up to the valley provided security from marauding English buccaneers patrolling the Caribbean. Sometimes that defense was successful, oftentimes not. Regardless, its narrow and irregular shaped valley left little room for a modern airport.

Although, it was just as well the Spanish located Caracas in an inland valley. For there was another topographical challenge for city planners in Venezuela. Along the northern coastline of South America was an escarpment several hundred miles long and a thousand feet high. It was the northeastern extension of the Andes and for virtually its entire length its cliff face dropped vertically into the Caribbean, leaving nowhere to build a city at sea level. Nor was there any flat land at sea level to build a modern airport.

Nowhere, that is, except for a small shelf of beach located at sea level and only 25 miles from Caracas. This fortuitous geological coincidence sat at the feet of the coastal cordillera and although it was just barely large enough for a modern international airport, it would do. And, that was how the tiny fishing village of Maiquetia became home to one of the busiest airports in South America.

Oswaldo let me fly the first leg for the three hour trip to Caracas. We initially flew over the same route as my very first trip to Nassau. But after passing Bimini we turned further south down Upper Amber 315 towards the South American mainland. The flight over the aquamarine Bahamian archipelago was as beautiful as it always was until we flew over the island of Hispaniola when the character of the earth below again changed. It was there where I was freshly reminded of the stark poverty in Haiti. That was because the island of Hispaniola was shared by both the countries of Haiti and the Dominican Republic. And even though they shared the same island, the Dominicans enjoyed a much higher standard of living. Although I may be overstating the concept of a high standard of living. The Haitians were desperately poor, while the Dominicans were merely dirt poor. And nowhere was this more starkly displayed in a single snapshot than when overflying the two countries. The Dominican countryside was lush, still covered by its primordial forest, while the Haitian landscape had been stripped clean of any vegetation in the incessant search for firewood. The view from our serene perch eight miles above the scarcity below revealed the marked contrast on either side of their shared border.

About that time, Oswaldo reached behind me towards a small galley located just aft of the copilot's seat.

"Would you like a roast beef sandwich, my friend?"

I agreed and he handed me a sandwich thick with fresh meat along with an icy Coca-Cola. I continued to contemplate the terrain below while I savored the mixture of warm meat, mustard, and a cold sugar drink. In that fashion, Oswaldo and I sailed on past the navigation beacon at Cabo Rojo without any further comment.

Once we passed Hispaniola, we continued on the same heading towards the island of Curacao. And it was on this next airway where we would have the longest leg of the trip. This leg was completely over water, over the main body of the Caribbean Sea, with no diversionary airports close by.

Normally, such a long over water leg would cause great concern to the pilots of a Lear 24 and result in the usual manic checking of the fuel state. The trip, however, had been placid and I realized not once since our preflight had Oswaldo checked the fuel gauges. Flying the Lear 36 with extra long range tanks was a luxury. We were sitting on our thrones in a strong and well-mannered airplane. Oswaldo as the captain was king, and I, as his copilot, was his heir. We had full stomachs as we watched the world pass below us. The weather was good across the entire Caribbean basin and we had plenty of gas. So much gas that we could fly on to Venezuela and then go all the way back to Miami if we had to. This was flying as it was supposed to be.

Once we passed Curacao, we began our descent towards Maiquetia and along the last 100 miles of the flight we parallelled the coastal cordillera. As we descended, the rugged coastline dominated more of our windshield until we went below the ridge line in preparation for landing. The landing itself was uneventful and we parked the airplane on a quiet section of the cargo ramp. Oswaldo was well connected in Venezuela and his boss was a powerful man. Therefore, we cleared customs routinely

Caracas

We then drove up the narrow mountain pass into the bustling metropolis that was Caracas. The city was surrounded on all sides by verdant green mountains and a ring of white cumulus clouds sat atop the ridgeline. Caracas enjoyed spring like temperatures year round and it was in this pleasant and bucolic setting where we ended up spending three days free of duty. In the daylight hours we slept in late, toured the city, enjoyed the local food, and fell easily into the Spanish tradition of afternoon siestas. In the evenings, we devoted our time to the party circuit with the Venezuelan elite. Every party went to sunrise as each host tried to outdo all the others with a lavish buffet of champagne, caviar, and beautiful people. All of which was freely available.

After three days, we were informed that our passenger would be spending yet another three days in Caracas before the next leg of our trip. And this extension gave me an opportunity to delve even deeper into the subculture of the Venezuelan upper class. As the week wore on, I came to realize that each party had the same tempo. Each one started out with a mix of disco, salsa and merengue, with a mass of people on the dance floor. As the night slipped into morning, the mood slowed with classical jazz and people split up into couples. Some of those couples left for home, some just stayed, passed out on the host's sofas. And it was during one of those parties where I met Adriana, the privileged daughter of a local oil family. Then, just as my Spanish was getting better we had to leave for Lima.

Chapter 32

··

Deep South

We were southbound at FL 430. Oswaldo was flying this leg with the autopilot engaged and it was tracking the Carousel inputs obediently.

Our route from Maiquetia to Lima was four hours. It was deeper into South America than I had ever been before and I studied the chart to orient myself. We were flying across the extreme western edge of the Amazon River basin and headed towards the Andes. For most of the trip our only potential diversion airport was Bogota. And, even then, it was far off to our north. In this lonely part of South America both the airspace around us and the land below us was empty. With no safe haven to divert, we could have just as well have been on an oceanic crossing.

We had left late and it was after midnight. As we approached the equator we flew towards the Intertropical Convergence Zone. The ITCZ as it was known was a belt of low pressure where the trade winds of the Northern and Southern hemisphere converged. At higher latitudes the trade winds were a benign breeze propelling explorers, empire builders, and merchants across the ocean, hence the name. In the Northern Hemisphere the trade winds blew from east to west and in the Southern Hemisphere, they blew in the opposite direction due to the Coriolis Force of the spinning globe. It was in the ITCZ where the tradewinds of Northern and Southern Hemisphere clashed and they formed a belt of thunderstorms girdling the globe along the equator.

Tonight, though, was mostly quiet. A few distant flashes of lighting were off our left wing but ahead was clear. Above us, the night sky was ablaze with constellations that I had never seen before. Nor was I familiar with any of their names. That is, with one exception. A single constellation famous throughout the Northern Hemisphere, even though most Northerners had never seen it.

And it was there, over the western Amazon basin, where I first saw the Southern Cross. The constellation that was both famous and spiritual. As we flew south, it hovered silently over our flight path and I marveled in its power.

The Southern Cross was elegant in its simplicity. Just four stars; and not terribly brilliant stars either. But they stood out prominently from the neighboring constellations and they were clearly in the shape of a cross. Although admittedly, different cultures saw the Southern Cross in different ways. Some non-Christians saw a kite, whereas other cultures saw images that were important to their own beliefs. Botswanans saw an eagle, Pacific Islanders saw a triggerfish, Maoris saw an anchor dragging across the Milky Way. The interpretations of the cross were as diverse as world cultures themselves. But to my western eyes, it was very much a cross.

The Southern Cross had been hidden from the view of Europeans from the beginning of time and was completely unknown to Christendom until the age of exploration. For those early European sailors who ventured below the equator, it must have been a powerful and comforting sight.

Those explorers were completely cut off from home. For countless years, they could only rely on each other as they clung to a rolling deck and felt their way blindly through treacherous waters. Their future was fraught with peril and their ultimate fate unknown. They had only their personal courage and faith to sustain them. For them, seeing the Southern Cross floating peacefully above them must have offered a powerful reminder of God's presence. Seafarers for centuries had remarked on it, poets had written songs about it, but it was not until I had seen the Southern Cross for myself that it made its full impact on me.

I looked down at the Carousel display. Its orange LED lights counted down the miles to Lima as it showed our estimated arrival time in just a few hours. I paused my celestial sightseeing to enter a few more waypoints on the navigation panel. And I again returned my gaze again towards the compelling image of the cross.

Sailors for millennia had navigated by the stars. And even until recently, airmen had used celestial navigation. Despite their primitive abilities, they made their way across oceans and back home again. But for me, the modern aviator, celestial navigation had become passe. Instead, I sat in air conditioned comfort and had constant computerized updating of my position and speed. It gave me some degree of smug satisfaction that I no longer needed celestial guidance. My modern and man made guidance assured me that I would arrive at my destination safely. However, I could not avoid a nagging disquiet: Was their navigational ability truly primitive? The ancient mariners had decades of experience navigating using the earth's subtle clues. Conversely, I was utterly dependent on a series of computer chips and a software programmer, much smarter than me. A programmer who was probably asleep in his own bed at the moment. Who, then, among history's world travelers, were truly the better navigators? I put the idea out of my head and reached behind me for a midnight sandwich.

We landed in Lima late at night and had only one day there to tour the city. Our hotel was in Miraflores near an ornate colonial church built in 1521. While touring the church, I wondered again about those early Spanish explorers. They built this church, a cathedral, really, only 30 years after their initial landing in The Bahamas. In that short time, they had sailed around the continent, toppled two of the world's most powerful empires, founded Lima as their capital, and raised this magnificent cathedral. As I was learning, the Spanish were, very much, not a people susceptible to their doubts.

Chapter 33

A Weakness Revealed

And then we were back in Caracas. It was another multi day layover where we again attended a long series of parties around the city. It was during these affairs where I was reminded frequently that the country was flush with oil money. And much of this money found its way to the local airport.

As it turned out, there was just barely enough room in the Caracas valley to squeeze in one small airport. It started out life as a military airport and over time became the hub of corporate aviation in Venezuelan. It was a dual use airport. As civil aviation grew, the Venezuelan Air Force maintained its presence there as well.

And given its dual use status, the airport also went by two different names, both of which were probably the two most romantic and beautiful airport names in the world. It was Miranda Air Force base located at La Carlota Airport.

In order to avoid the long drive down to Maiquetia, the airport was favored by the Venezuelan establishment and the ramp was filled with brand new business jets. And brand new jets required brand new pilots in order to fly them, which is how Oswaldo came to save my life.

You see, in addition to his other accomplishments, Oswaldo was also a civilian flight examiner. This allowed him the authority to give checkrides to Learjet pilots. And because of his examiner authority, he was requested to give a checkride to a local Venezuelan pilot who had just finished his captain upgrade training.

Checkrides are a constant and ordinary part of an airman's professional life. All pilots, whether commercial or private, must take flight checks. And it is during these checks that the pilot must show mastery over the airplane during both normal flight and simulated emergencies. Pilots are tested not only on their airmanship skills but on their ability to make good decisions.

Checkrides are stressful but that's the idea. The stress of a checkride simulates the stress of a real life emergency. A failed checkride involved a certain amount of professional embarrassment and would require more training. Failures would happen occasionally but the pilot who took his craft seriously was not just prepared for a checkride; he was over prepared in order to prove beyond doubt his ability.

Checkrides were sometimes given in simulators, which are completely forgiving of mistakes. You could "crash" a simulator but every landing was one you could walk away from. But in the world I lived in at the time, simulators were a luxury and checkrides were conducted in the actual airplane. And on that day, the checkride was to be in an oil company's brand new Lear 35.

Oswaldo asked me to join them as an observer and I accepted.

The Lear 35 was twin sister to the 36 we had flown to Lima. It had the same stretched fuselage with the same easy handling characteristics and high bypass engines. The only difference from the 36 was that it had a normal sized fuselage tank reducing its endurance to 4 ½ hours, which was still generous by the standards of the Lear 20 series. The extra cabin space was rededicated to passenger comfort making the cabin comfort match the range of the airplane. It was an ideal balance of endurance and cabin comfort. Ideal, that is for almost everyone. The pilots still suffered in the same cramped cockpit but nonetheless, the extra cabin space made it enormously popular among the people writing the checks. The 35 was a delight to fly and probably the best model of the whole Learjet family.

In the United States, checkrides were all business affairs. They were usually just a brief three or four hour professional transaction. However, in the Spanish style, this checkride was to be a day long leisurely affair involving both flying and socializing.

It began with coffee in the chief pilot's office. I joined Oswaldo with the student and his chief pilot who was an old friend of Oswaldo's from their days in the Venezuelan Air Force. This office was a complete departure from the office where I first interviewed with Ragsdale. It further reflected Venezuelan wealth with thick carpeting, sumptuous mid-century leather furniture, and modern art on the walls. Everything smelled new. A picture window provided a commanding view of the runway and the nearby mountains ringing the airport. I sat in the back corner of the room while Oswaldo and the student sat in plush chairs directly in front of the chief pilot's expansive polished desk.

The captain candidate was a young man, about my age who was the nephew of the owner of the oil company. His first name was Luis. He was handsome and well dressed. Perhaps, a bit too well dressed for a pilot. He was wearing a silk suit and enough jewelry to cover my salary for a couple of years.

The conversation was mostly in Spanish. It started with Oswaldo and his chief pilot friend sharing stories of flying the F-86 at low level around the Orinoco River Valley and how they were honored to provide air escort to Air Force One, which was carrying President Kennedy when he visited Caracas. After the chummy talk ended, the conversation turned to the matter of to-day's checkride. From what I could gather, Luis apparently had no discernible business skills that were useful to the family. However, Luis was a man with high expectations for himself. He informed his rich uncle that he was enamored with airplanes, and the chief pilot was then told to make room for him in the flight department.

The chief pilot then left the three of us alone so Oswalso could conduct the oral portion of the exam. This was conducted in English and went slowly. Luis's performance was halting not because of his English skills. He was actually very adept at English; but, instead, he had only a rudimentary understanding of the airplane. When asked a particularly hard question, he would fiddle with his gold watch, which peeked out from underneath his French cuffs, and then just tell Oswaldo to ask him something else. After a while Luis lost interest in the whole process and Oswaldo declared it was time for the practical test in the airplane. After witnessing this performance, I was not sure I would have passed Luis on his oral exam but Oswaldo was the boss so I followed along.

The airplane for that day was as new as could possibly be. It was factory fresh having just been delivered that very week from the Learjet facility in Kansas. The jet's blue metallic paint sparkled in the sun and the interior had matching blue leather. It smelled even more new than the chief pilot's office. We all climbed in and prepared for the checkride.

After a normal takeoff, we first flew to Margarita Island with Luis at the controls for practice instrument approaches. Some of those approaches were conducted simulating minor electronic failures. Once those approaches were successfully done we parked the airplane and stopped for lunch. Margarita was a popular tourist destination and we drove to a restaurant overlooking the Playa Concorde. It was there that I enjoyed a savory bouillabaisse. If I remember right, it contained lobster, clams, a local grouper, and corn in a tomato base. I'm glad it was delicious because it was very nearly my last meal on earth.

After lunch, we then flew to the city of Barcelona in eastern Venezuela for more normal takeoffs and landings. Oswaldo then instructed Luis to make the next landing to a full stop. Thus far, the checkride seemed to have been going well; better than the oral exam. But the next portion was when we were to practice the most demanding and hazardous of tests for a pilot.

We were parked at the end of the runway. Luis was sitting in the captain's seat. Oswaldo was in the right seat playing the role of copilot. But now he assumed command for a moment to brief the procedure so we all would understand what was about to happen. Our next practice maneuver left virtually no room for error and there could be no misunderstandings whatsoever. Luis now had to demonstrate a simulated engine failure on takeoff, sometimes called a V1 cut.

The procedure worked like this: We were to begin a normal two engine takeoff. We would accelerate down the runway to our Go/No Go speed, which was also called V1. This was the speed at which, if we had an engine failure, the airplane had enough kinetic energy so the remaining engine could provide enough power to continue accelerating the airplane and climb away safely. Conversely, it was also the speed when we didn't have enough runway left ahead of us to stop the airplane in the remaining distance. Before V1 the pilot could stop the airplane in the remaining distance. After V1, the pilot was committed and had to continue the takeoff. Hence, the expression Go/NoGo. At V1, Oswaldo would simulate an engine failure by retarding one throttle back to idle. At that point, the expectation was that the student would continue the takeoff and climb away on one engine. Oswaldo finished the briefing. It was a good and comprehensive briefing but he still asked if Luis had any questions.

The student nodded impatiently. Luis was eager to get on with the checkride and barked at Cordova in Spanish.

"Yes, yes! I understand. Let's go!"

I was seated just behind the pilots on a sideways facing seat. I had been leaning into the cockpit and was taken aback by the student's forcefulness. The seat I was using also doubled as a makeshift toilet. It was a simple plastic bowl with a holding tank underneath. It was framed in wood and leather for appearance sake and had a fold out curtain for modesty's sake. It was so rudimentary and lacking in privacy for use as a toilet that it was rarely used in flight for its intended purpose. However, I sat on it that day to give me a better view of the cockpit.

We lined up on the runway centerline and Luis advanced the throttles abruptly. The engines needed smooth control inputs and they paused as they waited for the fuel computers to catch up to the hurried throttle input. After the fuel computers made their necessary calculations to catch up to the throttle movement the engines then surged to 100% thrust jerking us forward. We accelerated down the runway and just as we passed V1, Oswaldo pulled the right throttle back to idle to simulate a failure.

This was the most difficult part of the maneuver. Not only did the flying pilot lose half of the airplane's power and then have to accelerate a crippled airplane; but with the left engine producing full power and the right producing no thrust, the airplane wanted to twist over on its side. This would require full rudder input to keep the airplane pointed straight. It was the supreme test. The climbout was the easier part. The student's prime responsibility was to maintain tracking straight ahead. Little else mattered.

And at this critical moment, Luis failed. He was supposed to continue tracking straight down the runway while keeping the airplane on the ground as it continued accelerating. This would get more lift over the wings and give the rudder more authority. This is a basic tenet of multi engine flying. Instead, Luis pulled back sharply on the yoke. With that one ill-advised reaction we leapt in the air, the nose pitching up steeply; much too steeply. With the nose up so sharply, the airspeed dropped off quickly. We barely had flying speed before the pitch up, and then in just a second our speed bled off even more.

Another second went by. Without enough air flowing over the rudder, and without enough rudder input by the student, the operating engine twisted over us. In one more second, the airplane snapped to the right. Luis then reached up to the autopilot control panel and stabbed the engage button. I couldn't decide what was worse; that he was trying to get the autopilot to save him or that he really believed that in such an extreme position the autopilot servos had enough power to recover.

I looked out the right passenger window. We were knife edge to the ground just ten feet in the air. I thought back to the student pilot who I pulled out of the airplane wreckage back in Fort Lauderdale. We were in the same attitude as he was after his mid air. We were banked at 90 degrees with no lift. Except we didn't even have the luxury of being 100 feet in the air. Three seconds ago everything was normal. But now I was going to die sitting on a toilet with a stomach full of Caribbean bouillabaisse. It was a simple realization on my part. I had no fear, no panic, not even resignation, just an acknowledgement. I figured I had about three or four more seconds to live. And I was alright with that.

I then heard cursing in Spanish from the cockpit and I looked forward again. Oswaldo had assumed control of the airplane. He was slamming the idle engine back to full power. This accomplished two things. It added more thrust, which gave us more life sustaining airspeed and once the thrust equalized it was easier to roll the airplane level. The problem was that such a sudden change in thrust would destabilize the airplane even more.

Simultaneously, Oswaldo applied full rudder and rolled the airplane level.

We were flying again.

Sort of.

We had lost so much airspeed in the pitch up, that we were then on the back side of the power curve. It was the exact worst place for an airplane at low altitude to find itself. It was the area of the performance envelope, where even with maximum power the airplane couldn't climb. We were only barely flying and we needed to descend to build up airpsed.

But we had no extra altitude.

We were screaming down the runway about ten feet above the concrete. I looked at the airspeed indicator.

"Jesus!"

Only 100 knots!

We were just above stall speed and I couldn't believe the airplane was still flying.

Fortunately, we were in a 35 which had the Soft Flite wing modifications. This gave the airplane much more gentle slow speed handling characteristics. If we had been in a 24, we probably would have already dropped a wing and cartwheeled.

With no extra altitude to spare, Oswalso couldn't descend aggressively to accelerate. Instead, he just nursed the airplane gently down, maybe sacrificing four or five feet to accelerate. The airspeed increased a few knots. That gave us a little extra margin but not enough to climb.

We were still roaring down towards the end of the runway. We needed to start climbing but first, we needed more airspeed. However, the landing gear was still down and its drag was slowing our acceleration. I thought that maybe we should just try to get the airplane back on the runway and stop. We would surely have slid off the end into the trees. However, at our speed that would have been a guaranteed fatal crash. I agreed silently that we should try to fly our way out of this. That would give us maybe a 10% chance of surviving.

I thought to call for gear retraction to reduce drag but it was a distraction that Oswaldo didn't need right then. Plus the gear retraction would have taken too long. No matter. One way or the other, in the time it would take to retract the gear, this was going to be over. The main priority was to start climbing before the trees met us at the end of the runway. But in order to climb, we had to first accelerate. I knew what Oswaldo had to do next, as counterintuitive as it seemed. He had to lower the nose just a bit more, just to coax a few more knots of airspeed. If we dragged a landing gear that will probably cause us to cartwheel but at that point we had nothing left to lose. As the old saying goes, "speed is life." Oswaldo knew it as well as I did, and he imperceptibly pushed forward on the yoke and we descended another foot.

The airspeed rose another few knots and I cheered inside. But there was still not enough energy to start climbing. I leaned forward in my seat trying to add impetus to our forward motion.

The trees were looming large and began to fill the windshield. We gained another few knots. I felt a slight lift in my seat and I knew what that meant. We had accelerated just enough that we were now on the front side of the power curve and we were flying like a real airplane again. We didn't have a lot of excess airspeed but we did have just enough.

Oswaldo had just enough excess energy that he was able to coax the yoke back so we cleared the tops of the trees. Once clear, we raised the landing gear; continued to accelerate and climbed normally.

Luis was unfazed by this whole event.

"I have the airplane." he said as he reached for the controls.

Oswaldo barked at him in Spanish and pushed Luis' hand away from the throttles.

He then flew the airplane to La Carlota by himself and nothing was said until we all went into the chief pilot's office where I was to witness a trial. The four of us were back in the modern and well appointed office. Oswaldo served as the prosecutor but he was too agitated to sit. Instead he paced around the room as he read the list of charges. The chief pilot was sitting back in his deeply upholstered leather chair. Luis stood off to the side and tried to interrupt Oswaldo. I tried to hide in a corner. As Oswaldo laid out the afternoon's events, what followed was a long rant in Spanish, heavily laden with new profanities that I had not yet learned.

I picked up part of it.

"Exact wrong thing."

"Almost killed."

"No sense."

"Arrogant."

Even though he almost killed me, I was embarrassed for my fellow aviator. However, as Oswaldo relayed the near fatal event in accurate detail, the defendant refused to acknowledge his mistake. The chief pilot has been friends with Oswaldo since they were in the cadets in the Air Force. But he was incredulous that such a thing could have happened and, instead, wanted to believe his own pilot.

Finally, Oswaldo pointed to me. He switched to English and called me to the witness stand.

"Ask him yourself, he saw everything."

A quiver passed through my stomach and I wondered if my testimony would hold any weight. After all, I was just an American asked to testify in a case against a well connected Venezuelan man.

The room went silent and everyone's eyes looked to me.

I had by then been alive for about two hours longer than I should have been. We had not had a chance to rest since then and the accumulated stress was bearing down on me. My mouth was bitter and dry so I took a second to moisten my mouth. I looked directly at the chief pilot and tried to be as forthright and unbiased as I could. I started out in Spanish.

"Esta verdad."

I paused. I then switched to English, figuring my testimony would be more powerful in articulate English rather than my inept Spanish.

I then had to confess that yes, I had a face full of Venezuelan asphalt staring at me. It was only through some magic divination on Oswaldo's part were we alive to talk about it. Otherwise, his precious new airplane would have been scattered all over the runway and the three of us would have just been a greasy spot on the runway in Barcelona. The chief pilot sat silently in disbelief and he ordered me out of the room to continue the trial.

I went back out to the waiting room and began to chat with the receptionist. It was Adriana who I had met a few days earlier at a party. She was standing by the door and it was clear she had been listening.

"Is it true?"

"Is what true?"

"That Luis almost killed you"?

"Well, you heard everything. Yes. We almost crashed up in Barcelona."

Adriana had backed up against a wall in the office. She was dressed in black dress pants and a crisp white business shirt. Her skin was porcelain and her straight black hair fell halfway down her back.

"Luis is a shit."

I was a bit taken aback by her forthright comment to me. We had gotten to know each other pretty well earlier in the week but really, I was still just a stranger.

"Why do you say that?"

"Luis is my brother. He has always been arrogant and he doesn't listen. He can't find a job because he argues with everyone. My uncle owns the airplane so he agreed to give Luis a job flying it. But Luis insisted on being the captain right away. He thought being a copilot was shameful. He doesn't have enough experience to be the captain but the main problem is that Luis is a bad pilot."

Of course, after what I just witnessed, I certainly didn't need her to tell me that, but I asked anyway.

"How do you know that"?

She stood taller than she already was and her eyes narrowed,

"I am a pilot too. I wanted that job and I'm a better pilot."

"Well, why didn't you get it?"

She let out an involuntary laugh. It was more a spasm than a laugh and her hot breath swept onto my face.

"What? You are kidding, right? This is Venezuela. I was lucky enough to just get flying lessons. They would never actually give me a job flying airplanes. And certainly not ahead of a man. My place is in the office…or home raising children. That is what they told me."

"So, they gave the job to Luis?"

"Yes."

She snapped her fingers and waved her hand across her body in a dismissive motion.

"They gave the job to Luis. Everyone knows he is a bad pilot but my uncle is a powerful man."

"I am sorry to hear that."

Then her annoyance turned to anger.

"Not as sorry as everyone would have been if you all died."

Just then, Oswaldo burst out of the office. His eyes were cold.

"Let's go, my friend. We have to leave. Get a taxi to Maiquetia. We're leaving for New York right away."

I followed him out the door with only the barest of goodbyes to Adriana. As we drove back down to the coastline, I was sorry to cut my time in Caracas short. Adriana and I had been invited to the same party that night and I was looking forward to seeing her again. She had even agreed to go out with me afterwards. I didn't know it at the time but I was to never see her again.

As we drove back down to Maiquetia, I was happy to be going home. It had been a long trip and the adventure had been tiring. Once at the airport, it was good to see our own airplane again. Although she was older and more battered than the checkride airplane, our old Lear 36 was already a comfortable old friend and I gladly slipped into the cockpit to prepare for our five hour trip to New York.

As usual, the passengers were late and we took off just after midnight. Once we leveled off we flew serenely along the lightly traveled oceanic tracks with three sleeping passengers in the back. We were tired ourselves so we were mostly silent but there was a question I could not let go. The regular copilot was meeting us in New York so this would likely be the last time I would fly with Oswaldo. I was reluctant to ask the question so I said nothing. But as the glow of the New York skyline appeared on the horizon, I knew I had to ask.

I drew a deep breath and tried to sound nonchalant.

"So, what happened in Barcelona?"

He glanced over to me and furrowed his bushy eyebrows. He knew what I meant but he paused as though he didn't want to answer. He was no longer angry but, instead, sobered by the episode.

He took a deep breath and sighed. He began to answer although he was still looking out into the distance.

"My friend, we were very lucky. He did two things wrong. First, he made a big mistake."

"He did the exact wrong thing. When you have an engine failure at V1 the plane wants to pitch up. You must push forward to pin the nose to the ground. Instead, he got scared and did the exact opposite. He pitched up. He said he was worried about going off the side of the runway and wanted to get in the air. But we were still too slow and the rudder couldn't hold the heading, so we started rolling over on our back."

"Yeah, I saw that."

"Yes, of course, my friend. The other thing he did wrong was he panicked and froze. Just when we needed him the most, just when the airplane needed him the most… he froze."

He looked at me and asked, "You know, my friend, we should be dead. We were lucky, my friend. Very, very lucky."

I nodded. Although I knew that luck had nothing to do with our outcome. It was Oswaldo's instant and expert reaction that saved us.

In the very near future, there were to be two separate crashes of Lear 35s conducting the same exact training exercise as our recent episode. In both accidents everyone on board was killed and in both accidents the accident investigation board laid the blame on the pilots.

Pilot error or not, both of those accidents further emphasized to me that the Lear was an airplane that made no accommodation for inattention and I said so.

"No Oswaldo, it was not luck. It was you. You are a hero. We should have died."

I repeated it for emphasis. "It was you. You saved our lives."

"A hero? No, my friend. I was only trying to save my own life."

It was now about four in the morning. The cockpit lights were dimmed. We were alone, Oswaldo and me, far off the coast of the eastern seaboard. We were suspended in that limbo of night flight. Halfway between the terrestrial below us and the celestial above.

He turned away from me and looked out the left side of the windshield as though searching for an answer. The flashing white strobe lights on our left wing tip silhouetted his profile.

He turned and looked directly at me. "Do you know the pilot's prayer, my friend?"

I was startled because his eyes were now different. He looked sad.

I tried to appear uncaring. It seemed like a good defense. It had worked for years, but inside, I yearned for an answer.

I shook my head.

He groaned and wiped his face with the palm of his hand. He had been sitting in the tiny pilot seat now for four hours and he shifted in his seat trying to find a comfortable position.

"The pilot's prayer, my friend, Let me tell you.

"When pilots get in trouble, they don't say 'Dear God, don't let me die.'

"No, they do not, my friend.

"Instead, the pilot's prayer is: 'Dear God, don't let me screw up'

"It is better to die doing everything right to save a bad situation that wasn't your fault rather than make a mistake and crash a perfectly good airplane."

He paused and his eyes stared straight into my own.

I asked, "But sometimes things happen by chance and the pilot has no control?"

He grunted a Spanish profanity.

"Yes my friend, that is true. Flying is like life, is it not?

"Sometimes we can control things. Sometimes, we are at the mercy of chance. Sometimes flying is a game of skill, and sometimes, we can control our lives. Other times it is a game of chance and we only think we have control. But we still get in the airplane. We still roll the dice. Why? Because we love it, my friend. We love flying. We have friends who die in airplanes. We face death ourselves but we always go back. Why? Because we embrace life. And life demands risk. We cannot help it. This is what humans do."

I remained silent and nodded.

New York Center broke the quiet and instructed us to a lower altitude and a new routing for the arrival into Teterboro.

Oswaldo reached up to the autopilot control panel to begin a descent and he then eased the throttles back to 75%. The autopilot began a gradual descent and I felt a pressure bump in my ears as the cabin pressurization surged gently to compensate for the change in engine thrust.

"A hero? No. I was just doing my job. You must give up those boyhood fantasies of adventure and heroics. This is a job. Yes, sometimes there is an adventure but it is mostly boring work. And you must always think clearly, even in the face of danger.

"The pilot's prayer, my friend…Remember that and you will do fine."

And that pretty much summarizes my first trip to Venezuela.

Chapter 34

The Storm/Disloyalty

It was mid afternoon and I was flight planning for a short hop from Fort Lauderdale to Tampa. I was in our dispatch office and I had just hung up the phone with the weather specialist at the Flight Service Station in Miami.

I frowned as I drew a line across the state of Florida. Both my line and the weatherman confirmed what Walpole had earlier warned me about when flying the tropics in the summertime. Winter weather was fraught with low visibility and icing but conditions were usually stable. Once a forecast was made, a pilot could reliably count on it.

The summertime was different. Early in the morning, the atmosphere was reliably sedate. However, the sky in Florida was almost always heavy with moisture. Once the sun began its daily ascent, the rising heat would spark a day long riot of thunderstorms. The daily summer forecast in Florida was as reliable as the sunrise itself: calm in the morning with afternoon thunderstorms. Although, I didn't really need a weather degree to tell me that. A glance out to the west confirmed a black and menacing sky.

My captain for the day was Benny and we were assigned a Lear 24. I had not seen him since our confrontation some months earlier when he thought I stole his trip. Like the rest of us, he had also advanced his flying career since then. He was now a new captain and as was common practice, a senior copilot was assigned to a new captain while they built their confidence. In his brief time as a new captain, word had gotten out around that most of the copilots did not like flying with him. So much so, that many of the copilots tried their best to avoid trips with him. However, for this trip, the dispatcher had the final say. She made her crew selection and that senior copilot was me.

Benny came into the flight planning room and I reported the weather.

"There's a line of weather running diagonally across the state. It's almost solid, only a few gaps along the line. The Flight Service Station also said tops were above 41,000 so we can't get above it."

Despite that report, he was uninterested in the weather.

"Have you preflighted the airplane yet?"

"Not yet. The airplane just got in. It came in from an all night air ambulance flight and the line guys just started fueling it. What about it?"

"It's filthy. I had the line boys stop everything and told them to polish the leading edges."

I paused to consider his change of plans.

Most Learjet pilots were meticulous about the appearance of their airplanes. The Learjet was a beautiful airplane and when cleaned and polished, each and every Lear was a jewel sitting on the airport ramp. It was not an exaggeration to say that virtually any Learjet chosen at random could have won an unannounced concours level inspection. Of special pride were the wing leading edges, which were made of stainless steel. They were consistently polished to a mirror finish. Some crews took this obsession to an even higher level and polished the landing gear.

However, this airplane had been flying around the clock for the past day. I hadn't seen the airplane since it landed but Benny was probably right. It was likely a little dirty but usually a quick swipe of the leading edge with a common household appliance cleaner would suffice when we were in a hurry. Which, this afternoon, as usual, we were. A detailed cleaning could come later.

"We're running late. How about if we just give the leading edges a quick wipe?"

"No. That's not good enough. The customer said he was bringing his new girlfriend and I'm not going to embarrass him. More importantly, I'm not going to embarrass myself."

"Don't you think he'd rather we show up on time with a dirty airplane? His girlfriend is going to be impressed enough getting picked up in a Learjet. I don't think she's going to scrutinize the leading edges. Besides, the rain we're going to fly through will scrub them clean anyway."

Benny stared at me for a moment and laughed. As far as he was concerned that was the end of the conversation. He stomped one foot to emphasize the point and left the room.

After a lengthy delay waiting for the leading edges to meet our captain's inspection we were closer to being ready. I waited in the left seat of the cockpit. Benny had graciously assigned me to fly this challenging leg and as I waited, I reviewed the flight plan and the procedures for turbulent air penetration. It was only 150 miles over to Tampa and we were sure to encounter bad weather. Even though we were going to climb up to 410 for the short hop, most of the flight was going to be climbing though the lower altitudes and then descending right back down again. We wouldn't have the luxury of cruising serenely above all the weather. Nor could we do much deviating around the weather on a short flight. The latest radar picture showed a few gaps along the way but they were unreliable. Thunderstorms were notoriously and always in a state of flux. What may have been a safe passage now could close up and turn deadly in ten minutes.

The flight manual said we should enter an area of turbulence at 270 knots. That speed would be fast enough to give us a safety margin in order to prevent a stall but slow enough that we wouldn't overstress the airplane. As an extra precaution, I'd turn on the engine igniters to continuous. That extra spark could prevent the engines from flaming out when flying through extremely heavy rain. It all seemed so neat. In hindsight, we should have delayed our flight but we had a customer waiting but that's not how we did business in the South Florida charter world. There was money to be made and more jet hours to log.

After my operational preflight duties were finished, I turned to my administrative chores. I filled out the logbook with the pertinent info for today's flight: the date, the name of each pilot, departure city and arrival city. The only thing left blank was the box for the captain's signature. Like a good copilot, I had everything ready so all the captain had to do was climb in and start the engines.

Satisfied the outside of the airplane met his cosmetic standards, Benny climbed in the airplane and closed the cabin door. The sky was now dark as the storm to the west blotted out the afternoon sun.

I glanced again at my watch. We were now even more late and I really wanted to get out before the storm came over the airport itself. However, Benny had other matters to attend. Rather than turn towards the cockpit to get things going, he went to the back of the empty passenger cabin.

That was unexpected. No other captain gave the cabin a second glance. They just boarded with maybe a cursory hello to any passengers and got on with the business of flying the airplane. However, Benny was in the mood to inspect the cabin.

The cleaning crew had already adjusted each seat belt so they formed an "X" across the bottom seat cushions just as they had been doing for years. But this failed Benny's scrutiny. He went to each seat and uncrossed each seat belt and then laid them straight out. He did this six separate times for each passenger seat on the airplane. He then stepped back to survey his work. Apparently unsatisfied, he returned to each seat and laid the belts back in their original X pattern. Still unsatisfied, he then pulled a protractor from his shirt pocket. He then laid the measuring device across each seat belt. He adjusted each seat belt, and then re-adjusted it, so the straps were laid across the seat at an angle exactly to his liking. He repeated this process for each of the six passenger seat belts onboard.

We were now over 30 minutes late but he continued his scrutiny of the cabin. He stooped over and inspected the carpet, which had been freshly vacuumed by the line boys. He studied the carpet and found a small piece of lint. He held it up with a flourish. For the first time, he turned to me and acknowledged my presence.

"You missed this."

He was delighted with his discovery. Although, I wasn't sure whether he was trying to be funny or proud of himself for finding an inconsequential oversight.

"Sorry about that. But just so you know, we have a clearance limit from air traffic control. They say Miami Center may shut down all departures soon and they want us airborne in 15 minutes."

He smiled broadly. "They can wait. You missed a spot so now I have to re-check everything." And he spent several more minutes combing the passenger cabin for any other oversights.

Benny finally climbed in the left seat and then performed another ritual. After he sat down and buckled his seatbelt across his lap, he then spent another minute ensuring his seatbelt was perfectly angled across his lap. Once satisfied with that detail, he then adjusted his tie so it was perfectly vertical down his shirt. He then ran his fingers down the front crease of his pants to ensure their sharpness.

I looked at my watch.

"We really have to get going. Our passenger is already at the Tampa airport waiting for us."

I was pretty sure that sincerity wasn't working so I added sarcasm.

"I'm not sure if you noticed but there's a storm cell just west of the airport. We need to get out of here before it closes the airport."

He was unmoved by my rationale. His eyes were without color and when he looked at me, he seemed to just look right through me as though I was distracting him from some important matter.

He laughed at my request.

He then pulled out a pocket comb and leaned forward towards the instrument panel. He searched for his reflection in the glassy glare of the flight director and proceeded to comb and re-comb his already perfectly parted white hair.

He again broke into a wide grin.

"You know, they really ought to install flip down mirrors underneath the glare shield so we can groom ourselves properly."

I held back a smirk. I was trying to decide first, whether he was kidding; and then second, whether his personal grooming was due to his desire to present a good image to the customer or from pure vanity. I decided he was not kidding and that he really was that vain.

It was now clear we were operating on Benny's timetable, not that of the customer or of real world safety concerns. The ritual continued.

Once he was satisfied that his seat was perfectly adjusted and his hair was perfectly coiffed he then raised his left wrist to admire his watch. It was a gold watch and it was a gift from one of our customers. Benny was enormously proud of it and he unclasped the wristband and adjusted so it was exactly centered on his wrist. He then wiggled it ever so slightly to ensure it would move out of position. However, like the seatbelts, he was unsatisfied that he got it right, so he unclasped the wristband again and recentered it on his wrist. He repeated that particular formality three more times as our line boy waited outside in as the thunderstorm closed in on us.

There was yet more to come. He then pulled out the airplane logbook, which I had already pre-filled out for our upcoming flight. Without a word he ripped that page out. My jaw dropped.

"You can't do that."

Any airplane's logbook was a federal document containing a record of its flight and maintenance history. It had to remain intact and be available for an audit at any time. If a pilot made an entry error, it could only be crossed out, not destroyed. A ripped page was sure to get the attention of a government inspector and probably incur a steep fine.

He dismissed my concern with a wave of a hand.

"Your handwriting is sloppy. I want the log entries to look more precise."

He then took five more minutes to redo the work I had already done, painstakingly filling out the form with perfect penmanship with each letter and number precisely centered in each box.

Satisfied that everything was in order he called for the Before Start checklist and things finally began to proceed rapidly.

We were assigned Runway 8 at Executive Airport. It was a takeoff to the east, and he assigned the takeoff to me. As we taxied out we could see the ominous storm clouds building just to the west of the airport. I turned on the airplane's weather radar to make sense of the storm. I made a quick assessment of its position and decided on a course of action.

"It looks like there's a gap just to the north of us. After takeoff, instead of turning directly towards Tampa, we should follow the shoreline to the north for a bit. Then we'll turn west though the gap in the line."

Given his stubborn nature, I was surprised when he readily agreed with me.

We took off towards the east and the sky ahead was clear and blue. It was deceiving because I knew what was waiting for us once we turned west. However, we had our plan of action. We had both agreed to it and I was confident we could slip through the gap unmolested.

Benny switched to Miami departure control and they gave us a heading of 360 degrees. That was a course straight north, parallel the shoreline just as we planned. We weren't the only ones who saw that gap. The controller was lining us up with other airplanes heading for the tiny opening in the weather. That heading also gave us an opportunity to see what was between us and Tampa.

And it was even worse than before.

There was a massive thunderstorm just west of us. It was fully developed and at its peak strength. I craned my neck to look up at it and the tops were easily above 40,000 feet. The storm was a jagged black mountain. The radar confirmed what we saw visually, a solid line of red radar returns. And both the radar and our visual sighting also confirmed there was a gap wide enough for safe passage to our northwest. Our plan was going to work and I was grateful we were going to deviate around the heart of the storm.

But Benny had apparently changed his mind.

He commanded to me, "Turn to a heading of 270."

"Benny, that's a bad heading. That will put us right into it. It's not even the right heading for Tampa. Why don't we just go wide? A heading of 310 will keep us out of it."

However, he was annoyed with my advocacy. Apparently it didn't matter that we had agreed to a different course of action.

"We're running late. I said a 270 heading… Now!…DO IT!.

A quick look at the radar told me what I already knew. A 270 heading would put us right into the heart of the storm.

He commanded again, "We can cut in on the inside. Turn hard left! Now!"

It was clear he was trying to cut inside to pass on the south side of the storm. There was a tiny gap on the south side but we didn't have enough maneuvering room to make it. We were too fast and our turning radius was too wide. Despite my own counsel, I obliged anyway.

I was hand flying the airplane and I leaned forward to push my forehead as far as possible against the cold plastic windshield, as though an extra fraction of an inch would have given me a better view. I again looked straight up at the jagged clouds. We were headed straight into the heart of the roiling storm.

Walpole had trained me in thunderstorm penetration. And after my lesson with him, I thought I knew what was about to come. I flipped my sunglasses back over the top of my head. I wouldn't need them in a minute and besides, I always thought that wearing them over my head made me look both competent and carefree.

I turned the storm lights on and they flickered to life. I didn't think I needed them but I turned them on anyway. That was my last rational act before I had to fall back on animal instinct.

I looked ahead and saw the hard clouds just ahead of us. They had now turned a cold, icy blue. We were about to plunge into the cloud and I looked back down to focus on the instruments.

Two seconds later we flew into the storm. We were immediately assaulted with a solid wall of water and the airplane lurched backwards. I was thrown against my seat belt like a rag doll and I exhaled violently as the seat belt cut into my pelvis. My sunglasses flew off my head and fell somewhere near my feet. Outside of the thunderstorm it was a bright summer afternoon but inside, with heavy rain and thick clouds blocking the sun, it was midnight.

Inside our little plexiglass bubble, the storm lights bathed the cockpit in a stark white light. In a thunderstorm, we had no pretense to maintain night vision. There was nothing to see outside anyway and any night sight would be destroyed by lightning strikes. My main goal was to follow the guidance of the brightly lit instruments.

There was a moment of calm and I was able to reach up to make one last throttle adjustment. I slowed the airplane to 270 knots. It was the turbulent air penetration speed. And just as I did that, I was slammed again by a wind gust. This time, I was pushed down against my seat back and a second later, I was slammed forward again.

The storm had us in its grip and we were tossed like a rat shaken by a terrier. I saw 60 degrees of right bank on the attitude indicator. That extreme roll angle was surprising. I had to decide quickly. Was that an accurate indication or have the gyros tumbled? I cross checked with our other two attitude gyros and yes, we really were at 60 degrees of bank.

We were at the verge of tumbling out of control and I had only a second to corect.

The Lear was evolved from a fighter jet. It had an eight spar fail-safe wing. I knew it was strong enough to handle this storm and worse. Or, at least, I had been told it was. The weak link was not the airplane. Instead, it was me.

I still had to be supremely careful. I had to aggressively fly the airplane through the tempest but I had to avoid over controlling. That mishandling could overstress the airframe and could cause inflight break up. Or if I over-controlled, I would lose control of the airplane myself. Either one was really bad. I had to be gentle but firm; and despite the vertigo tearing at me, I had to trust my instruments. If the storm tore us apart or I lost control, it would be pilot error, plain and simple.

I rolled the airplane back to wings level. The pounding rain was beating the windshield so loudly that I couldn't even hear the engines anymore. Another sharp jolt and we rolled sharply to the left. I recalled Walpsole's soothing advice, "Be firm but gentle, let the airplane's natural stability do its job.

Only correct for large deviations but always bring the airplane back to level flight smoothly."

I didn't want to make any fatal mistakes. I concentrated on the attitude gyro. It was just a five inch square of glass and spinning metal but, at that moment, it was my whole life.

We hit another updraft and the nose lurched down. The airspeed indicator jumped up 30 knots. I eased the nose back up a bit to bleed off a little airspeed. But I didn't chase the airspeed. I was still letting the airplane's natural stability do most of the work and just trying to maintain a constant attitude.

I left the throttle untouched. Using the throttles to chase the airspeed would further destabilize the airplane with excessive inputs. I knew the throttle setting I had selected would give me a constant 270 knots so I didn't mess with it.

The other rule in a thunderstorm was to not turn excessively and certainly not to turn back. Trying to maneuver the airplane just increased the strain on the airframe. We were committed to this heading but I wanted to know what was ahead. At our speed, we should be out of the storm cell in another minute or two…

I hoped.

But still, there was a very real possibility that we might be flying into the very core of the storm and that really could be more powerful than the airplane itself. I wanted to adjust the radar to get a better look at the storm but I dared not take my hands off the yoke, or my attention off the attitude indicator.

I asked for help.

"Benny, tilt the radar down, I want to see what's beyond this cell."

There was no response.

"Benny!"

Nothing.

It was noisy in the cockpit so I repeated the command louder.

"Benny! Tilt the radar down!"

Still nothing.

I looked over.

He was frozen.

He was staring straight ahead, holding the microphone tightly in his right hand.

I swore to myself. I was on my own and had no choice now but to continue on this heading. I only could hope that we would break out soon and that my flying partner could, at least, control his bladder.

I gave up on adjusting the radar. Then, as impossible it was to believe, the rain had gotten harder. We had flown into the very core of the storm and the rain was like a waterfall. At my power setting we had slowed 20 knots.

I couldn't believe rain could be that thick and I then had a new concern. I yelled to myself.

"Godamnit! The engines!"

Although, by now, the din was so loud, I couldn't even hear myself.

The engines suck air into their intakes and then mix that air with fuel in their combustion chambers.

With this much rain, the engines could flame out from water ingestion.

Now, I had to act. I had forgotten to turn on the igniters as a precaution before entering the storm. I should have remembered but I was distracted by trying to talk sense into Benny.

I could live without adjusting the radar but I had to protect the engines.

The switches were on opposite side of the cockpit. I had to take my right hand off the controls. I gripped the yoke even more tightly with my left hand, trying to maintain control with just that one hand. I reached over and flipped both engine igniters to "Air Ignition." That gave me continuous ignition in the combustion chambers. And then for good measure, I switched hands again while still fighting the airplane to turn on the engine nacelle heat with my left hand.

Hopefully, with those actions, I could keep the engines from flaming out. The continuous ignition would keep the combustion going in the engines, and the engine heat would prevent any ice from building up on the intakes and choking the engines.

I returned my full attention to the airplane. I was too busy to be scared, thus I had no room left for panic. We had drifted a few degrees off course, but the finer points of navigation was not much of a concern to me. I let the course error stand.

I briefly wished Walpole or Coe were with me. Their years of experience made them completely unflappable. Instead, my flying partner was still of no help leaving me entirely on my own. I had gotten used to the bedlam surrounding me and I was able to think a little more clearly.

With no one to turn to, I began to coach myself.

"Gentle movements"

"Just go with the flow, like a swimmer caught in a riptide, don't fight the current, just ride the waves, and wait for it to spit you out."

We had been in the storm now for over two minutes and fighting for survival had become routine. I had been on the razor's edge balancing between keeping the airplane from tumbling out of control and trying to be gentle on the controls. I was pretty sure we were going to make it but I was getting tired. The adrenaline rush had passed and now flying the airplane was just work.

We were flying at over four miles a minute. We should have been out of the storm cell by now. The storms in Florida are intense but they are much smaller than the monster squall lines in Kansas. People called them "popcorn cells." It made them sound kind of cute and harmless. They were localized and scattered. If you got into one by accident you could usually pop right out quickly.

But not this time. The rain intensified and beat the windshield harder. The sky darkened even more. The pelting of the rain against the airplane's aluminum skin hurt my ears. We got hit with another jolt. Worse than any of the others. My hips hurt from the strain of the lap belt.

I was getting worried. By now, I was confident that the airplane could take the continued strain but I didn't have much left. I was afraid I might now lose control of the airplane. My muscles ached but I drew deeper into my reserves.

The sky lightened momentarily and then darkened again. Another downdraft slammed us hard. Again, a streak of light appeared and then disappeared.

A ray of light meant hope. Maybe we were approaching the outer wall.

And with that thought, the storm then tired of us, spitting us out into the brilliant sky.

One moment ago I was fighting for survival; then we were in smooth air streaking higher, straight and free.

The airplane shook off the last flutter of turbulence and settled down into stable flight. I corrected my course a few degrees to the right. Except for the rain droplets shearing off the windshield, it was as though nothing had happened. Once we left the malevolent cloud behind, the sky was bright blue all around. In the calm air, I was able to replace my sunglasses in their usual jaunty position in order to resume the facade of a dashing pilot.

A look ahead revealed the moon was hanging in the midday sky. At night the moon was cold and shimmering. But on that day, floating in the blue sky, the moon was soft and warm. Ancient societies often worshipped the moon as a benevolent female deity. Although from my current vantage point I was unable to philosophize on the exact gender of the moon. However, after our passage of stark terror, its presence, regardless of gender, was, indeed, a great comfort.

We proceeded to Tampa uneventfully, the air continued blue and sleek for the twenty minutes we had left. I made an unremarkable landing and we taxied to the corporate ramp area on the southwest side of the field. We both climbed out of the airplane and I breathed the soft warm air deeply.

My knees were weak and I steadied myself against the side of the airplane. Most of the stress from our wild ride had remained. So, I decided to break the tension.

"That was a helluva ride. Remind me not to do that again."

A comment like that was a hallmark of the pilot fraternity. When either faced with an upcoming challenge or after having completed an especially difficult flight, the proper response was avoid any reference to your own abilities and down play your performance as being particularly inept. Conversely, the other pilot would play along with this charade and make an equally disparaging remark.

For instance, let's say after making a textbook approach and landing into a mountainous airport in low visibility, the conversation would go something like this: "I really wasn't paying much attention to the airplane so by the time I realized it was time to start down, we were way too high. It was a total screw up on my part and we had to ask the air traffic controllers for relief from our crossing restriction. Fortunately, the copilot reminded me to use the speed brakes so we were able to slow down enough to start the approach. Once we were on final approach, it took me several tries to get lined up on the runway properly and really, it was only by coincidence that I landed on centerline just as we were passing though it for the fourth or fifth time. It was a pretty smooth touchdown but only because I lost control of the airplane at the last second and the airplane just landed by itself."

Conversations like that were all great fun and designed to self congratulate while at the same time maintaining a sort of humility that wasn't humble at all.

The other pilot listening would then continue the game. Their response, while sounding derogatory, would also be a half compliment/half insult.

Usually, something like, "Yeah, you did pretty good but, you know, you really should get your pilot's license one of these days. Your passengers would appreciate it."

It was a finely tuned art form that most pilots had mastered.

It was good to have escaped from the storm and I wanted to congratulate myself on surviving a crisis. Maybe, more importantly, I wanted my fellow pilot to acknowledge my achievement. I was faced with an unexpected challenge and I did my job. And I did it well. It was time for us to play the game of making equally derogatory comments. This end result of this self-deprecating intercourse would be a way to cement mutual respect and admiration.

However, my fellow pilot saw it differently. Benny, the captain of the perfectly crossed seat belts, the sharply creased slacks, and the perfectly coiffed hair, had regained his composure. He decided that was not the game he wanted to play.

He was the one who insisted on flying into a thunderstorm, and he was the one who froze in a moment of crisis, but rather than examine his own performance, he decided to critique my flying technique.

"Well, that was really bad control of the airplane. You were flying the wrong airspeed and you got about ten degrees off course. You should know your operating manual better."

He went on to harangue me about several other perceived miscues until, as a final exclamation point, he stomped his right foot and walked away. Leaving me to stew in my own indignation.

I am not sure why he decided to cut through the storm. He never offered an explanation. Benny never explained himself. Everything was always someone else's fault. Was it to save a few minutes? Maybe because listening to his copilot would have hurt his own self image? I didn't know and I never found out.

His other copilots had warned me that loyalty was a one way street with Benny. He would demand total obedience but never, in turn, support his copilots. To him, we were simple automans, only there to obey all of his commands, immediately and exactly as instructed.

It wasn't supposed to be that way. Pilots were a fraternity and in the face of danger we learned that we had to trust and rely on each other. It was a matter of pride among pilots to be considered trustworthy. But it wasn't that way with Benny. Therefore, his flying partners learned he was not to be trusted, either as a pilot or as a friend. And in just the last hour, I had learned that lesson myself. He was not to be trusted. But more than that, I began to pity him.

Chapter 35

The Panamanian Captain

A heavy rain was falling over the isthmus of Central America and somewhere below us lay our destination. I peered out the thick plexiglass windshield but the cloud mass was thick and sticky. It gave no clue as to our location so I reverted my gaze back to the comfort of the flight director to guide me to safety.

It was eight in the morning and we were trying to find the city of David, located in the western hinterlands of Panama. Also below us were mountains surrounding our destination. That was pretty typical though. There were almost always mountains to contend with in Latin America. I double checked the navigation charts for the Minimum Safe Altitude (MSA) in this sector and read them off to the captain.

"Volcan Baru is 12,000 feet high. The minimum sector altitude is 14,000 but this airway keeps us to the east of the highest terrain. The minimum airway altitude is 7,000, so as long as we stay on the airway, we're good to descend down to seven." The plan being that once we descended to 7,000 feet, if we were still in the clouds, we could then fly overhead the airport and start an instrument letdown into the valley.

Allen was my captain on this trip. Over the past several weeks, despite the random nature of pilot pairings, we had been flying together frequently. Only a week prior, we had a week long layover in the Virgin Islands where we chartered a sailboat in lieu of a hotel layover. We had spent an entire week in the tropical sun cruising between ports, alternating between diving, partying, and gorging on freshly caught lobster. Sailing was Allen's main passion. He had grown up on the shores of Connecticut and had spent much of his childhood sailing the waters of Long Island Sound.

Although he had mastered the complexities of sailing, it was well known among all the copilots that he was less than able in the airplane. The copilots didn't mind him terribly. He wasn't their favorite but he wasn't the worst. He flew the airplane well enough but had a tendency to not stay ahead of the airplane. He was often surprised by slowly deteriorating conditions, whereas a more diligent pilot would see a developing crisis and take early action. In other words his judgement wasn't the best so you had to watch him. That was the bad part but, at least, he wasn't abusive. When it came to which captain was the favorite of the copilots, Allen was in the middle of the desirability spectrum.

His only response to my earlier observation about the mandatory minimum altitude was to light another cigarette. It was my leg so I continued in this manner circling down through the murk until we broke out into visual conditions. However, once we were in clear sky, we were faced with another obstacle. There was a fog layer obscuring the valleys of the Cordillera. Only the peaks of the mountain range were visible making the mountain range appear to be an archipelago floating in a frothy sea.

We knew the airport was located in one of those frothy bowls but it was served only by an NDB approach in a non radar environment. This meant we had to use a fifty year old, and marginally accurate, technology for navigation without the guiding eye of a radar controller; leaving us to feel our way down through the valley. It was a procedure in which I had become quite accustomed. It was another routine matter of affairs in all of the smaller cities in Latin America. However, despite these challenges, we were able to find the airport and landed in an ordinary manner.

Once we landed, we were informed that the plans had changed. We had expected to fly back to Panama City, in the humid lowlands along the Pacific Coast; but instead we were told to prepare for an overland trip deeper into the misty green hinterland.

Upon hearing the news of our trip to the mountain compound, he was characteristically ambivalent. His main criteria for where he lay his head was only dependent on whether there was a steady supply of gin at the destination.

Our passenger that day was a wealthy Panamanian journeying to his mountainside lodge for a long retreat. The great man traveled like a middle eastern potentate with a combination of advisers, security men, toadies, and groupies following in his wake. At the last minute, he decided that we were also to be a part of his entourage.

Although we were not part of his usual retinue, we had a special role to play. It turned out that he had many enemies and he didn't like being isolated.

Therefore, it gave him great comfort knowing that his pilots, and his airplane, were close by allowing for a quick escape if necessary.

A convoy of military trucks was waiting for us at the David airport and picked up the main body of the entourage while we stayed behind to close up the airplane. A second but much smaller convoy then waited for us to finish so we could follow about a half an hour behind.

We were assigned a young Panamanian Air Force officer to be our escort and see to our various needs. He was an amiable type who spoke excellent English. He said his name was Reymundo, but he preferred to be called Rey. Rey was tall and slim with black hair swept straight back. Despite his military standing, everyone in the entourage was on holiday and he wore a pair of dark blue jeans, a light blue cotton button down shirt, a white polyester baseball cap with the emblem for the Panamanian Air Force, and brown Adidas sneakers. Allen and I were still in our civilian pilot uniforms although we had taken off our epaulets in a futile attempt to fit in.

We were assigned to ride as passengers in a brand new white Ford sedan. We loaded our bags and Allen and I climbed in the back seat with Rey in the front right seat. We then left the airport to begin the climb into the misty Panamanian highlands. The road we were on roughly paralleled the Rio Caldera, which flowed down from the continental divide. The road itself was as sinuous as the river it followed and was mostly paved. In parts though, the road had washed out from when the river had overflowed its banks. In those sections, we had to disembark and climb aboard one of the army trucks accompanying us. The trucks then pulled the sedan through the mud so we could continue our ascent. The higher we climbed the more frequently we had to repeat that process.

At the halfway point in our journey, Rey decided it was time to stop in a hamlet for lunch. Our stopping place didn't even have a name and I'm not sure it was even big enough to be called a hamlet. It was just a plywood hut overlooking a narrow section of the mountain stream. The wood was unpainted and it had a flimsy tar paper roof. It had one window overlooking the rapids and a tin metal chimney with smoke billowing from its top. On one side of the hut was a rusty sign nailed to the building proclaiming that they served the local Panamanian beer.

In order to reach the hut, we had to make a precarious crossing over a homemade wooden bridge. Although, it was actually more just a plank laid across the narrow rapids. Outside the hut there was an aging lion lying in a rusting cage open to the elements. He was languid and mangy and was disinterested in the goings on around him.

Rey, Allen and I entered the hut while the drivers remained with their trucks and waited on the side of the road eating some sort of military rations. Inside, we settled in on primitive wooden benches. I ordered the local beer, the same one advertised on the side of the building. It was branded Cerveza Panama and tasted like fizzy piss water. They were so weak, that I figured I could put down about ten of them with no problem but we had to move on. We only stayed long enough to eat a quick meal of chicken and rice before we were on our way again.

After several more hours of travel through the misty wilderness, we arrived in the town of Boquete. It was a fairytale town, filled with alpine style architecture. It was considered the Switzerland of Central America and we checked into the Hotel Fundadores.

The hotel was a modest affair. Unlike the Hotel Oloffson in Port-au-Prince, which still managed an old world elegance, this hotel was more like a roadside motel one would find along a 1950s highway in the rural United States. The main building was squat and constructed with inexpensive lumber. The facade of the hotel was styled like a sad imitation of Mad Ludwig's castle in order to fit in with the other buildings in Boquete. The front desk clerk assigned me to an outbuilding which he assured me was one of their best rooms.

I walked outside the lobby to my room but first had to navigate a circuitous breezeway overgrown with ginger and crotons. There was a small stream just in front of my door and I crossed over another makeshift plank to enter my room. Once inside, I saw what one would expect in a cloister for a religious retreat. The room was large but under furnished. A single twin size bed was located in one corner. The bed had a threadbare green bedcover. Against the white side wall was a single small dresser and an even smaller mirror just above it. The bathroom was separated not by a door, but by a burgundy colored curtain. Off to the side was a small kitchen area. The room had jalousie windows all around and they were covered by yellowed sheer curtains.

And of course, located in the wall was the same kind of ancient window air conditioner, ubiquitous to the region. It had brown plastic fake wood paneling. I looked at the label. It was a Chrysler Air Temp. Designed in the 1950s, it had old rotary control knobs. I rotated the knob to turn it on. The knob was stiff and the switch moved with a loud click. Once it was turned on, the compressor deep inside the unit groaned, made an attempt to start to life, and then stalled out with a hiss. Cycling the switch again resulted in nothing and I gave up. Instead, I cranked open the jalousie windows. It was about 65 degrees with a nice breeze and the curtains lifted instantly as the sweet mountain air filled the room.

I noticed an ice cooler besides my dresser was filled with bottles of Coca-Cola and beer. The beer was the same cerveza Panama at the hut with the sad lion where we had lunch. On the dresser were glasses, several bottles of rum, along with a carton of Marlboro cigarettes. Flip tops. That was important. My military escort had earlier told me that I would be hosting a party because I had the biggest room. I guessed he wasn't kidding. It looked like we were in for a long night of partying and conversation. I cracked open a bottle of the local Panamanian beer while I waited for the party to start.

A knock came on the door. It was Allen, the captain. He already had a drink in his hand. He was followed by Rey, our Air Force escort. He was accompanied by another officer who was the personal helicopter pilot for our passenger.

Rey sat at the linoleum kitchen table and opened a beer.

"I was educated in the United States," he announced proudly.

"I could have stayed in the United States but I decided to come back to Panama because I wanted to make my country a better place."

I really didn't care all that much but I figured I had to say something.

"That is an honorable thing," I said, complimenting him.

"Panama is a great country but we have many challenges. We owe our existence to the United States but we have never been allowed to be fully independent. The canal is one of the most valuable pieces of land in the world. And everyone wants to control it. During the Second World War, both the Japanese and Germans had eyes on it. But the Americans, with the Monroe Doctrine, kept a firm grip on the canal.. and on us.. for decades."

His story sounded an awful lot like what I had heard in Haiti from the university professor. It was a combination of respect and resentment for the role of the US in the region.

He paused and took a long draw from his beer.

"Do you believe in the Monroe Doctrine?"

This was a common line of conversation in Latin America. For as much as they seemed to dislike American interference, they were obsessed with knowing what we thought.

I sidestepped the question.

"I suppose there are good and bad things about it."

Allen was in the corner, lost in a cloud of cigarette smoke and probably on his fourth gin and tonic. Or maybe it was more than four. I had long ago given up counting his drink consumption. And I had even more definitely stopped trying to keep up with him drink for drink.

Speaking of drinking too much, by now Rey had drawn down half a bottle of rum. He was mixing it with Coca-Cola so it was going down pretty easily. So much so that his true feelings were exposed.

"The Spanish were here first and the English were satisfied to leave this part of the Americas alone. But once the United States separated from the British Empire, that was when things changed for us. Once the United States became independent they decided they wanted an empire of their own and they had their eye on Spanish America. But they had a problem. They were a republic not an empire. They couldn't make us a colony but they didn't want to actually include us in the United States. We had too many Spanish. They only wanted land that was either empty or already Anglo. So instead, they came up with the Monroe Doctrine. They gave themselves the power to control the whole hemisphere without actually owning it; and, more importantly, without giving us the same rights as their own white citizens. It gave them an excuse to interfere with our governments on almost any pretext."

Ricardo paused to take a long draw of his rum and Coke.

I wanted to remind him that the local indigenous people were actually here first, not the Spanish, but that was off topic and it would only have likely antagonized him.

He then went off on a tangent.

"Do you know why so many Latinos revere Castro?"

I only knew that in the United States, particularly in Miami, Castro was one of the most reviled of all dictators. I was uninformed that he was admired around the region.

He was getting agitated and continued without waiting for an answer.

"It is because he is defiant to the United States. The US constantly meddles in the foreign affairs of countries around the region, invading and toppling governments if it doesn't suit them. But Castro is independent and has even embarrassed the United States."

"Do you see that, my friend?" He asked righteously.

I couldn't stay silent any longer. He had me cornered and he demanded an answer. I tried to stay non-confrontational.

"Well, yes, I see what you are talking about but aren't there some good things about outside influence? Isn't it good to have others help you?"

I was satisfied that my answer was sufficiently friendly. Although, even with that non-committal answer, Rey had plenty to drink by then so I wasn't sure whether I was to get a further barrage of anti-American sentiment or a finding of common ground. It could go either way.

Instead he became philosophical. He paused to pour several fingers worth of rum into his glass. You know, the cheap kind of scratched up glassware found in seedy hotels all around the world.

"My friend, remember this: The day you are born, you are given a nationality, a religion and a family name; and you are expected to defend all three for the rest of your life."

I should have stopped to take in the enormity of what he just said but I was, as usual, a little too slow to understand the nuance. Instead, it became a debate and I pursued my original line of reasoning. "I can see that but isn't it important to be open to new ideas?"

"Perhaps, but it is very hard to unlearn old ideas. It is much easier to go along with what you are taught. You tell me I should be open to new ideas, I think that you too, must also be open to new ideas. Remember too, here we do not have the same luxuries you have in the United States of free speech. You can say almost anything you want. Here in Panama, if I were to say certain things I would end up in jail...or worse."

I had no answer for him. He was right. I came from a totally different world than his. Even though I was only middle class in America, I still had enormous privilege. Especially in South America, being American and white placed me automatically at the highest levels of their society. However, there was always that combination of envy and resentment that I saw time and time again. There was very little I could do to understand his world and trying to change his mind was simple arrogance.

With that realization we decided to call it a draw. The trash was filled with empty beer cans; the rum bottles were almost empty and it had gotten very late. With the windows open, I could hear the distant gurgling of the mountain stream as I reflected on what he had said. The night had held an epiphany for me. It was here in the highlands overlooking the city of David, named after the righteous King David of the Old Testament, where I realized that righteousness often depended on what side of an issue you happened to be sitting. It had become starkly apparent to me that the world was not at all as clear as I was taught as a child; nor would it fit into my preconceived notions. In my sad little hotel room, far from home, this realization had left me unsettled.

We said our goodbyes and everyone walked out on wobbly legs. Once they left, I was grateful to be alone and I closed my door with the reassuring click of the flimsy latch.

The next morning there was another change of plans. We were told to cut short our stay in Boquete and to reposition the airplane to Panama City. Once there we were to await instructions.

Chapter 36

A Bad Guess Can Kill

I was working a thorny math problem while standing in the 96 degree heat of the midday tropics. The wing of the Lear was at hip level so it made for an ideal desk where I had laid out a navigation chart in front of me.

The airplane was parked on a remote section of ramp at the Paitilla airport, which was nestled in downtown Panama City. The sleek and shiny airplane stood in sharp contrast to its surroundings. Weeds sprouted out of the cracks in the concrete ramp and the aircraft fueler was waiting patiently for my answer. He was wearing a greasy yellow T-shirt. It was too short and his hairy belly peeked out from the bottom. Emblazoned on the front of his shirt was the faded red logo of the Shell Oil company.

I had mostly mastered flying the Lear, so I was now also assigned responsibility for all flight planning as well as the tedious paperwork for the various government bureaucrats that were in our way. At the moment, I was trying to figure out the proper fuel load for our flight and I was working the math one handed. My other hand was occupied to keep the chart from floating up in the fetid breeze blowing off of the Pacific Ocean. My polyester slacks were soaked with sweat and clinging to my skin. I was eager to get back into the air conditioned cabin of our airplane and get on our way. But first, I needed an answer.

I was still flying with Allen and he had tasked me with the three dimensional problem of calculating our flight plan from Panama City to Medellin, a city in Colombia, which was of sudden interest to our customer.

I calculated we would require about 2,000 pounds of fuel to fly to Medellin. That was the easy part. But, there was an unknown. I didn't have Medellin weather, so I didn't know if I needed to add extra fuel for an alternate airport.

Normally, the answer given by many Learjet pilots, including myself, would have been to just top off the fuel tanks but there was a second and more immediate complication. Paitilla was not the main international airport with its luxuriously long runways. Instead, Paitilla was the downtown airport tucked in between the business district of Panama City and the mud flats at the edge of the runway. It was originally designed in the 1930s to defend the Panama Canal and the prop driven air defense fighters of that era didn't need a lot of runway. Hence, the runway was only 5,000 feet long. We couldn't carry a full load of fuel out of Paitilla. The weight of full tanks would have lengthened our takeoff roll beyond the length of the concrete available. Simply put, a comfortable fuel margin would make us too heavy for takeoff.

Allen came out of the customs office with our departure clearance. A cigarette was dangling from his thin lips.

He was only 38 years old but aviation had not been kind to him. He was slightly built with thinning brown hair and watery blue eyes. It had been 12 hours since his last drink and the palsy in his hand seemed a bit worse than usual.

"Are you finished yet? The customer will be here soon and the fueler is waiting."

"Not yet, I can't make the numbers work. If we load enough gas to make Medellin and then also enough fuel for Bogota as an alternate, we'll be too heavy for takeoff."

The breeze picked up and I slapped the chart down again.

I pointed to a line drawn on the chart between Panama City and Medellin. Allen only half-heartedly paid attention.

"It's 200 miles from here to Medellin. I figure about 2000 pounds of fuel to get there."

"What's the Medellin weather?"

"The only report I have is 12 hours old. The weather office here doesn't have anything more recent. Either Medellin is not reporting or they just can't get it."

"Well, that would be important to know. Medellin is in a valley and they don't have any instrument approaches. It has to be visual conditions there… We have a light load. You know we have only one passenger, right?"

"Yeah, but that doesn't help us. It's the fuel. We should probably load at least 4,000 pounds but the runway isn't long enough."

I looked at the numbers again on my scratch paper and I was unhappy that we were assigned a Lear 25 for this trip. It was larger and heavier than the 24 we normally flew. Worse yet, the 25 was an even more profligate user of fuel, even by Learjet standards.

"I wish we were flying the 24. It needs less runway and uses less gas."

I regretted my wishful thinking as soon as I said it.

"Well, they gave us a 25."

"Can you take a look at my math?"

He instead gave me the nebulous command, "You can make it work."

Uncertain as to whether that was an actual command or wishful thinking on his part, I went back to my calculations but I couldn't make the math work. I couldn't put on enough gas to fly to Medellin, then an alternate, then reserves, and contingency. At least, not without going off the end of the runway on takeoff.

Since there was no clear answer I started weighing the odds and I decided to make a wager.

I was going to bet that the weather in Medellin would be kind to us and we'd pick up the airport visually. We could forgo some extra gas.

"The weather in Medellin is usually good so I won't add alternate fuel."

Still uncertain, I looked to Allen for approval and he only shrugged his shoulders.

I continued the conversation, hoping to get him more engaged and suggested a better solution, one that made me feel better.

"We could hop over to the international airport, just to top it off, and then we'll have plenty of fuel for Medellin and an alternate, and any contingencies."

"No, the customer won't like that. He's already running late and that will take almost an hour."

I wiped my brow in the unrelenting heat. I was unhappy with how this was heading.

I then tried to work the problem backwards, but my stomach hurt as I still came up with the same unsatisfactory answer.

I tried the math again, probably, for the fifth or sixth time. This time speaking aloud as I did my math, partly to assuage my nerves, and partly hoping to have Allen cross check my work.

"OK, assuming no alternate required, then we just need 2000 pounds to get to Medellin, another 1500 for the minimum legal reserve. That's a total fuel load of 3500 pounds, which makes us just light enough to make the takeoff. Is that OK?"

At the same time, I turned my worksheet to Allen, hoping for his approval.

He only grunted a noncommittal answer.

"Yeah, I guess that will work."

And he walked away, leaving me alone by the side of the airplane.

In aviation it is said that there are three things useless to a pilot. It was one of the first things we learned and every pilot knew to repeat it at any time as a form of a ditty. The things most useless to a pilot were: "Altitude above you, runway behind you, and fuel you left in the fuel truck."

Even knowing full well the value of that aphorism, I was about to make a decision that would take something important and render it useless.

Setting aside my doubts, I then convinced myself of the accuracy of my calculation and I decided to leave fuel behind. I decided we could make it to Medellin with only 3500 pounds of fuel on board and as a result, our tanks would only be about half full.

I then had to give the fuel order to the fueler in gallons so I subtracted the fuel we already had on board and worked the math to convert my desired fuel from pounds to gallons of fuel into gallons and proudly announced in Spanish to the fueler, "quatrocientos galones, por favor."

He responded with a wide smile and began pumping the fuel from his rusty truck.

After he had finished, I signed the fuel slip and paid him in cash. I didn't realize it at the time; but that signature on the fuel slip, instead of an acknowledgement of delivery, would instead be a signature on my own death warrant.

Chapter 37

An Ill-Advised Departure

Our lone passenger arrived in his Turbo Porsche. The car was steel gray and chauffeured by his Panamanian bodyguard. He quickly boarded and we taxied out blind to my bad decision.

Allen was flying this leg and as we prepared for takeoff he seemed less engaged than usual, even for him. It was not that Allen didn't care because he did, but his reputation for lacking foresight was proving true. It didn't allow him to think ahead or to catch my own bad decision. Mountain flying, especially in South America, left very little room for error and unbeknownst to either of us, I had already made several serious errors.

No matter. We were headed to the Andes, and not to just any part of the Andes, but to one of the most treacherous airports in all of the Americas. This was going to be only my second time into Medellin, and the captain's first. We were carrying barely enough fuel to meet all of the legal requirements; and we were departing with a weather forecast that was stale by several hours. I should have paid more attention to the warning signs but I didn't.

We arrived at the end of the runway and dutifully waited for our takeoff clearance. While we waited, we checked and rechecked the fuel gauge. Finally, we were given the go by the control tower and Allen turned onto the crumbling end of the runway. He lined us up with the nose pointed straight down the runway and I saw the Pacific Ocean lapping against the far end of the runway. He then came to a stop and held the brakes.

Now, there are two schools of thought on how to best make a takeoff from a short runway. The most dramatic method is to hold the brakes and then push the engines all the way up to full power before rolling. The idea is that you are not wasting runway rolling towards the end while the engines are still accelerating. Conversely, the other school of thought disputes this technique. They say the holding the brakes is just for show. All you are doing is churning the air and scaring the passengers. Their preferred method is to just make a smooth rolling takeoff and expeditiously advance the power to full.

We decided to use the high drama method. Allen, held the toe brakes down hard and at the same time pushed the throttles all the way up. I watched the tachometer needles roll up to 102% of rated thrust. Not being an aeronautical engineer myself, I was uncertain as to which technique was best but this was the technique we had chosen on that day. And it made me feel better.

Once Allen advanced the power to full, we had 6,000 pounds of thrust trying to push us forward. Behind us, thick black exhaust was screeching out of our tailpipes. The airplane wanted to go but we were holding her back. She lifted up on her struts in protest, like a sprinter lifting on her toes on the starting blocks. The airplane wanted release and the brakes shuddered from the stress, but we were holding back on the bit as hard as we could.

I looked off to the front of the airplane. The thunder from our engines prevented any work and dozens of eyes around the airport were turned towards us. It was already a hot day and the heat pouring out of our tailpipes was scorching the grass behind us. Allen held the brakes a second or two longer; longer even than proponents of this technique would deem necessary.

The air continued to churn.

The airplane strained forward.

The engine tachometers had rolled up to 104% of power and had no more to give.

Allen then released the brakes and we jerked forward.

Even though the runway was short, we were still relatively light for using this much power and we accelerated quickly.

I then called out, "Thrust is set! Engines are stable!"

Then, "Airspeed alive!"

But I must admit, I announced those mandatory calls out with more hope than certainty.

As we built up speed, the engines were getting some ram effect from our forward motion, which in turn provided more thrust, and the acceleration built up more quickly.

However, we were nowhere near flying speed and the end of the runway was coming up even more quickly.

"100 knots!"

I watched the end of the runway rushing towards us. It was going to be close. Fortunately, there were no obstacles at the runway's end. Only the flat Pacific Ocean.

Another few knots of speed.

"V1!"

We were now committed to go!

I saw the end of the runway slip under the nose of the airplane.

"Rotate!"

The airplane didn't know the length of the runway and since we were light, she leapt into the air and we accelerated quickly.

With that hurdle behind us, we began our normal climb and Panama Control gave us our initial vector on course. We dutifully turned south, towards Medellin, where its narrow valley lay in wait.

Chapter 38

Down the Dragon's Throat

Medellin was just 330 miles ahead. As we climbed to altitude, the humid and sticky air of Panama peeled away behind us and the cool conditioned air in the cabin began to dry my sweat soaked pants. Although, that didn't make me feel better. Ahead, the jagged cordillera of the South American continent appeared on the horizon. Its coastal mountain range appeared as a prone dragon waiting to catch the unsuspecting aviator in its jaws and I was reminded of Coe's admonition when I first became acquainted with Andean flying.

He introduced me to Medellin with a rhetorical question. The very same one Zimmer posed when we were heading to Guatemala for the first time.

"What are the two things in common on every mountain top in South America?"

"A cross and an airplane crash site."

At the time, it seemed funny. Coe was highly competent and flying with him was comforting. On my first trip to Medellin with Coe, the approach and landing went uneventfully under his experienced hands. It was just another romp in the airplane.

But now?

Not so much.

Allen leveled off at Flight Level 410 and I again scanned the horizon. We were sailing serenely in a blue tropical sky but far ahead it was different. The placid sky gave way to a gray and brooding cloud mass hiding our destination. It was then that I began to have a nagging doubt. We still had some runway to spare on takeoff and I regretted not adding more fuel. I suppose we also could have re-thought our decision and turned back to Panama but we continued on.

I put those thoughts aside as I returned to my navigational chores and looked again at my hastily scribbled flight plan. I had drawn a line on the navigation chart between Panama City and Medellin. The chart told me we would be flying over some of the highest terrain in South America. However, much of that was conjecture, because, underneath my line were large blocks of blank space containing the phrase "Terrain Data Unavailable."

What I did know was that the Medellin airport lay at the floor of a narrow valley. The airport itself was at 4500 above sea level but mountains surrounding it were at 12,000 feet. This setting may have been ideal for the Spanish to defend their mountain Eldorados in the days of mule trains and horse borne soldiers, but it was much more problematic for aviators 400 years later.

Approaching the Colombian border Panama Control handed us off to Bogota Control who controlled all the airspace over the country. Once we were in contact with them we were cleared to Medellin via the main airway into Colombia, Upper Amber 323.

Ahead of us, the gray cloud mass had taken on more definition and I could see we were heading towards a wall of towering cumulus clouds. Allen turned on the radar to scan ahead. The radar revealed there was nothing dangerous ahead. That was good so we wouldn't have to waste fuel deviating around storms, however, the radar did show that there was a solid sheet of showers blanketing northwestern Colombia.

I checked the fuel again. We still had enough to make Medellin and with some to spare. Although, by now, it didn't matter. We were more than halfway to our destination and we didn't have enough fuel to turn back. No matter what was to come, we were committed to Medellin. I looked up from my worksheet and the windshield was opaque. In just the last minute we had become enveloped by the gray and brooding cloud layer.

The air traffic control frequency was busy with the comings and goings of local airliners. The locals seem unfazed by the weather, although I found the chatter disconcerting. I wanted to recalculate our fuel burn but I couldn't concentrate. I asked Bogota Control for the latest Medellin weather.

There was some lighting in the clouds and the static charge affected the reception. This much I heard:

"Medellin weather is overcast clouds at 8,000 feet, visibility 5 miles in light rain," which I dutifully report to Allen. And I follow up with my own observation.

"It's technically visual in the valley but I think the overcast layer is obscuring the ridgeline. I'm not sure we'll be able to pick up the airport visually from

the airway." That was an important consideration because the standard procedure for mountain airports with no instrument approaches was to descend to
a minimum safe altitude on the known airway; slow down to approach speed,
find the airport, and continue the descent into the valley visually. However, as
a pilot naive in the ways of South America, I was still learning that not very
much in the region was standard, and certainly not standard by the norms I
was used to in North America.

I was getting increasingly uncomfortable and I redid my math. If we descended to Medellin, we wouldn't have enough to climb back up and go to an
alternate but I wasn't feeling good about getting into Medellin. Maybe, we
had enough fuel to continue to Bogota where the weather was good. Maybe
we could make it to Bogota, but only if we diverted now and even then, we
would only land on fumes. I looked at the scribble on my notepad and it was
even more sloppy than before. I sunk in my seat as my math revealed the
truth. All of our options had drained away. Bogota was out of the question.
We were landing in Medellin, or not at all.

My chest tightened and my stomach was about to retch as our little world
closed in on us. I felt like I must do something. I looked to Allen for guidance
but he was passive.

I wanted a firm answer and I wanted it from someone… anyone. If the
weather report was nebulous, then I would ask a direct question. I picked up
the microphone to call air traffic control.

"Bogota Control, this is Learjet 5 Whiskey Bravo. Is Medellin airport open?

The answer was immediate.

"Si capitan, the airport is open. Expect no delays. Descend now to Flight
Level 250."

Every airplane has a built in clock that determines how long it can stay
in the sky. This clock is in the form of fuel remaining in the tanks; and like
grains of sand in an hourglass, each minute that inexorably goes by is a minute closer to the end of the flight. This limit is fixed and inviolable. Our precious fuel was draining away rapidly and my main attention was focused on
getting back onto the ground, preferably, on a runway.

The answer from Bogota was definitive but still unsatisfying. Allen was
unfazed and I then became the one compulsively toggling the fuel switch.

I wanted to escape, to run. To find an airport with long runways on an open flat plain with clear skies. But I couldn't. There wasn't one within what little range we had left.

Regardless of that. Air Traffic Control had ended my internal debate by giving us that descent clearance to Medellin. Allen pulled back the throttles. I was relieved to see the fuel consumption drop off at idle power but my stomach continued to tighten as we descended into the murky unknown.

We descended quickly and after being handed off to Medellin Approach Control we were instructed to steer directly to the Medellin Navigation beacon. It was a homing radio perched on a ridge on the south side of the valley.

Medellin controllers did not have the capability to guide us via radar to line up with the runway. They could only clear us to the navigation beacon with a descent to 11,000 feet. After that, we were on our own.

We followed their direction and leveled off at 11,000 feet. The ridge line was at 9,000 leaving us 2000 feet of clearance. At that altitude, we expected to see the airport so as to proceed visually.

As we flew over the Medellin navigation beacon we were still solidly in the clouds.

Allen turned hard to the right and entered a holding pattern over the ridgeline.

We had 30 minutes of fuel left.

We knew Medellin airport was only 7 miles away and about a mile below us but we were completely enveloped in a thick cloud. Rivulets of rain streaked back on the windshield.

Looking for an answer, I keyed the microphone button to ask the same question.

"Medellin Control, this is Lear 8WB. Is the airport open?"

And I received the same answer.

"Si Capitan, the airport is open. Visual conditions at the airport. Airplanes arriving with no delay. Report the airport in sight."

We had enough gas to land but only if we found the airport quickly. Other airplanes may have been getting in, but we were still solidly in the clouds.

Allen lit another cigarette. By my count, it was his fifth since takeoff. He had the navigation chart clipped to his yoke and for the first time that day, he advocated a plan.

"The ridgeline surrounding the airport is 9,000 feet. We'll hold here until we see the airport, then we'll spiral down into the valley."

We were still doing 250 knots. Much too fast. Too fast for any holding pattern and certainly too fast if we're trying to enter the valley. We should be back to about 210. Preferably, even slower if we were to drift gently down like Coe had taught me earlier in Aspen.

The cockpit was closing in on me. I had the same claustrophobic sensation when trying to land with Walpole in Springfield with the weather at minimums. But this was different. Springfield had an air traffic control system with radar controllers guiding us to a modern instrument landing system. It was guaranteed to guide all the way down to a safe landing. Here, we were lost, and on our own. We had to find the airport visually, or not all.

I glanced at the fuel gauges. We were down to about 23 minutes. Walpole's "time to live" had new meaning for me now. If we were going to have any chance of a safe letdown into the valley we needed to slow down. And we need to get down. But Allen had again disengaged from our problem solving. I heard multiple airplanes on the frequency calling the airport in sight but I began to tune them out. My entire world was then reduced to just that tiny cockpit.

I asked Allen, "We're doing 250 knots, let's slow down a bit?"

He said nothing but he reached up and tweaked the throttles back a half an inch with his unsteady hand. The airspeed needle slipped back only 10 knots.

We were still too fast and we didn't know what to do. We were stranded in the holding pattern like a lost kitten crying for his mother.

I had been afraid before in my life but now I was experiencing a different sensation. This was real fear and my own hands began to shake.

The fight or flight reaction rose in my mind.

I chose flight.

"We're in solid clouds here, I don't think we can make the visual let down. Let's go to Bogota."

I realized as soon as I said it that it was a nonsensical suggestion. We had 22 minutes of fuel and Bogota was 40 minutes away, at least.

Allen answered curtly, "Not enough gas"

Then he went silent again. He offered no other plan.

I searched frantically for an answer myself. But I came up with nothing. That's because there was no answer. Other than we were going to die.

"I'm ducking under," he said.

Allen's suggestion violated every rule of instrument flying and I registered my protest.

"That's suicide. We can't leave the charted airway, especially not into a valley. We don't know where the hills are. We'll just end of hitting the side of the valley."

"We're dead if we do nothing."

I had to admit. He was right. When I made my decision on the fuel load, I made a wager that everything would work out just right. And here we were, on solid instruments with only minutes of gas remaining. Nothing had gone our way and I had lost the wager.

However, in order to have a chance at surviving, we had to make a second, even more desperate wager. We didn't have enough gas to make it to Bogota and we couldn't sit in the holding pattern indefinitely. It was a go for broke moment.

Allen's suggestion reeked of desperation but his logic was impeccable. It had two possible outcomes. Either we would descend blindly and hit a mountain in the first minute or we would pop out into visual conditions, and find the airport. The first outcome meant we would only be dead a little sooner than waiting to run out of gas; the second outcome meant we would live. It seemed like a reasonable trade-off.

Allen clicked off the autopilot. His shaky hands pulled back on the throttles as we prepared to blindly descend down into the dragon's throat.

"I think we're lined up parallel with the valley so it should be clear of terrain ahead."

He then rolled the dice and began the descent below the minimum holding altitude.

I thought of my mother briefly. Her first husband was a bomber pilot and he was killed in an airplane wreck during the war. I don't think she ever recovered from his death. Once she would receive news of my own crash, she would be devastated. I was sorry I disappointed her. I was sorry that I disappointed everyone in my life. I should have listened better.

I tensed my stomach muscles in anticipation of impact. At least, if we hit a mountain, it will be over in an instant. I recalled the morbid joke.

"When you're in the clouds, what is the last thing you see, before you hit a mountain?"

"Nothing."

I looked out ahead but my eyes had nothing to focus on. We were descending rapidly, still lost in a swirl of clouds. Although, I did not have to wait long; just 400 feet into our descent we broke out with the green valley filling our windshield. And I cheered inside!

However, our relief was short lived. We were below the cloud deck but the visibility in the valley was just three miles; although that depended in what direction you looked. We had some ground contact but the visibility in every direction was obscured in mist. The city of Medellin sprawled out below us but we couldn't see the airport. I looked around but nothing was recognizable. We were still descending and the airspeed indicator showed 240 knots.

As every second passed our thirsty engines drank more of our lifeblood fuel.

On the radio, I could hear airplanes all around us calling the airport in sight. But those were local pilots who knew the valley intimately. They were navigating by memory in the murky valley and they knew where the unforgiving granite lay. Conversely, we were a blind man trying to navigate an unfamiliar room.

Worse yet, instead of heading down parallel the length of the valley, we were crossways to it and descending straight towards the opposite ridgeline.

I called out "We're crossways to the valley. Turn right, we need to line up parallel."

Before I could check the captain's response, I was distracted by a red light on the forward warning panel.

It was both expected and unwelcome as I read it.

"LOW FUEL"

It was cold and impassive.

It told us we had about 20 minutes of fuel left, although we didn't really need a reminder. 20 minutes to live, that was if we didn't hit the side of the mountain first. I killed the messenger and punched the Low Fuel light off.

Allen had led us into the valley but he was still heading straight towards the mountain wall. I called out to him.

"Turn right!" I looked over to him and saw palsy had taken over his whole body.

My captain, the man who I depended on, was panic stricken and then seeing that, the panic visited me as well. It replaced my garden variety fear.

The panic rose up into my throat and began to choke me. I had never experienced it before but I knew what it was. It tasted like cold metal and I tried to jam it back down.

Our sole passenger came up and stuck his head through the small passageway and asked if everything was alright. Even a layman smelled the panic welling up inside of us. Our passenger was a self made man. He was comfortable commanding a business empire across three continents. But despite his silk shirts, Ferrari cars and expensive girlfriends, he was still innocent in the ways of aviation. Even more naive than me. He had nothing to offer and I wanted him to please be quiet, and sit patiently while he awaited his fate.

I barked. "Yes, it's fine. Just sit down."

He withdrew.

But we were not fine.

I looked out again. The green ridge was ahead, passively waiting for us. And we were pointed straight at it. At 240 knots, impact was about 30 seconds away.

Chapter 39

Death Pays Me a Visit

I looked to my left and was able to choke out a plea to Allen.

"We need to slow down, we're heading right to the opposite ridgeline." But I received no response. I again looked outside hoping to see something. Instead, I see we had flown into a scud layer. We had lost visual references again and we were heading straight to the ridge.

Then the mood shifted suddenly.

A door opened and I felt a chill. I looked through the windshield and just ahead of us, I saw an apparition. It was something I thought only existed in fairy tales.

It was death. We had lost the second wager and he had now come to collect.

Death... I had seen him once before, on the day of the midair collision, but on that day, I was of no interest to him, and he only brushed past me for his intended victim. Today, however, he was looking at me straight in the face and reached out for me. He poked his icy finger in my chest. I reared back but the cockpit wall stopped my escape.

I cried out. "No!"

My captain will protect me.

I screamed at him. "I need you!"

Still no response. I looked over to my left.

Allen was parayzed. He had succumbed fully to panic as death reached out for him also. Death took a step closer. And I was ready to accept it.

My entire body felt cold and weak. I was both afraid and calm.

And then I knew. Death was going to be easy.

I was ready to give up and I was ready to take death's hand.

And this is how I would die, in a green valley in the Andes...far from home.

Death beckoned. "It will be over in a second and then everything will be all right."

He smiled.

"Come."

He was right. It would only hurt for a second, and then it would be peaceful to lie in the green grass. I looked one last time at Allen. He was going to be the last human I would see. I could see that he had given up as well. I looked ahead. We were out of the scud layer and there was a wall of South American granite now just a mile ahead. At our speed we were just 15 seconds away and I went limp.

But in an instant, I changed my mind.

The fight or flight instinct returned and this time I decided to fight. I would NOT surrender!

What happened next I will leave to the psychologists who study how the gray folds of the human brain make decisions; or perhaps it is better to ask the priests who are more comfortable explaining divine intervention.

Whatever it was I do not know, but in that instant, I willed myself to live.

Death was still watching me although he had receded back into the doorway.

And I then had a moment of total clarity.

There was no time left for talk or coaching.

"Give me the airplane!"

I took the controls from Allen and rolled sharply to the right.

I don't know why I rolled right but I did. It was just instinct.

As I rolled the wings perpendicular to the ground we banked away from the mountain face. It was an unconscious and desperate act with no rationale behind it. Then I followed it with another instinctive act. I looked straight down.

"There's the airport!!"

We were right over the airport the whole time! That's why we couldn't see it.

And in a split second, I was again a rational, thinking being. With the airport in sight, I had a firm point on which to navigate. And, on this, our second bet against death, we won the wager again! Death stepped away, disappearing into the mist and the door closed.

Like a shipwrecked sailor, I was overjoyed at the sight of land but we were not yet safe. We still had to swim madly for the shore against a strong current.

I checked the fuel gauges again. The center and tip tanks were bone dry and we only had about 400 pounds in each wing tank, just minimum fuel sloshing in the wing tanks. I next checked the fuel flow. It showed we were burning 2200 pounds per hour. When we entered the valley we barely had enough to make the airport but we had burned too much searching for the airport. We now knew where the airport was but we still had to circle around to line up with the runway and there was only three miles of visibility. And once we extended our flaps and landing gear, the extra drag created meant our engines were going to consume even more of what little fuel we had left. But still, we should be able to make it.

That was if the gauge was accurate.

...And if the fuel pumps didn't cavitate from the fuel sloshing around in a steep turn.

...And if we didn't have to add power unnecessarily to correct any more of our mistakes.

...And if we didn't lose sight of the airport again.

Those were a lot of ifs that still had to go our way before we were safely on the ground; and we had already used up a lot of our luck so far.

I was still flying but I asked Allen, "Want me to keep on flying?"

And he came awake, the same as me.

"No, I've got it. Just give me headings."

We had just 17 minutes of gas left and it was going to take 10 to maneuver into proper position for landing. And in order to line up properly, we needed to maneuver on a downwind leg away from the airport to line up on the active runway.

I did some quick math in my head.

"Fly a heading of 010 degrees."

I didn't want to fly away from our safe haven but we had to.

Allen turned away from the airport and it disappeared behind our right wing

I punched the clock on the instrument panel to time our outbound leg. And I began to do my math aloud. But unlike when I figured our fuel back in Paitilla, this time I was much more accurate. I had to be.

"We are doing 240 knots, about 4 miles a minute."

But that was still too fast.

"Slow to 210 knots."

But this complicated my math because I then had to factor in the deceleration and calculus really wasn't my strong suit.

"We want to go about 4 miles outbound. 240 knots is 4 miles a minute but we're slowing.

Let's make it 90 seconds outbound before we turn back… No, make it a hundred seconds."

It was what we called a WAG, a wild ass guess, but it would have to do.

Despite our desperate fuel state, it was better to extend a bit too far out rather than turn too tight. The Lear had a high speed wing and she didn't like to be yanked around at very slow speeds. I didn't want to make it this far just to spin in on a base leg that was too tight. Although, if we crashed now with no fuel, there wouldn't be much of a fire. It was hardly a comforting thought.

I continued my calculations for a nice wide and gentle pattern back in towards the airport. But I had only a narrow window. The visibility was merely three miles so I couldn't make the pattern so wide that we risked getting lost again. We had to fly a wide enough traffic pattern to avoid stalling the airplane but tight enough to avoid another fog bank.

As we proceeded outbound, we found ourselves skimming over the green valley floor. I ached for more altitude but the gray mist above us held down. Not only did we have to hold course exactly, but our altitude was limited by the clouds above us and the jagged green valley below us. Scud running it was called, and it was the last effort of a fool. It was bad enough in a slow airplane but in a jet whistling by the surface at 210 knots we were still tempting suicide. Worse yet, fuel was always a precious commodity in the Lear. Fuel was always to be used in the most miserly way but with all this low altitude maneuvering we were squandering what little we had left. Maybe death was going to win after all.

We had a few more seconds before our base turn so I took in some sightseeing. We were now over the northern suburbs of the city. This part of town was a combination of well kept enclaves with tidy terracotta roofs and lush gardens alongside wretched slums. Regardless of the economic status of each resident, most here shared the same circumstance. Medellin was once a city of peaceful and productive citizens but now it was witness to the many turf wars of the various drug cartels. It was among the bloodiest cities in the world. If we crashed, three more lives added to the daily carnage would be hardly noticed.

A small knoll appeared out of the mist. Allen squeezed back on the yoke and deftly maneuvered just over it.

It was almost time to make our turn.

"Let's slow down some more." I suggested.

At this point, the slower speed would help us. I was still worried about overshooting our lineup so slowing would tighten our turn radius.

With the finish line close by, we were no longer panicked, merely frightened, and we had mostly gained our composure. We were just two men with no pretense who were making decisions together. Our thinking was barely able to keep up with the speed of events so we were both relieved when the other offered the next step. And we continued to work like that. Each of us alternated making a move across the chessboard. Never seeing beyond that one move, and letting the other pick up the strain, while the first rested and so on.

Finally, and with great relief, the second hand swept around to show 100 seconds had passed. We could turn back to the airport.

"Turn right to a heading of 100 degrees. Hold that for about 30 seconds. I'll call your turn to the final."

I hacked the clock again and hoped that my geometry solution would align us to the runway properly.

We continued our turn around towards the final approach and the greasy slab of concrete that was the runway at Medellin swung back into view. We were aligned properly and at the right altitude for a normal approach. With our safe harbor in sight and directly ahead, the remaining four minutes of flight was ordinary. Or, as ordinary as possible when worrying about flaming out both engines short of the runway.

We landed uneventfully and turned towards the cargo ramp of the airport. A signalman dressed in dirty green overalls directed us to a stop alongside an derelict Arca Cargo DC-8 with deflated tires.

Allen set the brakes and brought the thrust levers to cut off; and with that action, the engines gave up with a descending whoosh. No one had to know that the engines only had a few minutes of life giving fuel. We were just another crew concluding a routine flight. We finished the parking checklist, switched the batteries off and the airplane went quiet.

Our passenger was already out of his seat unfazed by our brush with death. I quickly got out of my own seat, opened the cabin door and bid him goodbye. Our passenger then scurried off to do his important business. As I saw him drive away, I had to wonder.

Did he realize how close we came to killing him?

Did the airplane realize how close we came to killing her?

With the last bit of energy, I slumped back in the passenger seat and looked into the cockpit to see Allen still in the left seat. He was staring at the fog bank closing in around the airport. We were the last airplane to land. And even the local airliners were by then diverting to their alternates.

Chapter 40

Reflection

O ur ride to the hotel was a quiet one. We were scheduled to stay at the Hotel Intercontinental in the foothills of the Aburra Valley. The hotel was a majestic mid century masterpiece built by Pan American Airways to house their globetrotting passengers. Like the Hotel Oloffson in Port-au-Prince, it was perched on high ground and had a commanding view of the city below.

While driving through the city, I reflected on our encounter with the impassive mountains. They were innocent and uncaring, yet they held a deadly venom for those who ventured too close. My performance for the entire day was an embarrassment and yet, there was a paradox.

Did I show cowardice? Yes, we both did. But alternately we also exhibited bravery and calm under pressure. When I was too overwhelmed to think clearly, Allen saved me from myself and I did the same for him. We each relied on the other to save us from ourselves.

Perhaps then, this was the measure of all human existence. We are never fully brave or fully cowardly and we can't survive without the help of others. I looked back at my life and saw I had a column of both brave and cowardly behavior. Over time, they tended to balance out. I wondered if that's how life was: Just a series of transactions, and the best we could hope for is that the accounts were balanced at the end of our lives.

That was certainly the case today. When tallying my columns for the day, I saw I was equally a coward and a hero. It was a draw. It didn't make me feel any better, but at least the columns balanced today.

We then pulled up to the hotel, and Allen remarked, "I need a drink."

That comment made me angry. And I thought to myself that he always needed a drink. Even though our accounts balanced, I wanted to blame him. Maybe if his mind hadn't been so muddled, or if he had been a better captain, we could have avoided all this.

I realized that most of my flying up to this point had been mostly joy rides, just blindly taking orders from my captain and going along without thinking, and without contributing meaningfully. I was seeing that, novice or not, I was just as responsible for my own life on the airplane; and that blind trust was for fools.

Allen and I met later in the hotel cocktail lounge. It was lavishly decorated in a modern style with Calder artwork on all of the walls. It had large wraparound windows overlooking the green mountains. They were the same impassive mountains that almost killed us.

The waiter came to our table and asked for our drink order.

Allen ordered his usual gin and tonic and the waiter nodded. The waiter then looked at me and waited patiently.

"Señor?"

The waiter was wearing black pants, a white shirt and a black bow tie. And in the Latin fashion, he had no order pad. It was a matter of professional pride for the waiters here to deliver all orders, no matter how complicated, from memory.

I looked at him and I hesitated.

Previously, my preference for alcohol leaned towards beer and sweet mixed drinks, in the style of a college boy.

I began to speak but instead, I thought of a prior layover with Ragsdale and remembered his drink preference. I then changed my mind.

"A scotch please. A double… no ice."

The waiter returned quickly and I cupped the glass in my hand. The heft of the cut crystal glass was comforting as I gripped it tightly and I found the brown liquid gratifying as it burned my throat.

I stared out at the hills for a while. We should have been a black smear on the side of the valley and someone else should be in these seats commenting on the crash. We continued to sit in silence, Allen and me. I never looked him in the eye, never talked about what went wrong.

We looked out the window exchanging an occasional pleasantry about the return trip home. But mostly, I sat there to wrestle with my own failures. As much as I wanted to blame someone else for what had happened, I knew I had failed at a critical moment, more than once, and I knew that I was every bit as responsible for the flight as the captain.

The fear I faced was to be an important part of my training. I was slowly realizing that in order to become fearless, one must first have learned how to act while being fearful. Other captains had been trying to make a pilot out of me, and for that I was deeply appreciative. They were also teaching me how to think. But more importantly, I now knew there was something more; something more deeply intrinsic. And with that realization, I vowed that from then on I would take responsibility for my own actions.

Chapter 41

....

Rededication

I was sitting in a black leather Eames chair located in the main lobby of our flight department. It was a chair normally reserved for our best customers but I was sitting in it, nonetheless. We had just arrived from Medellin late the night before and when I got home, Rags had a message waiting for me on my answering machine. He wanted me to meet him as soon as I could get to the airport. So, even on one of my rare days off that's what I did.

From my comfortable chair I had a commanding view of the departure end of Runway 9 Left at Fort Lauderdale International. That's because the southern wall of the lobby was made of floor to ceiling glass that soared 25 feet above the ground. As I waited, I absentmindedly watched a steady parade of Eastern and Pan Am jets take off for destinations mostly in the northeast United States, places decidedly less exotic, and safer, than where I had been flying.

I thought it would be nice to fly for one of the big trunk carriers. I loved flying the Lear but the practice left no room for error. Our brush with death in Medellin was about the same time that a Lear 25 crashed in Newark. The crew of two on that flight were alone, on a night cargo run. Coming in from Chicago, they were late and trying to make up time. As the investigation would show, the crew did several things wrong, any one of which was easily preventable. The airplane's unforgiving nature did not help but the blame for the accident rested solely at their feet. The pilots could have salvaged a bad situation but instead, like Allen and me, they knowingly pressed on into clear adversity. And both men died. By all rights we should have been killed on our little Medellin escapade also. But we weren't. We were alive, although I knew we didn't deserve to be.

Flying for the airlines in domestic service would be mundane, perhaps even dreary duty. Up and down, back and forth on the same routes all day long, like a bus driver. Flying for Eastern Airlines was still an unattainable dream but the economy had gotten better so I thought that maybe I could get a job at one of the local airlines flying to the Florida Keys. That seemed like easy duty. A dull routine would be nice for a change; only day time flying, and maybe even home every night. That would certainly make my dating life a lot easier. The nice thing about airline flying was that all of the dirty business was taken care of by the airline. All the bureaucratic hassles, the filing the flight plans, the arranging for fuel in the middle of the night, and the payoffs to anyone who happened to be blocking your way. All of that was taken care of by the local station people. The only thing the airline pilot had to worry about was flying the airplane. I didn't care if it was mundane, It would be nice to just watch the excitement from a distance and not have to live it every day.

Yes, perhaps it was time to take a break from the Learjet.

I had been running away from home seeking adventure for years. I expended a lot of time and energy and I still didn't know what it was I was seeking. I certainly had enough experiences now to last a lifetime. Maybe going back home would be OK now. I was going to give Ragsdale my resignation that morning. That was, if he wasn't going to fire me first. I was sure that by then he had heard about my Medellin performance.

Rags came in the side door with a cup of coffee in one hand and a Pall Mall in the other. He was wearing the same worn suit as when I first met him.

"Hey tiger. Let's go to my office. We need to talk."

And there I was again with Ragsdale; in the same dismal office when I was first interviewed, with Rags in his same squeaky chair, and with the same cold air conditioning blowing on my neck. The difference was this time I was allowed to sit.

Just like our first meeting, he was in no rush. First, he sipped his coffee, pretended to review some papers, took a long last pull on his cigarette, and stamped out the stubby remains.

"So tiger, tell me what happened in Medellin."

"Not much. We got to Medellin no problem, although we were a little tight on gas. No big deal. We descended into the valley and couldn't find the airport at first, but Allen did a good job and he got us in OK. Just mostly routine."

My statement really was the truth because almost every flight into South America was finished with minimum fuel, and flying into narrow valleys entailed some degree of uncertainty. Therefore, by our usual standards, the Medellin trip was routine. And that's all I wanted to say; partly because I was ashamed of my performance, but mainly because I didn't want to betray Allen.

"Is that everything?

"Yeah, pretty much…although, I gotta' say, after spending six days in the city, the women in Medellin are pretty nice looking."

Rags didn't respond. Instead, he leaned back in his squeaky chair; pulled out another cigarette and went through his cigarette lighting ritual.

He snapped his lighter shut and looked at me for a moment as he drew in another long pull of his cigarette.

"OK tiger, if you say so, but there's one other thing I have to tell you."

Yep, here it comes, Rags was going to fire me, but as it would turn out, not for the reason I thought.

"The owner is selling the airplane so we are closing down the flight department. We're letting everyone go. Effective immediately."

And with that announcement I let the relief sink in. I was done with charter flying and I didn't have to quit. The decision was made for me.

I shrugged my shoulders and I decided to be polite.

"Thanks for letting me know in person."

Although, I was actually thinking that I wanted to get out of that cold cave that was his office and head straight over to Bahia Cabana where I could drink and let myself melt in the hot sun.

"Well, if that's what you want but I've got you lined up with Corky Zimmer, up at the executive airport. He has a couple of new airplanes and they're looking for pilots. He remembers you from your Guatemala trip and he'll take you on as a new captain."

"But, I'm not ready."

I left unsaid the fact that just a few days ago I nearly killed myself.

"Besides, I'm not sure I really want to do this anymore. I hear the airlines are starting to hire again. Maybe they'll take me."

I smiled. After all, wasn't it every pilot's goal to fly for the airlines?

I waited for his approval that wasn't coming.

"That's ironic. A year ago you were practically begging to work here. Now you want out?"

"Well, things change."

"Sure you could go to work for the airlines but is that really what you want? If you get hired, you'll first have to be a flight engineer for several years flying between here and East Bumfuck. It's pretty boring. In the Lear, you are doing a lot of interesting flying. You're needed here and you're good at it. You can't just go and be the new guy at the airline. That's not you."

He slid Zimmer's business card across the table towards me.

"Stop by his office. He is expecting you."

"Thanks, Rags."

He then called me by my first name for the first time I had known him.

"Greg, you were right. You are a fast learner. Just keep on doing what you're doing and you'll be OK."

I got up to go and as I slowed to pull the office door open. He stopped me.

"There's one other thing…"

I paused and turned to look back at him.

"…About Medellin… Allen told me everything."

"Oh yeah? What's everything?"

"Look, I appreciate your loyalty. You did the right thing. Whatever you think of the other pilot, you still have to support each other because if you don't, then neither of you are any good. I would want the same for myself. But do everyone a favor. We're part of the team too. If there is something wrong, we need to know about it so we can fix it."

I thanked him again for his advice and walked out to the next part of my life. I never saw him again and I still regret never having told Ragsdale, or Coe for that matter, that I appreciated the opportunity to fly jets that they gave me so long ago.

Chapter 42

Another Mountain to Climb

I walked into a place I had never visited before on a sunny Tuesday afternoon. This hangar was at the Fort Lauderdale Executive Airport, located on the east side of the airport, and was much larger than the one I had previously called home. It was filled with an entire fleet of Learjets and an assortment of other corporate jets, each sparkling under a coat of fresh acrylic paint. It was not unusual for private jets to be compulsively clean but these were all better than new. As I walked through the hangar towards the flight office I noticed the condition of each airplane and whistled to myself.

"Jesus, even the landing gear are polished."

The hangar was also home to some World War 2 era warbirds owned by some wealthy collectors, and each of those were in pristine condition as well. All the doors were open and a nice breeze sailed through the building. The hangar floors themselves were painted in a high gloss, swimming pool blue and the parked airplanes floated on the shimmering floor like jewels set in a turquoise tiara.

I stopped in front of the side door of the charter department and looked at the sign in gold plated script. It read "Personal Jet Charter." I turned the knob and stepped inside the reception area. It was lush and opulent, decorated in a pale beige. The walls were wrapped with leather, and the carpet was a plush silk. Everything else in the room was either polished mahogany or gold plated.

Once inside this private new world I was met by the company dispatcher. Her name was Lyndee. She got up from behind her broad desk to greet me. She was wearing a pink silk Hawaiian shirt, a black leather mini skirt, and high heel mules. Her outfit was in sharp contrast to the monotone background of the reception room.

"I heard you were coming… welcome! Corky is in a meeting but he'll see you in a minute. Want a coffee?"

"No thanks."

"OK, suit yourself. Have a seat while you're waiting."

I sat down and leafed through a flying magazine while discreetly observing the woman who would likely be in charge of my life for the foreseeable future. Lyndee was just 21, blond, muscular, and tan. In our little charter world dispatchers had total authority over scheduling of both airplanes and pilots and I knew it would be important to stay on her good side. I was to later find out that she had come from a dynasty of prosperous industrialists in Pennsylvania. As a result, her family background trained her to be quite comfortable and adept with responsibility despite her young age. She drove a brand new silver Camaro Z28 and ran the charter department with aplomb.

As I killed time, I heard the whine of Learjet engines approaching. Lyndee looked up. "Excuse me. I gotta' run. The boys are coming in and they owe us some money." She leapt out the front door to meet the airplane. Once outside, she pushed a heavy generator cart into position to power the airplane once it shut down. Despite her expensive clothing, she obviously didn't mind getting dirty to get the job done.

She waited to greet the passengers coming off the airplane. It was a brand new Lear 35 with the generic registration number N39292, although the airplane itself was not all generic. It was painted powder blue with navy and gold accent lines. Once the airplane door was opened, I could see the interior was slathered in a lavish lambskin and silk, all in powder blue and with the same gold plated trim as the office waiting room. I watched Lyndee conduct her business and wave goodbye as the passengers drive away in a chauffeured Town Car. I stood there admiring the airplane and was transfixed by watching the pilots deplane. I was measuring myself against them when I heard a voice behind me.

"That's 292. It's hard to believe she was destined for the scrap yard."

I turned to the voice. It was Corky Zimmer. I remembered him from our trip to Guatemala last year. He was wearing designer jeans with a green polo shirt that was about two sizes too small. His hair was graying and was folded in a huge pompadour several inches higher than his scalp. He had a pair of mirrored pilot sunglasses pushed up over the top of his forehead.

"We bought that airplane from an Australian air ambulance operator. God knows what they did with it. Flew it all over The Outback on gravel strips, I guess. It was a wreck when we bought it."

"That airplane was a wreck? It looks brand new."

Corky laughed. "Well, it's a testimony to what a few hundred thousand dollars can do at the paint and interior shop. We sent it to Duncan Aviation, up in Lincoln, Nebraska, for the past six months. We just got it back. Come on, let's go up to my office."

I obediently followed Corky up to his office, which was on the second floor of the hangar and had a view of the entire airport. Unlike my interview with Rags, this one went much more easily and ended up with a handshake and a job offer.

"We've already got you scheduled for training tomorrow."

"Thanks Corky, see you tomorrow. I appreciate it but I have to ask. When we were in Guatemala, at that dinner party where I asked all those questions about the Communist insurgency, I didn't think you'd want to ever see me again..."

He interrupted me. "Jesus, that was some stunt! But, yeah, I didn't think we were going to get out of there alive. That one guy was about to bust a gut but his boss pulled your ass out of the fire so it turned out OK. Hell, I was young and stupid once too. You'll learn. Just fly the airplane, do what it takes to finish the trip, and keep your mouth shut."

Corky paused and stared out the window for a while. His interlude lasted a while, much longer than to just collect his thoughts. I stood next to him and waited. He started to speak then stopped in mid word. He paused to look outside again for another lengthy lull in the conversation. Finally, he looked back at me. This time his eyes were stern as he reinforced his policy, "Yeah, the way we do it here is you just fly the airplane. Our customers like their privacy. If anyone asks, you didn't see anything and you didn't hear anything. That keeps us all out of trouble."

Chapter 43

The Upgrade

The next morning I was reintroduced to Farmer. We hadn't seen each other for some time but our acquaintance was re-established due to the nomadic ways of South Florida flying. That's because charter pilots were mostly gypsies migrating between whichever company happened to be the busiest at the moment. The economy had been improving so Farmer and I had both washed up on the shores of Corky's operation, and Farmer was assigned to be the instructor for my captain upgrade.

The airplane for my training was the latest version of the Lear 24. The D Model. It was equipped with the larger and more powerful Dash 6 engines. It did have a few system improvements but it was still equipped with the original wing optimized for high speed flight, making it the true hot rod of private aviation.

The earlier models of the 24 were already high performers but the 24D was the aviation version of the American muscle cars of the same era. That is to say, the design philosophy of the decade was driven almost solely by performance. Engineers would simply place enormously powerful engines on small and lightweight airframes. The idea was to fly higher and faster, and with heavier loads. And like muscle cars; fuel economy, creature comforts, and a sweet temper were of secondary concern. Given its high performance and unforgiving handling characteristics, the Lear 24D was hardly the ideal airplane for training.

Of course, the ideal would have been to conduct the training in a simulator but they were very expensive and only the province of the airlines and well funded corporate flight departments. Instead, all of the Lear charter operators in South Florida chose to conduct training in the airplane itself; and flight training in the Lear was not something to be approached lightly. The airplane was difficult enough to fly normally, but when flown by a trainee practicing emergencies…well, let's just say that training accidents claimed many more lives than they should have.

But that's just how it was. In the extremely cost conscious world of charter flying we got the training we could afford, which is to say, only the least expensive and barest minimum to satisfy the government inspectors. And, without the use of simulators, we could only practice emergencies that could be safely replicated in the airplane.

There was, of course, so much more that could go wrong in an airplane and that was why simulators proved so valuable. Things that would either be too dangerous or impossible to replicate in an airplane such as electrical fires, hydraulic failures, pressurization loss, trim failures, and complicated navigation problems could be practiced to perfection in a simulator; and practiced safely. And it was through this practice of rehearsing a wide range of emergencies in the simulator that allowed airline pilots to become the ultimate aviation professionals and how they achieved such an enviable safety record.

But back in our charter world, training in the airplane was what we had; and we were pretty much limited to practicing engine failures ad nauseum. Being prepared for an engine failure was, of course, an important skill but given the overall reliability of jet engines, more people had been killed in training accidents than were killed in actual engine failure events. With all of this in mind, I was informed that in preparation for my checkride I would get three hours of training, and only three hours. That is what the charter company could afford and that is what I was to get. The rest of my education was to come later, on my own, while flying real revenue trips with real passengers on board, and with a copilot even more inexperienced than me.

And, so, after those three hours of cursory training, I met with Captain Bill Conrad for my checkride on a sweltering August afternoon. Conrad was 75 years old and a South Florida legend. He was, by far, the oldest active pilot I had ever met, and he made Rags seem like a kid. He was a former captain for Pan American but he was not just any captain. He was a throwback to the earliest era of aviation and was close friends with Charles Lindbergh. In the 1930s, Conrad flew a Fairchild 91 seaplane to scout new routes in South America. He would later fly those same routes in the massive Boeing 314 Clipper flying boats out of Dinner Key in Miami. He then finished his airline career as the head of training for Pan Am shepherding the global airline into the jet age. Conrad was also a member of the revered, but long since defunct, fraternity of aviators known as the Silent Birdmen. To say he was aviation royalty would not have been an overstatement. Now, in semi retirement, he was designated as a pilot examiner with the authority to issue Learjet type ratings.

Not only was Conrad the oldest pilot I had ever met but also the tallest. He was 6'6" although he surely must have been taller in his prime. However, he was so stooped over with age, his upper body was nearly perpendicular to the ground. In that posture, as he walked, his eyes were pointed almost straight down. When we met, he strained to stand more erect to shake my hand but he still had to look at me through his bushy black eyebrows.

"Let's get to it young man."

Conrad directed me into a back conference room for the knowledge portion of the exam. And just like my first meeting with Rags, I was in a small and unattractive room to defend my future in aviation. The difference was that my interrogator was three times my age and his conversation never paused. Conrad had wisdom of his seven decades but also the alertness of a twenty year old. The oral exam was a non stop and fast paced two hour discussion about the Learjet, its systems, and operational characteristics, as well as the vagaries of flying in South America. In those two hours he attempted to find, without success, any shortcomings in my understanding of the required knowledge.

During that time, I had a chance to examine Conrad. He had a full head of white hair that flaked dandruff on the collar of his baggy red golf shirt. He was wearing a pair of white golf slacks. His clothing was the loose and the out of fashion style of an old man but he was still dignified and muscular. His voice was graveled with age but still self assured, and his faint body odor wafted through the air.

The oral exam went well and Conrad seemed satisfied with my knowledge; but he wasn't done yet and he went down a new path, one that explored the more nebulous area of Lear operation. He leaned back in his chair and pushed back his white baseball cap. The cap had large silver and blue embroidered wings on the crown.

"Tell me how you operate the pitch trim."

This was Conrad's favorite gotcha question. The pilot network had warned me it was coming and even though the exam had gone well so far, I nodded to him eager to supply the answer to his favorite question.

Trim tabs were small but powerful control surfaces on every airplane. The Lear had trim tabs for the elevator, ailerons, and rudder. They were designed to reduce workload by not requiring the pilot to exert constant pressure on the control yoke. A properly trimmed airplane could be flown almost effortlessly with just fingertip pressure. However, the pitch trim, which controlled the elevators, was the most powerful and most commonly misused aspect of the Lear.

The pitch trim needed adjustment whenever the airplane changed speed or power settings, and there was a right way to operate the trim and a wrong way. Many Learjet pilots had gotten lazy, and had become overly reliant on using the trim system in the wrong way rather than relying on their own airmanship skills. The pitch trim was controlled by a small switch under the pilot's thumb on the control yoke. It was not uncommon to see a Lear pilot begin a climb or descent by first squeezing in elevator trim rather than using the control yoke. This was an area of great irritation to Conrad. In his mind, pitch trim was a secondary control and using it as a primary method of pitch control was lazy airmanship; and that lazy technique made him wonder in what other areas a pilot may be lazy. Hence the question.

Conrad was the consummate old school pilot. Therefore, I gave him the consummate old school answer. More importantly, given the extremely delicate handling characteristics of the airplane, it was also the correct answer.

"I only use the pitch trim as an aid to trim our control force. When I have to make a pitch change, I first adjust the pitch of the airplane up or down using pressure on the control yoke. Once I have placed the proper input on the elevators manually, then, and only then, do I use the trim to take out the control force."

He then raised his ancient body up from his chair.

"Very good, young man. Let's go to the airplane."

Farmer was already waiting for us and he greeted Conrad cheerily. The two of them had done this before with other students and they both knew the drill. Farmer would serve two roles today: Legally, because I was not yet a rated captain, Farmer would be the pilot in command of record. However, for the purposes of the checkride, I would play the role of captain and make every decision as Farmer played the role of copilot. He would do what I asked of him but no more. This was my show, and during the checkride I would sink or swim on my own.

As I strapped into the left seat, Farmer gave me one last word of advice.

"You fly a nice airplane but remember. You're not here to impress Conrad with how smooth you can be. Smoothness is important when flying the paying customers but today you have to fly as precisely as possible. Don't worry about being smooth, just show the old man you're master of the jet."

He then quoted verbatim his favorite part of the FAA Practical Test Standards "You must show that you are master of the aircraft, with the successful outcome of the maneuver never seriously in doubt!" It was one of his favorite lines and he laughed at his own joke.

It turned out that Conrad had other peculiarities. Once he had boarded, he placed himself squarely on the center of the rear settee. Most check pilots would sit right behind the cockpit to see everything that was happening. Some like Oswaldo would administer the checkride from the copilot's seat. But apparently, Conrad was able to tell as much of a pilot's ability by feel, as by watching. And from the very rear center seat of the airplane, his body was aligned directly over the longitudinal axis of the airplane. This way, he was more attuned to the proper coordination of my maneuvers. It was true seat of the pants flying and made sense given his background. Since he held my future in his hands, I didn't question this particular peccadillo.

The result of his seating position created another peculiarity. Rather than give me verbal instruction of what he wanted to see during the course of the checkride as things progressed, he had given Farmer a list of the various maneuvers he wanted to see me perform. They were all in a predetermined order and Farmer had them clipped to his notepad. Conrad would remain mute for the duration of the ride and make his assessment from the back seat.

We took off from Fort Lauderdale and headed west towards the Florida Everglades. It was there, in the middle of the state, where a 10,000 foot long slab of abandoned concrete was waiting for us. It was the only remnant of what was to have been a mega jetport designed to serve Miami in the new era of supersonic transport. However, the project was abandoned in 1971 after the objection of environmentalists.This left a modern runway that had been surrendered to nature, taken over mostly by alligators, panthers and egrets. It was originally named The Everglades Jetport but the runway was then repurposed as a remote training field and renamed Training and Transition, nicknamed "TNT." It was there, far from the congestion of the east coast where I was to spend the next hour sweating under the tyranny of Conrad's list.

TNT was only forty miles away from Fort Lauderdale and we flew over there quickly and Farmer began to run me through Conrad's list of maneuvers. The first few were mundane like steep turns, an approach to a stall with a recovery, and two engine instrument approaches. They were designed as a warm up as well as a gauge of my general airmanship skills. We ran through them quickly before we landed at TNT and came to a full stop.

It was then time for the important V1 cut. This was really the make or break maneuver of any checkride. I briefed the takeoff and planned departure profile. Assured everyone was ready, we began our takeoff and accelerated down the runway. Once we passed the Go/No Go speed of V1, Farmer reached over to pull the left throttle back to idle. I remembered my lesson from Barcelona and promised myself there would be no similar mistakes. I pinned the nosewheel down with forward pressure on the yoke and simultaneously came on hard with right rudder to keep pointed straight down the runway. The rudder pedal was almost at the stop, for the Lear was a powerful airplane, and with its one engine operating the asymmetric thrust wanted to twist the airplane over on its back.

The amount of rudder necessary for a V1 cut was actually easy to modulate. I pressed the rudder all the way to the stops. For, as the Lear instructors would say when asked how much rudder to use, the answer was always the same.

"We've never seen anyone use too much rudder."

After the engine failure, I continued to accelerate to proper flying speed before rotating. Thus, with the airplane under positive control, we took off, retracted the landing gear and climbed away flawlessly.

Once we leveled off one one engine at 1500 feet, I turned back to TNT for a simulated single engine landing. While circling back, I got distracted briefly, let up on rudder pressure and the airplane wobbled a bit.

Despite his age, Conrad was not past his prime. He proved himself fully aware of the airplane's condition and yelled from the back.

"Rudder!"

I looked at the slip indicator.

"Son of a bitch," I muttered to Farmer. "That old coot is right."

Everything was centered looking, good except the airplane was skidding sideways, ever so slightly, away from perfectly stable flight. I squeezed in a bit of rudder and I swore to myself that Conrad's ancient buttocks would feel nothing more out of the ordinary. We then made a successful single engine landing at TNT to a full stop.

And then we were done.

All that was left was to make a normal two engine takeoff from TNT and head for home with a two engine ILS at Executive airport. All very routine.

We taxied back to the end of the runway past the alligators sunning themselves on the side of the runway and we lined up for takeoff. We had burned a lot of fuel maneuvering down low for the past hour and we were very light, so the airplane leapt into the air as I rotated. We were climbing through 100 feet and 150 knots as I called:

"Gear up!"

As I waited for the gear to retract, I congratulated myself on a successful checkride. The only thing left was a normal two engine landing back in Fort Lauderdale. Something I had done hundreds of times. We still had plenty of gas and it was a beautiful summer afternoon. At this point, nothing could go wrong.

I continued accelerating: "Flaps up!"

Instead of complying to my command, Farmer had bad news to report.

"We got a problem. The gear won't come up."

I looked over and saw three red lights. Those lights meant that all three landing gear were halted in transit, hanging just halfway; neither fully retracted or fully extended.

I looked at the hydraulic gauge.

"Damnit! Check out the hydraulic pressure. It's down to zero."

I would normally have accelerated to 250 knots for the flight back to Fort Lauderdale. However, with no hydraulic pressure, the flaps were also frozen in the extended position. I didn't want to overspeed the flaps so I pulled way back on the throttles to keep the speed back as I leveled off at 3,000 feet.

Farmer looked over to me. He was the pilot command but now this real life emergency had just become part of my checkride. Farmer was an experienced hand and he already knew what to do but with Conrad still watching this was my show. Checkrides are not only about demonstrating flying skills but also about demonstrating leadership and general mastery of the craft. I had already proved my flying skills but now I had to show Conrad something more. I had to show him I was just not a good pilot but that I could be a captain who could make decisions and lead in an abnormal situation.

I turned to Farmer.

"OK, here's the plan. We're only 40 miles from Executive airport. We have enough fuel to make it back even with the drag of the gear hanging down. Just call Miami for a vector to Executive airport. I'll fly slow and we'll work the problem on the way home."

Of course, I already knew the direction to Fort Lauderdale. These were the same Everglades over which I had spent hundreds of hours flight instructing and every pilot pretty much had an innate sense of direction. As I gave Farmer those instructions, I was already turning towards home.

I turned back to Conrad.

"We lost our hydraulic system. We're going to run the checklist and land back at Executive.

He nodded.

But getting back to home base was the easy part. We still had to get the gear down. The problem was that in the interest of weight saving and simplicity (it was those grandmothers again) the Lear had only one hydraulic system. And something had happened to that one system. We couldn't get the gear up; but more importantly, we couldn't get it back down.

We had only one alternative. Located in the hell hole was a canister filled with high pressure nitrogen and it was installed for just this purpose. The nitrogen was used to blow the gear down using pneumatic force; but it too, had a limitation. Once we blew the gear down, it was locked down permanently until a mechanic reset the system on the ground. The question for me then, was when to use it. If we extended the gear too early, then we might burn too much fuel with the added drag. But we had to extend it early enough that we could finish our checklists and fly a stable approach.

Conrad was watching and I continued my exercise in captaincy.

"OK. Declare an emergency. We want priority handling to Fort Lauderdale, once we're in range we'll do the checklist for loss of hydraulic quantity and blow the gear down."

Farmer nodded, "How about the drag chute?"

"Yeah, let's plan on that."

This one simple failure had implications for multiple other controls. We had not just lost the normal capability to lower our landing gear but we had also lost the ability to fully lower our flaps, to use spoilers, and have normal brakes. As a result, we would be landing at much higher than normal speed; and then, after touchdown, we were to have no ability to dump excess lift; and finally, we were going to have diminished wheel braking. Essentially, everything we needed to slow the airplane to a stop was inoperative.

Even though the runway waiting for us was dry, it was only of medium length. This was going to be a serious problem. However, the engineers had given us other cards to play. This airplane was equipped with alternate wheel braking and a drag chute.

The 40 miles to Executive airport went quickly and we hurriedly read through our checklists and briefed each other on who had what responsibility. We approached the airport and once we were ten miles from touchdown, we read the last steps of the abnormal gear extension checklist.

Next to my right knee was a small red tab. It operated the emergency gear extension. Once the checklist prompted us, I pushed it down with a sharp movement and we heard a slight whoosh of nitrogen and a thunk. The gear locked down instantly and to my relief three green lights appeared on the instrument panel.

Now, we were only five miles from touchdown. The gear was down but with only partial flaps we approached the runway at a speed about 30 knots higher than normal and that 30 knots of excess speed would translate into about another 3000 feet of runway being used.

On very short final, I looked to the far end of the runway. The runway was almost a mile long, plenty by normal standards, but at this speed, and without normal braking, it was only barely long enough. The landing data chart said so. We only had the drag chute of our guarantee of a safe landing. And neither of us had used it before. Not in training, and certainly not when we needed it for real.

I began to worry about my decision. Maybe we should have gone to Miami with its runways twice as long. It certainly would be bad form to run an airplane off the end of a runway but even worse to do so with a government representative on board.

I looked at Farmer. It's my checkride but he was still the real captain. Maybe he should make the landing.

He knew what I was thinking.

"You're looking good. Just do everything like you briefed it."

It was good advice but it was also the only advice. We were now committed to the runway right in front of us. With the gear locked down, we didn't have enough fuel to make it to Miami.

With just two miles to touchdown the landing became like any other. I became completely focused on just the small world outside my windshield. I was on speed and on glide path on a textbook approach.

But I still wanted more. I was still focused, like a cat, straight ahead. Without looking his way, I announced to Farmer.

"I'm going slightly low. I'm aiming right for the runway end."

Normally, an airplane crossed the runway end about 30 feet high and touched down a thousand feet or so down the runway. That technique makes for a more relaxed approach and gives the pilot a little margin for error if he was a little too low unintentionally. But we didn't have that luxury. I again reminded myself that runway behind you is one of the most useless things to a pilot. In a dire situation, a pilot would often aim for the very end of the runway or what was sometimes called "the first brick."

And that's what I did, I touched down just a few feet past the runway threshold.

I then lowered the nose wheel quickly and called out:

"Drag chute!"

On the copilot's side of the cockpit rested a silver pistol grip shaped handle. It was by Farmer's left leg. I was very familiar with that handle, because like every other Learjet copilot that protruding piece of aluminum had cut into my thigh for untold hours. It took up valuable space in the cramped cockpit but now all those hours of discomfort were worth it.

Farmer reached for the handle. He squeezed the trigger and pulled the handle upwards in a swift motion. Back by the tail of the airplane the chute deployed and blossomed out behind us. We were thrown forward in our seats, decelerating from 150 knots to taxi speed in just a few seconds.

My earlier anxiety was unfounded and we had come to a complete stop in just two thousand feet, less than a third of the available runway. I actually needed to add power to turn off to the nearest taxiway. Once off the active runway Farmer unbuckled from his seat and ran outside to collect the deflated chute. We then shut down the engines leaving us and our beautiful airplane stranded on the taxiway, where we were eventually towed ingloriously back to our hangar.

Once we pulled in, Conrad unfolded his large frame from the tiny cabin and stood by the side of the airplane waiting for me to exit. He remained silent then spoke in his deep voice.

"Come inside. We have to talk."

I dutifully followed him into our original conference room, where he was already seated. He already had all of his paperwork laid out on the table. We sat in silence as he filled out an accounting ledger detailing his humorless observations during the checkride.

I was tired and even though I thought I had done a good job, I stopped caring. If I had to go back out for a recheck, well, then a small black mark on my record wouldn't be the end of the world. You just never knew about checkrides. Examiners were notoriously fickle; and the pilots from Conrad's era were known to be unforgiving of even the slightest error.

He paused and looked up.

"Young man, after the V1 cut you had got distracted and the airplane began skidding after level off. What were you thinking?"

I mumbled an apology and pointed out that I corrected immediately along with a further explanation that showed my full knowledge on the subject.

He nodded and took some more notes.

"Now, that hydraulic failure."

I waited. This was it. He was going to fail me on the partial flap landing. It was an emergency with no clear guidelines and there were probably as many different ways to land the airplane safely as there were different pilots. Anything I had done could have been called into question.

"You used the pitch trim too much. You had told me in the briefing you knew how to operate it properly and I saw you use it properly early in the ride but you got sloppy during the emergency procedure. What happened then?"

My mood began to darken as my old resentment towards authority began to percolate to the surface. I knew I had flown a good ride but here was this old man criticizing me. The cold air conditioning in the room chilled my mood further and I prepared an argument.

Instead, I held back my temper and I mumbled another apology while he again took some more notes.

He pushed back away from the table and clasped his hands together.

"Well, that was a textbook handling of the hydraulic failure and everything was excellent. You are a good little pilot. I have nothing more to debrief."

Conrad, the great man, then leaned forward again and continued filling out some extra paperwork finishing by signing his name with a great flourish. And he then awarded me a cherished slip of paper. It was a brand new temporary airman certificate with the additional rating, "LearJet." He left me with one last brief admonition as he shook my hand.

"Remember, this is just a license to learn. You are a good pilot but don't be reckless. It takes many more years to become a true aviator."

He slowly gathered his things and shuffled out of the conference room, and my time spent with the great legend was over. Farmer, too, added his congratulations and bid me farewell also. He had just been recalled to his airline job leaving me without any senior Lear captains to mentor me.

I stood in the office alone and I looked down at the freshly inked document.

It was official. At the age of 26, by proclamation of the United States government, I was no longer just a Learjet pilot... I was a Learjet captain.

Chapter 44

An Apprentice Again

The months to follow were a repeat of my early days as a new copilot. I was first assigned the less demanding trips to build my experience and do some more on the job training. I was also assigned to fly with our more experienced copilots. The ones who were almost ready for their own upgrade. We could look out for each other that way.

I took to the captain seat easily and the next few months proved to be a lovely autumn. My flying alternated between operating around the northeast United States, where I watched the leaves change color; and our usual flying around the Caribbean in what can only be described as the best flying in the world.

Overall, it was easy duty. Although Rohwedder and I did do one trip to Wichita in a 24 where we had to fly an approach down to minimums in heavy icing and blowing snow, followed by a landing on a runway with nil braking. But that was the exception. I was mostly assigned the simple trips. Well, mostly. There was another trip in a 35 with Inderbitzin where we had a runaway pitch trim while trying to get into Peoria. But that was it…Oh yes, and I almost forgot, there was also another trip with Chipman where we made a nighttime approach into St. Thomas using the emergency standby gyro. And I did fly a few trips with some brand new copilots because those were the only guys available when a trip popped up. But, overall, those were the exceptions.

The plan was that once I became more accomplished, I was to be given increasingly challenging flying. Of course, as was often the case, the whims of the scheduling gods placed us in situations in which we were ill-prepared.

Chapter 45

Captaincy Earned

I was lying in bed still recovering from the previous night's New Years festivities when the phone disturbed my sleep.

It was Lyndee.

"Have you ever been to La Paz?

I was pretty sure I knew what she meant but since there was more than one La Paz, I asked.

"You mean in Bolivia?"

Her answer was curt.

"Yes… In Bolivia."

She knew full well the answer so I avoided her earlier question.

"What's going on?"

"Eastern Airlines called. They have a missing airplane. It was due to land in La Paz a few hours ago. The Bolivian controllers lost radio contact with them and no one knows what has happened. They want us to fly a few of their people down there."

I tried to shake the sleep out of my head. "What time is it?"

"It's 11 PM. Get to the airport as soon as you can. You'll need to reposition the airplane to Miami first. The Eastern guys are waiting for you there. I'm assigning Rohwedder as the copilot."

La Paz was one of the highest airports in the world lying atop the howling altiplano and the surrounding terrain was the highest of the entire Andes chain. I had heard of a few other Lear operators that had been there but beyond that, I knew nothing other than it routinely ranked as one of the most dangerous airports in the world. It was a challenging trip and would require several fuel stops on the way.

"Yes, Rohwedder is good. He's almost ready for upgrade himself and I could use the help. Tell him, I'm on my way to the airport right now."

I hung up and dressed quickly.

When I arrived at the airport, the hangar was brightly lit and the line boys had already pulled the airplane out of the hangar.

I rushed past them.

"Just wings and tips on the gas. We'll top off in Miami. We're leaving right away!"

I continued in a rush to our flight planning office and once inside, I reached first for the thick leather Jeppesen binders that contained all of our South American navigation charts.

I thumbed the tissue paper thin pages and there it was… "La Paz, Bolivia."

Below the name of the city was the name of the airport itself "El Alto." In my basic Spanish, I translated it roughly to "The High One." I had some experience flying around the mountains in the Rockies and northern Andes, and it had become routine for me. Aspen was at 8,000 feet, and the mountains around Medellin that reached up to snag Allen and me were at 11,000. But this was different.

My finger went down to the line to read the airport elevation at La Paz.

I stared at the number.

13,300 feet above sea level. And that was the elevation for just the airport. I moved my finger over a few miles away on the chart. I pursed my lips hard against each other. There was a mountain peak adjacent to the airport. The chart showed it at over 22,000 feet. And we were going to arrive there bone tired, after flying all night long.

Ten minutes later, Rohwedder showed up to finish the preflight. He was a couple years younger than me and had grown up on the beaches of Fort Lauderdale. He had a leathered deep tan with dark curly hair and cold blue eyes that easily saw all the absurdity in life. He was our hangar truth teller and he did it without being cynical or mean.

Fifteen more minutes after he showed up, Rohwedder and I lifted off from Executive airport. He was flying and we leveled off at 4,000 feet for the short hop to Miami's International Airport. Once we leveled, I started transferring fuel from the wings to the center tank. A cold front had just passed through leaving the night crisp and cloudless with the entire metropolitan area sparkling below us. It was after midnight and we had the sky to ourselves.

On the 10 minute hop I briefed Rohwedder on the trip.

"Eastern is missing an airplane. They were supposed to have landed in La Paz a few hours ago. It's a 727…That's all I know…Hell, I think that's all they know."

"How many people were on board?"

"They never said."

"Do you think they diverted somewhere without radio contact?"

"Not likely. Big airliners don't just disappear. No matter where they would have gone, someone would have at least had a phone to call La Paz."

"Yeah, that's what I was thinking."

"We're picking up their chief pilot and a few other people. I didn't have a lot of time to figure the route all the way down there. I just did most of it in my head. I filed for Panama City on the first leg. We would make it a little further south but I didn't want to refuel in Colombia. There's no sense making a fuel stop in a challenging mountain airport. We'll just head to Panama and that will get us started down there."

We were in a hurry and flying fast as Miami approach control cleared us for a visual approach to Runway 9 Left. Once Rohwedder pulled the power back to idle, we were 250 knots of silent kinetic energy gliding into the traffic pattern and he made a perfect landing.

We turned off the runway and we were instructed to a section of the airport that had previously been forbidden to us. It was the Eastern Airlines headquarters complex. Among South Florida charter pilots, Eastern Airlines held a mythic status. It was widely considered the dream job for almost everyone, but their department in charge of pilot hiring was a fortress and it was impossible to even get an interview there.

A follow me truck led us into the ramp in front of the monolithic Eastern maintenance hangar where we parked alongside a line up of Lockheed L-1011s.

I opened the door and an Eastern rep greeted me.

"Captain. Are you here for our La Paz charter?"

I suppressed a grin. An Eastern manager was calling me "captain."

I gave him a crisp nod.

"Yes, I am. We'll be ready to go when you are."

"Good, follow me."

Before I left, I gave Rohwedder instructions.

"The clearance to Panama should be ready and they should clear us as filed. I requested Upper Lima 780, the whole way. Flight Level 410. I know we can make it that far with plenty of gas to spare. I listed Balboa as the alternate. Once we get going we'll figure out the routing south of Panama."

Rohwedder smiled. "Sure thing. And while you're in there, ask what a guy has to do to get a job at Eastern."

We both laughed at that statement because that quip was a running joke among the local Lear pilots. Eastern had finally started hiring pilots after a five year hiatus but there was a long backlog of highly qualified applicants. The rumor was that Eastern had thousands of resumes on file to fill just a few spots. The wags said Eastern wouldn't even consider a pilot unless he had 10,000 hours of jet time and two lunar landings.

With my meager experience I didn't stand a chance of getting hired but I was about to march right into the heart of the Eastern Control Center as an honored guest.

The Eastern manager led me into the maintenance super bay filled with a variety of Eastern airplanes. The hangar itself was monstrously big; football field size, at least. It was 1 AM and the midnight shift was busy at work. I counted three L-1011s and two DC-9s, each covered with scaffolding, each in various stages of disassembly and overhaul. Every corner of the hangar was illuminated by high intensity light, leaving nowhere to hide from the on-slaught of industrial luminescence. I had never been this close to an airliner but here I could touch them. I knew airline pilots were better men than me and an airline job was unattainable but being so close to those airplanes made them even more desirable.

We continued to wind through a labyrinth of work platforms to find a set of stairs in the back of the hangar. We climbed one flight of stairs, and then transitioned to a second. We walked down a dark hallway and passed through a door. Once it opened, I was suddenly in the very heart of Eastern Airlines. The door had opened into their operations control room. It was the size of a small gymnasium and the room was also brightly lit with fluorescent lights. Banks of TV monitors surrounded the room, dozens of dispatchers were hunched over computer terminals; and a massive TV monitor displaying the entire Western Hemisphere covered an entire wall. Off to the side, several dozen teletype machines clickety-clacked their essential messages. There was a hushed urgency about the whole thing.

I was then led to the every center of the room where a small group of people had clustered.

The tight circle opened to allow me to enter.

"Captain?"

A distinguished gentleman reached out to shake my hand. He was 6 feet tall, thin, patrician, and dressed in an expensive business suit.

" I am Edward Stone. 727 chief pilot for Eastern."

It was all I could do not to beg for a job right then and there but I played it cool.

Eastern was one of the world's most envied airlines and selected only the very best pilots. Moreover, Eastern was considered a pilot's airline meaning the pilots answered, not to ground based managers who were not aviators, but only to each other. Captain Stone represented the very pinnacle of professional commercial aviation. And there was me, all of 26 years old. A product of the sleazy and oily side of general aviation. Compared to his blue chip pedigree, I was a pretender of the worst kind.

He was in a hurry and he started out without any small talk.

"We have a 727 that left Asuncion a few hours ago. It was Flight 980. They were on their descent to La Paz but the air traffic controllers lost radio contact with them."

I noticed he referred to the flight in the past tense.

"We're not sure what has happened to them. It could have been a crash, or a hijacking, or maybe a forced landing. It's been over six hours without any radio contact so we are sending a team down to investigate. We chartered for four people but now there will be seven of us. Can your airplane carry that many?"

"Yes, sir. We can hold eight passengers plus their luggage."

"That's not necessary. We are traveling light."

He then changed the conversation to the flight itself.

"It's 2600 miles to LaPaz."

"Yes, I know."

"How many fuel stops will we have to make?"

"Probably two. We're filed for Panama first. We'll work the rest of the flight plan to LaPaz on the way to Panama. "We'll have three hours on the first leg to figure it out."

"And after that?"

"Probably Guayaquil. From there we can make La Paz non stop."

"Do you need any handling on the way? Those are all Eastern stations. We have lots of people here to help."

"We're used to handling ourselves down there, but, yes, any extra help would be appreciated."

Then he stopped to inspect me further.

I waited for his next thought.

"The terrain around La Paz is extremely difficult. And we require all of our pilots to go through an extensive checkout before going there. Are you familiar with LaPaz?"

I knew what he was getting at, but I gave him an indirect answer.

"Yes sir, I have flown around the Andes extensively."

He wrinkled his brow. He knew I was avoiding giving him a direct answer so he then expressed his skepticism more openly.

"That's not what I meant… I must ask you directly, have you ever been to La Paz before? You must have had at least one entry there for us to go. It is an insurance requirement for us."

I was taken slightly aback, not only at the directness of the question but the forcefulness. I have never had any passenger question my ability or qualifications. Of course, I had never had a professional pilot as a passenger before, especially one who knew what to ask. It was not so long ago, that after being questioned by an authority figure, I would have gotten defensive. But after being an authority figure myself for a little while, I could now stand on my own. I decided that I was his equal and would answer him accordingly.

Although, I had a problem. The fact was that I had never been to LaPaz before. But before I confessed to that fact, I gave myself a second to review the consequences of my answer. I had two choices. I could have told him the truth and then gone home. Or I could have lied and flown the trip.

I looked straight in his eye and I took another second to decide.

I straightened up and raised my chin..

"Yes sir, I have."

I even decided to add a little book knowledge to make it sound better.

"El Alto is on the altiplano at 13,300 feet. The highest terrain in the area is Mount Illimani at 21,000 feet high. But we'll be coming in from the north over Lake Titicaca. From that direction, the terrain is a little less challenging so we'll be OK."

"Good, then let's get on with the briefing."

And twenty minutes later, we were airborne on our way to Panama.

As we climbed away from Miami, there were nine of us huddled together in the tiny cabin and we were on our way to find a missing airplane deep in South America. Once we leveled off at 410, I looked to the cabin. The cabin was lavishly upholstered in a rich beige leather like the lobby outside Corky's office. I had instructed Rohwedder to keep the cabin on the warmer side. Everyone had taken off their jacket and the mood was relaxed.

Our passengers included Captain Stone and someone who I think was his assistant. They were leaning over a topographical chart of Bolivia that was illuminated by a single shaft of light from the overhead. The other passengers were various department heads from dispatch and maintenance. They were sprawled out uncomfortably trying to get some sleep in the otherwise dark cabin. One of the passengers included a man wearing a dated beige polyester leisure suit. The suit wasn't the only thing notable about him. He had an artificial arm.

Rohwedder had filed the flight plan to Panama Tocumen International Airport. It was the airport I wished I had flown out of when trying to get into Medellin with Allen. It was located at sea level with long runways. We knew it would be open in the middle of the night and be able to give us a quick turn. As the lights of downtown Miami disappeared behind our tail, I checked the ship's clock. It was now just after 1 AM. I had been fast asleep two hours ago and I was now flying to one of the highest, most treacherous airports in the world with not much more than a perfunctory briefing and more than an average amount of bravado.

It was a quiet and smooth night. After one hour into the flight we had passed Cuba and were about to put Grand Cayman under the nose. We were looking at another two hours of empty sky before making landfall in Panama. There wasn't much to talk about and I just stared ahead at the stars thinking about La Paz but after a while Rohwedder broke our silence.

"You know as well as I do what really happened down there, right?"

I shrugged my shoulders.

"Well, we shouldn't jump to any conclusions."

"Sure, if you say so. But you know they hit a mountain, probably Illimani… All those South American routes that Eastern is flying? That's all new flying for them. They were flown by Braniff Airways for decades. Braniff started flying there in the 30s and, along with PanAm, trail-blazed most of those routes.

Not only did they fly into those airports, they helped build them, installed the nav-aids, and created the entire route structure.

"Yeah, I know, What are you getting at?"

"Well, when Braniff went out of business two years ago, Eastern bought up all their South American route authority. The problem was the Eastern guys had spent their whole lives just flying up and down the east coast of the US. Mostly sea level airports with very little in the way of terrain. They had no idea what was waiting for them down here.

"Braniff had been flying the Andes for decades. They were the old South American hands. They offered to come over and help train the Eastern guys. And Eastern refused to hire any Braniff pilots in order to learn from them. Not even as consultants temporarily. They basically told the Braniff guys to go fuck themselves. All of a sudden, all that experience was gone as the routes were handed over. The Eastern guys thought that just because they flew a few trips to Puerto Rico, they were South American experts too. So now they hit a mountain... Dumb shits. It serves them right. I am surprised it took so long. I'm just sorry they killed some innocent passengers."

I had to admit Rohwedder was right, as he often was. But it wasn't doing us any good to dwell on it. We had our own challenge ahead of us. And like the Eastern pilots we were unprepared. But we pressed on anyway.

After a while, Captain Stone came up to the cockpit and sat on the side facing seat just behind the copilot. He was facing right at me and he asked a few questions regarding the airplane. He seemed to be genuinely curious about the Lear but I guessed he was still concerned about my experience and was trying to feel me out. We had a pleasant exchange as equals and he eventually returned to the back of the cabin for a nap.

The refueling stops in Panama and Guayaquil went smoothly without any of the usual delays caused by bureaucracy and corruption. In both cities, Eastern had a large presence and we were aided by a mass of Eastern agents and their political heft. No mordida required from us. Whether Eastern agents paid it at the airport, or lobbyists paid it in the hallways of the presidential palaces, I didn't know and I didn't care. I was tired and just glad to be on our way.

By mid morning of the next day, we were over central Peru on our last leg to La Paz. I had been up for over 24 hours with two more hours to go. El Alto was waiting for us and I knew it was important for me to stay alert.

Captain Stone came up again from the back of the airplane. After watching me now flying for seven hours and two landings he had gotten more comfortable.

"When we were in Guayaquil, I called back to Miami for an update. No other airports have reported our airplane landing. So, it wasn't a hijacking. There is still a tiny possibility they may have made a forced landing off airport somewhere but I don't think so."

He paused. He was leaning forward with his arms crossed over his knees. Captain Stone had been awake now for as long as us and probably under a lot more stress. He was no longer the blue blooded and aloof chief pilot. Instead, he was just another aviator sharing his fears with fellow pilots.

"At this point, we're pretty certain they crashed. The only saving grace was that there were only 29 people on board. A very light load, so it could have been much worse."

I remembered Rohwedder's prediction but I reserved any judgement.

"Any ideas what happened?

"Their last position report was just south of the airport. But the question is where exactly? We know they were close to the airport when they crashed. They made a position report at 7:37 PM local time with a landing ETA of 7:47. That would have put them just 25 miles from the airport. The airway they were flying passed alongside Mt. Illimani. That's one of the highest peaks in South America. They were probably in the clouds with no visual references, got off course, and hit the mountain on their descent to La Paz."

I put myself in the place of the accident crew.

At night and in the clouds, descending into the mountains; every nerve should be on edge, checking your navigation over and over again. You had to navigate like your life depended on it... because it does... but somehow a very experienced crew got off course and slammed into the mountainside.

Traveling at over 300 knots with an impact against the vertical granite of the high Andes the end would have been instantaneous. They probably didn't even realize they had killed themselves. It would have been that quick. And at that altitude, they were above the treeline. There was no wildlife to have heard the impact, and no foliage to have been burned. But the end was still certain. We all knew it and we didn't need to go into details.

Captain Stone asked me, "Do you have a chart?"

I handed him my Jeppesen chart neatly folded with La Paz right in the center. He pointed his finger to La Paz and then traced it backwards on an imaginary line back towards Asuncion; from where Eastern 980 had originated. As he traced his finger south on the map, he stopped 25 miles south of LaPaz.

Next to his finger was the peak of Mt. Illimani. I looked at the altitude of the peak.

The chart showed Illimani at 21,000 with a minimum safe altitude of 25,000 feet.

"We think they hit the mountain at around 20,000 feet. For some reason they were about twenty miles east of course.

We were then over Lake Titicaca and had just begun our descent. Captain Stone continued:

"I have a favor to ask you. Can you circle around to where we think the crash site is?"

Rohwedder and I exchanged a glance.

I then checked the fuel gauge. I figured that we would land at la Paz with almost two hours of fuel.

I answered, "We have some time to linger but we're a high speed jet, we're not designed for low and slow search and rescue."

I paused to consider the proposition. As much as I didn't want to do an impromptu search and rescue, especially without a solid plan, it was still a challenge that I couldn't refuse.

"Yeah, we can take a look."

Captain Stone was pleased with my answer but still concerned.

"Are you sure that's OK?"

"Yeah, as long as we keep to the airway and obey all the minimum altitudes we'll be all right."

I turned to Rohwedder to brief my plan.

"They were on Upper Mike 657 inbound. We'll overfly LaPaz and fly that airway outbound. We can retrace their steps. The minimum enroute altitude there is 250, so we'll descend down to that altitude. The terrain will be 4,000 feet below us and it's a clear day, so maybe we'll be able to see something."

Stone was listening to the briefing and once satisfied we weren't going to kill him in a misguided attempt to play hero, he left to the back of the cabin again.

I looked to Rohwedder. "You OK with all that?"

"Yeah, just as long as you stick to the plan. I don't want you freelancing after that. We're good if we stay on the published airways. But actually, I'm more worried about cabin pressure and the tire speeds."

"I was thinking about that. What do you think?"

"As we descend into La Paz, we'll have to depressurize the cabin down to field elevation. 13,000 feet is pretty damn high."

"Yeah, I know. Well, we just do what the airiners do. You and I will go on 100% oxygen starting when the cabin climbs above 8,000 feet and stay on oxygen all the way until we park the airplane."

"Sounds good. Also the tires... I did the math. At 13,000 feet field elevation, we'll have a much higher true airspeed on landing than at sea level. Close to 200 miles per hour. That speed is right at the tire limit. I just hope the tires don't disintegrate."

"Well, there's not much we can do about that. Although, we should be OK. The dispatcher told me that as soon as they got the trip, they had maintenance do a quick tire change. We've got brand new rubber all around."

With that small amount of extra comfort we passed the La Paz VOR outbound and descended to 250 to begin our search.

I hugged the airway like it was my lifeline and at a point 25 miles south of La Paz, Mt. Illimani loomed off of our left wing. It was a clear day and Illimani was laid out in full glory below us. The mountain was not the highest in South American but it was considered the most beautiful and it stood high above the surrounding altiplano as a sentinel overlooking the city of La Paz. The mountain was a dark brown granite, almost black, and the top third was cloaked in a brilliant white snow cap. A few wispy rotor clouds trailed off of the peak.

"OK. Let's enter a holding pattern now at our present position. We'll make right turns, away from the terrain. I'm slowing to 210 knots."

I then gave control of the airplane to Rohwedder so with the mountain on my side I could look for anything unusual. When we made our turn and reversed course with the mountain on his side, we swapped flying duties. Seven other pairs of eyes in the back of the airplane joined the search.

However, we were just too far away. I didn't want to slow up any further and I certainly didn't want to leave the safety of the airway. At our altitude, the air was just too thin and our lift was compromised for any further maneuvering. We were a high speed jet, not at all designed for low altitude and low speed search patterns.

As we re-entered the airway on our second orbit in the holding pattern, we flew into some wisps of cloud obscuring our vision and I began to have some doubts about our impromptu search mission. We were still protected by staying on the airway but the outcome of the exercise was becoming obvious. Our spirits rose and fell with each orbit in the holding pattern. Every time, we turned away we were discouraged that we couldn't see anything. Every time we turned back inbound towards Illimani we became encouraged anew; thinking that maybe we could see something. We flew in and out of the cloud layer. And everytime we flew back into clear sky we searched frantically during the few moments afforded us. But there was nothing but empty sky and the silent sentinel that was Illimani. Conditions were worsening. The wind at altitude was picking up and I could see snow blowing off the top of the mountain.

But I still wasn't ready to give up.

I dialed the emergency frequency on our back up radio and picked up the microphone.

"Eastern 980, are you on frequency?"

But there was no answer. The frequency was silent as well.

I called again.

"Eastern 980!...

"Are you on frequency?"

It was a pointless radio call. But maybe, just maybe, I continued with the hope there might have been survivors working an emergency radio.

We continued in our fruitless search for a couple of more turns, each time braying our lonely call on the radio and with each orbit becoming more dispirited.

However, after our fourth orbit by the crash site, the clouds began to close in again. It had been a lost cause from the start but one we had to try. But by this time, there was no further point searching for our lost brothers and we then made a hasty retreat back to El Alto.

Later in the day, the Bolivian Air Force mounted a search and rescue mission of their own using some helicopters capable of high altitude flight. They made a heroic effort but they found themselves with the same problem we had. The conditions were just too treacherous to conduct a meaningful search of the area. The helicopters could fly by the peak of Illimani but the air was too thin to hover. The wreckage might have well been on the moon.

We ended up spending a few days in La Paz while the team conducted what investigation they could. Although they were limited by the lack of a crash site. Ultimately, they returned to Miami empty handed. The mystery of Eastern 980 was never solved. Although, over the ensuing decades, various alpinists braved the face of Illimani only to find a few scraps of tantalizing debris. And, to this day, the remaining clues to Eastern 980 remain locked in the Bolivian ice pack.

During those few days we waited in La Paz, Rohwedder and I would normally have toured the city and even gotten in some hiking. However, we were both suffering from food poisoning and altitude sickness, as well as a general malaise from the accident, so we didn't venture very far during our time there.

What we did find out, in the days following the crash, was that the flight engineer on the accident airplane had just been hired by the Eastern. And, of course, because Eastern was a dream job for many of us in South Florida, the flight engineer ended up dying doing a job that many of us had wished was ours.

Chapter 46

....

An American Samurai

After our brief odyssey in Bolivia, I was relieved to be assigned to some easy trips around the United States. And I found myself flying with Rohwedder again on a five day trip in a Lear 24 that zigzagged across the country. The first of those legs included a trip from Fort Lauderdale to Carlsbad, California, with just one passenger on board.

Normally, a transcontinental flight in a 24 would require two fuel stops but the headwinds were light that day and we were able to stretch the first leg to make it as far as San Angelo in central Texas.

The line girls in San Angelo met the airplane wearing hot pants and Stetson hats. They were on their game and we turned the airplane in San Angelo in just 20 minutes. I was flying the second leg and I had just engaged the autopilot as we leveled at 410. Carlsbad was 1500 miles ahead and the weather ahead was forecast to be agreeable. It was going to be an easy leg with a nice layover in California waiting for us. Rohwedder and I had already agreed to have dinner at a local diner known as Pea Soup Andersens. It was my favorite restaurant in that part of the state and I would always gorge on their signature split pea soup. After dinner and brief rest, we were then scheduled to pick up a different set of passengers and fly an all nighter to Grand Cayman with a fuel stop in Houston.

Our single passenger was a pleasant older gentleman whom we had flown several times before. He was Asian and he always wore expensive silk suits. He knotted his necktie in a large Windsor and he never took his jacket off while we flew. He wore dark framed glasses with thick lenses, the kind of lenses that made his eyes appear watery. He was a small man and said very little. We didn't know much about him other than he was very rich and very unassuming.

The first time I flew him, I had mischaracterized him as an affluent Hong Kong businessman. I don't know why I misjudged him, but I did. Therefore, the first time we spoke with each other, I was taken aback when he spoke perfect American English. His name was Jonathon Taguchi.

He was an enigma. He would always sit quietly in the back of the airplane and was never demanding. He never told us about his business. We thought he was a banker but because anonymity and discretion was a large part of our business service in the world of Learjet charter we never asked. No matter, he was undemanding and he would always tip generously. In short, he was one of our favorite customers.

We eventually climbed up to 450 and were level. The airspace in the high altitude sector of American Southwest was quiet and we were enjoying the solitude. However, in a move that was out of character for him, Mr. Taguchi came to the front and sat in the side facing seat just behind the copilot. He sat demurely with his hands between his legs and watched us silently for a while. We were used to these intrusions in our work space. Unlike the airlines where the pilots were sealed off from the passengers and hence, aloof. The Lear was a small airplane and although we had a small partition separating the cockpit from the cabin, we were on display for all the passengers to see.

I looked back to say hello and I noticed he had a crumpled road map in his hand. His right index finger was loosely pointing to a feature on the map. He sat silently for a few minutes straining his neck forward to see out of our windshield and alternately looking out the large side windows.

He again leaned forward.

"Excuse me, I was wondering, where are we?"

I didn't mind the intrusion. After all, Mr Taguchi was a favorite and I liked playing tour guide.

"We are over southwestern New Mexico, Tucson is about 200 miles ahead."

He nodded and looked at his map again.

"You know, I used to be a pilot so I like to do my own navigation and follow along."

His comment was, I knew, going to be the beginning of what was a common conversation with our passengers. It was not at all unusual for many of our male customers to confide in us that becoming a pilot had been a boyhood dream. However, like so many other dreams, they were usually swept away by life's other distractions and priorities. And if they had done any flying at all, it was usually just a few elementary experiences in training airplanes before needing to quit aviation. Many of our passengers marveled at flying and envied us in our career choice. Even if just a little bit.

Some pilots resented these attempts at camaraderie. In their minds, professional pilots and private pilots were completely separate from each other. However, I welcomed their desire to befriend us. One of the things I was slowly learning was that it was important for men to be respected by other men. When a passenger told me that he was also a pilot, no matter their level of experience, they were proud of their history. Therefore as a man, I would honor their experience. It was important for a man's ego.

So, as I did with all of the people who wanted to share, I decided to show respect to Mr. Taguchi. I smiled and shared the brotherhood of flight with him.

"Oh yeah, what kind of airplanes did you fly?"

Of course, I already knew what the answer was going to be, probably a light airlane of some sort. I waited politely, ready to compliment him and make him feel good about himself.

Mr. Taguchi leaned back a bit. Most other passengers would smile a little as they made their pronouncement. But not today. Our passenger was stone faced and then he frowned. He hesitated and then he nodded before asking me:

"Do you really want to know?"

"Yes..."

That was odd, I thought. Why would I not want to know?

He looked down for a moment and then leaned forward again. He looked at me.

"I flew Japanese Zeros in the war."

His answer was completely unexpected and he said it just as a matter of fact if he was ordering a coffee. I tried to process that fact. World War Two was only forty years in the past and many veterans were still alive. It was quite common to run into American war veterans of all types. The story of their heroics was common knowledge among all American pilots. I had even met a few German aces. Their stories were less well known but still, not unheard of.

But Japanese? That was a first. I had read about the kamikaze pilots, who were martyrs but other than that, I knew nothing about Japanese pilots. How did he emigrate to the US after the war, I wondered?

I was trying to figure it all out but nothing would logically follow.

This was too interesting not to follow up. I had to ask for more detail. I then assumed he emigrated to the United States after the war, although that would be the second time I misjudged him.

"Zeros? In World War Two? How is it that your English is so good?"

"Well. That is a long story. Do you have some time?"

I didn't need to look at my own chart. I knew we were still 90 minutes out of Carlsbad. We were over some very lonely airspace with little demands. I looked to Rohwedder. He was just as interested as I was. We had the time and he now had our full attention.

"Do I have time? Hell, yes!" I thought to myself.

I shifted in the tiny confines of the cockpit and turned my whole body toward him.

"I am Japanese-American. My parents immigrated from Japan and I was born and raised in San Francisco. I grew up speaking both English and Japanese in the house. San Francisco in the 1930s was a beautiful city. Located on the west coast, far from the rest of the United States, on the tip of a peninsula, it was isolated from the rest of the country, almost like an island really. I grew up attending public schools and spent my summers fishing in the bay with my father. We watched the Golden Gate Bridge being built as we fished.

"In 1939, when I was 19, my parents sent me back to Japan for the summer to visit my aunts and uncles. I didn't think much of it but was looking forward to meeting my cousins. When I cleared into the port of Yokohama there were representatives from the Japanese Army waiting at the port. They told me that as far as they were concerned I was Japanese, subject to the dictates of the emperor. They confiscated my passport and they drafted me in the army. Right then and there. That night I was in an army barracks. They let me write one letter to my parents to let them know.

"Two days later, I was in boot camp training to be an infantryman.

"There was nothing I could do so I decided to just cooperate the best I could, but it didn't do me any good. I was an outcast. I spoke Japanese but I was still American. All the officers were suspicious of me. They hated me actually. And my platoon mates were afraid to befriend me. I just barely survived.

"After a few years, they selected me for flight school. By then, my Japanese had gotten better. The war with the United States had started and they were getting desperate for pilots. I had the advantage of an American education; and being raised as an American I was not as timid as a lot of the other recruits. That made me better material for flight school.

"I received a commission as a lieutenant and after graduation I was selected to fly Zeros."

"They let you fly a front line fighter?"

"Yes, I trained to fly Zeros."

"Then, why didn't you just ditch your airplane on your first mission in front of an American destroyer and surrender? That's what I would have done."

"Of course. That's exactly what I would have done also. And the Japanese command wasn't naive. They knew it too. After graduation, they said they didn't trust me in combat for that exact reason. Instead, I flew a seaplane version of the Zero. I did mostly rear echelon flights shuttling satchels back and forth between the generals."

"That's where I got lucky. You know, the war was not kind to Japanese aviators. We had a 90% attrition rate. By the time the war ended, all my classmates had been killed. I only survived because they didn't trust me to fly front line combat against the Americans."

I glanced across to the copilot. Rohwedder was monitoring everything but he was still riveted. I had read a lot about World War 2 aviation but it was almost always from the side of the victors.

"I am sorry. I have never heard about the war from the Japanese side."

Mr. Taguchi leaned against the seat to stretch his back. He then ran his fingers through his gray hair and rubbed his neck.

"When the war ended, my unit was in Korea and we surrendered to the Russians."

He paused.

"You surrendered to the Russians?"

He really didn't need to say anymore. The plight of POWs in Russia were well chronicled.

"Yes, It was a terrible time. 6,000 of us surrendered in 1945. They sent us to Siberia, it was a two day train ride. Then a three day march to a work camp. They kept on saying they were negotiating our release. While we waited, cholera and starvation took many of our lives. Surrender was very shameful to many of my men. Many died of the shame or from being homesick. So, many just gave up. In the end, only 10% of us made it home."

He paused and rolled his eyes back as though to recall something. And he choked back a sob.

He then spoke slowly. "We lost five thousand, four hundred, and thirty of our men… I know that number exactly because I kept count. By the time we were released, four years later, I was the senior surviving officer."

"Didn't you tell the Russians you were American?"

"For what purpose? They wouldn't have believed me. And by then, I had a duty to my men. Even if they released me, I would have never left them behind. I stayed with them and we survived together.

"Once the Russians were tired of us, we were first sent back to Korea by train. There, a ship was waiting for us to take us back to Tokyo. Some of my men were ashamed to return home after surrendering but I was elated. Maybe it was different for me because I was American. I knew I would be seeing my parents soon. But it was going to be a while yet.

"Once we arrived in Tokyo, we were sent to another prison. This one was run by the US Army. It was there, we were processed and interrogated. I was interviewed by an army intelligence officer, a captain, he was younger than me. He was surprised I spoke such good English, although it had been ten years since I last spoke it so I was a little rusty.

"At first, he didn't believe I was American but I gave him my parent's phone number back in San Francisco. He finally relented and called the number. They then sent me back to my cell.

"The next day, they released me.

"Then they said because I was bilingual, I was drafted in the US Army, and I then served two years on MacArthur's staff as an interpreter.

"It was there, while I was back in Japan, that I found out that during the war my parents had been sent to an internment camp in Arizona; somewhere just below us, I think."

He paused again. He leaned back in his seat, closed his eyes and sighed.

I waited for more but his catharsis was done.

"That is all really. I finally made it home and I have been living in San Francisco ever since raising my own family. You seem to enjoy flying for a living but I must admit to you, I don't enjoy flying. I did like flying when I first started. It gave me an escape, even just for a short while, from the stupid and mean officers in the Japanese Army. But I haven't flown an airplane since 1945. After the war, it never held any joy for me."

He took a deep breath and straightened himself up in his seat. He then thanked us for our time and went to the back of the cabin while I pondered his story.

Mr. Taguchi was like Odysseus. They both left for what was to be a short trip. A lark almost. Both fought a brutal war and both lost many comrades. Although, Jonathon was alone for many of those years.

I wondered if he cried during his time away from home.

Odysseus, at least knew what he was doing. He was already a king when he left. Mr. Taguchi was just a boy when he started out and then he had his youth immediately stripped from him. Although, he didn't seem bitter. He had returned to the United States, started a family, and had a successful business career.

I turned towards the front and looked out at the dusty horizon. And I thought of some of my own friends I lost. Those losses, and my own brushes with death, were nothing compared to his experiences. I remembered that Oswaldo had warned me that we all make bets in life. Some are successful; many are not. Mr. Taguchi probably had to bet his life almost every day for those 12 years he was away. He said he was lucky but he was being modest. He only could have survived by a combination of both luck and his wits. He was a young man who fought for his life every day. Every day he wagered his life, and in the end, he won. He made it home.

Chapter 47

An Airplane Forsaken and Unloved

A few days later, Rohwedder and I were back home ourselves. He had been getting ready for his own upgrade to captain and it was my job to get him ready. Therefore, rather than the two of us flying in a rotation with other pilots we were flying together consistently.

For our next trip, we had been assigned to ferry an empty airplane to its new owners in Montana. It was to be a fairly easy trip. It would require one or two fuel stops depending on the winds, and then we'd grab an airliner home, but we first had to solve a problem. The fuel burn numbers from the airplane's most recent flights didn't look right.

We didn't know much about the airplane. It was a Lear 23. One of the very first airplanes off the assembly line back in 1965. In her early days, she was one of the most glamorous airplanes on the ramp. However, the years had not been kind to her.

She did not at all look the part of her more glamorous stable mates. She had just shown up in our hangar one day. We didn't know much about her other than she was clearly an unloved airplane with faded paint and a badly scratched windshield from God knows what. She had spent the past few years in Brazil where it was rumored that she had been flying between remote dirt runways deep in the hinterlands of Brazil. That rumor was believable given the underside of the airplane was dented and caked with red mud.

The airplane had been delivered the previous day by a crew of Brazilian pilots who ferried the airplane as far as Florida. Normally, when one crew hands off a strange airplane to another there is a brief period where we discuss the idioscyranices of the airplane. Instead, these Brazilian pilots were eager to get back home and as they ran to their taxi, they left us with only a cursory remark.

"Here is the airplane, you can have it."

Inside our flight planning room, Rohwedder spent an unusually long time pouring over the airplane records. He discovered the record of recent fuel receipts but they didn't match the previous fuel burn history. The airplane was burning much more fuel than the flight manual predicted; a significant amount more. Rohwedder was a careful aviator but even more importantly, he had a profound instinct. However, this math problem left him stumped.

I triple checked his computations but none of it made sense. There was no way the airplane could be burning that much fuel. We went back and started all over again and checked and rechecked the performance charts and came up with a conclusion that seemed plausible. Someone down in Brazil was probably stealing gas and concealing the theft by showing it as a higher burn rate. Thus, we talked ourselves into an assumption that the airplane's history of overburn was not real. Knowing how business was done differently in the deep south it made perfect sense. We congratulated ourselves on that great insight and proceeded with the rest of our flight planning.

We planned to make our first fuel stop in Wichita. It was at the edge of the airplane's range but the weather was good everywhere; and from there, Billings, Montana, our final destination, would be a comfortably short leg. We ordered a full load of fuel and headed out to the jet.

We were a bit unfamiliar with the instrument panel layout of this older airplane, and it took us slightly longer to finish our cockpit checks and start engines but it was only a minor inconvenience for two professional pilots. It was a beautiful day for flying and I felt that hand flying the airplane on such a fine day would be enjoyable so, as was my prerogative as captain, I decided to fly the first leg. Once we made the fuel stop in Wichita, I'd switch seats with Rohwedder and he'd fly the second leg from the left seat getting more practice as a captain. We'd probably do some engine failure training along the way.

We taxied to the end of Runway 8 and began our takeoff roll. We were relatively light and I expected to use only about 4,000 feet of the available runway. But as I pushed the throttles up, the airplane was sluggish. On takeoff roll, it didn't really have the same rocket like acceleration all the other Lears were known for. As we accelerated, I made an excuse for the airplane and attributed its lethargy to a set of tired, old engines. As I rotated, the airplane didn't leap into the air, as Lear would always do, instead, the airplane had to be nursed into the sky

Once airborne, the airplane felt draggy. We weren't flying; instead we were sloshing through the air and it took more than the usual amount of physical effort to fly.

I turned to Rohwedder.

"What the hell? The airplane is flying like a pig."

He had been watching my struggle; and nodded but offered no insight.

It was not unusual to climb to FL 410 in less than 15 minutes, but after half an hour we were still struggling through the mid 30s. We climbed so slowly that I was getting impatient.

"OK. There is something definitely wrong with the airplane. Any ideas?"

We then checked everything. The power was set at 100%; the airplane was trimmed properly; the flaps, gear and speed brakes were all tucked in tight. After that, we had run out of ideas.

I clicked through the fuel gauges, checking all five tanks.

"Well, we are definitely overburning on the gas. Let's keep an eye on it and see what it looks like in a little bit."

And then I added some wishful thinking.

"Maybe, the burn will normalize once we level off."

When we finally did reach 410, I reduced from climb power back to our normal cruise RPM setting of 90%. Normally, the airplane would then settle down into cruise flight, accelerate slightly, and the fuel flows would drop down to a comfortable level.

As soon as the power came back, I felt the back of the airplane drop and the wings began to wallow in a Dutch Roll. I focused on the flight director trying to keep the airplane level.

Rohwedder called out:

"Watch your airspeed!"

"Damnit! We just lost ten knots."

I pushed the throttles back up to maximum power just to stay at flying speed; and even with the power firewalled, our speed continued to roll back, getting close to a low speed buffet.

"Jesus! What the hell!"

I needed to unload myself so I could work the problem with Rohwedder. I wanted to engage the autopilot but the early generation autopilots were notoriously prone to failure and I dared not engage it. But I had no choice. I ensured the airplane was straight and level and as stable as possible. I stabbed the autopilot engage button but the plane immediately jerked to the left.

"No good!"

I quickly disengaged the autopilot.

Since the autopilot had proven itself an unreliable partner, I continued hand flying. But I was really working at it. Even on a good day, the early Lears were difficult to fly at altitude but this was different.

I was grunting from the physical effort required to control the airplane and worse, I was so focused on flying that I was distracted from our performance problem.

Finally, I stole a glance at the fuel flow meters.

"Christ! Look at the fuel flow! It's almost double the normal. What's going on?"

Rohwedder was perplexed, as well.

"I don't know."

We were struggling to maintain 410. The speed had stabilized but it was dangerously slow.

I decided we had to do something. Going lower would burn even more fuel; fuel that we needed but I didn't have a choice.

"The airplane is flying like shit up here. We're just mushing along here. Let's go back down. Ask ATC for 390."

Rohwedder agreed and dutifully called air traffic control who then issued us a descent clearance. I pulled the power back slightly and the bottom dropped out from us. I was caught by surprise.

"Whoa, the speed dropped off again!"

I pitched down aggressively to maintain flying speed and with this increase in descent rate, FL 390 came up quickly. A 2,000 foot altitude reduction wasn't enough.

"Ask for 350! We need even lower."

Rohwedder was watching me struggle with the floundering airplane and asked, "Do you want to declare an emergency?"

I grunted through the effort.

"Not yet, lets see how it does lower."

ATC offered us FL350 and once we leveled off, I was able to maintain some semblance of control. I pushed the power back to maintain altitude but we were still at almost full power just to maintain 350 at a comfortable speed. I had better control of the airplane in the thicker air and I handed it off to Rohwedder so I could unload my brain.

The fuel flow meters were showing a burn several hundred more pounds an hour than usual. The engines were not producing enough thrust and we were burning too much gas. The combination didn't make sense.

I thought back to my lessons with all the captains who mentored me but nothing I was taught about turbojet engines, or the Lear, fit our problem.

"What the hell is wrong?"

Rohwedder then voiced what I was just beginning to think.

"We can't make it to Wichita. Not like this."

I was pretty sure he was right but I wanted to probe his thinking.

"What do you mean, we can't make it? Can't make it at all, or we'll just be tight on fuel?"

"No. We can't make it at all, As a matter of fact, I think we need to find an airport to land now. We're already way over burn. We need to stop in Meridian, Mississippi. It's just a hundred miles ahead. It's got a 10,000 foot runway and the weather is good."

He was right. We had been overburing for the whole flight and it wasn't going to get better. Better to get the airplane on the ground and figure things out with the luxury of time and with solid ground underneath our feet. Flying this airplane was like balancing a broomstick on one finger and having to juggle with the other hand.

"OK. Meridian it is. Let ATC know we want a destination change and lower."

As soon as I reduced the power, the airplane descended much more steeply than normal. I had to add power to keep from plummeting. Meaning still more fuel burn.

I hazarded a guess.

"It feels like the airplane is overweight."

"But we're empty."

He motioned to the back of our cabin, devoid of even passenger seats.

"I ran the weight and balance and we were way below max weight."

"I know, but there's nothing wrong with the engines. At idle, they're showing normal fuel flow. But it's only when we're trying to maintain flying speed, the fuel flow is way high."

We continued to descend and it was with great relief when it was clear that we could make it to Meridan. We landed there uneventfully with about 45 minutes of reserve, although the fuel flow on approach was way higher than usual. Rohwedder was right. We would never have made Wichita.

After we shut down the engine we were informed that we had parked in the wrong spot. Meridian didn't have a fuel truck available for us so we had to taxi over to a fixed fueling area. We then had to restart the engines to reposition the airplane.

We did as we were instructed and once the right engine started, it then immediately flamed out.

"That's odd. I wonder if we have a fuel controller problem."

The problem was now obvious but I was still too dense to understand its exact nature.

I then tried the left engine. It started normally and then we taxied only 50 feet before that engine flamed out as well, right in front of the fuel pump.

Rohwedder was still sitting next to me.

"I don't understand it. We are still showing several hundred pounds."

I was still misdiagnosing the problem.

"Something is wrong with these engines."

Before we re-fueled the airplane, I reported our problem back to our chief pilot who gave us instructions to leave the airplane in Meridian and just airline home. Another crew would pick it up and fly it to its new home and we gladly complied with those instructions.

Back in Fort Lauderdale, the next day, I stopped into our maintenance office and sat down in front of our chief mechanic. Bob was his name. He was a big man and formerly played football in college. He had black hair and a full beard. His small office was cluttered with spare parts and once he took his seat there wasn't much room for anything else.

Like many mechanics, he didn't have a lot of time for small talk and he started right in.

"You are one lucky son of a bitch."

"I wish some of that luck would rub off on my airline applications. What are you talking about?"

"The maintenance logbooks on the airplane just arrived."

"Oh yeah? This should be good. Those engines are junk, right?"

"Just the opposite. Those engines saved your life."

I leaned back and unwrapped the cellophane from a fresh pack of Marlboros.

"Oh yeah? How's that?"

"It turns out the airplane had an accident a few years ago in Manaus. They had a hard landing and the landing gear collapsed."

"So?"

"Well, when they rebuilt the landing gear they placed 500 pounds of steel plates in each fuel tank to anchor the new gear struts. So, the airplane was 1000 pounds heavier than what you have been using for your fuel burn calculations. That's why the fuel burn was so high and that's also why the airplane was so sluggish. You were way more overweight than you thought. Those engines have been working their hearts out ever since that accident. It's surprising they are running at all. You can thank General Electric for that."

"OK, I'll remember to do that."

"That's not the worst of it."

"There's more?"

"Oh yeah. Those steel plates? They took up some space in the tanks that would normally hold fuel. So when you topped off the tanks you didn't have as much gas onboard as you thought you did."

"Well that explains why it was so slow to climb. But what about the fuel controllers? They probably need to be changed out."

"Man, you don't know jack shit about engines. I'm telling you, there's nothing wrong with the engines."

"So what happened?"

"That's the reason why you ran out of gas right on the ramp in Meridian. After they added the steel plates inside the fuel tanks, there was less volume in the fuel tanks but they never recalibrated the fuel gauges. So they were showing more fuel than you actually had on board."

"The airplane has been flying for years like that. The Brazilians apparently knew about it and took it into account but when they dropped the airplane off, they neglected to mention that very important fact. When you left here, you had about a quarter of a tank of gas less than you thought. Then on top of that, you were burning way more than usual because you were dragging around another 1,000 pounds of steel. You finally realized you couldn't make Wichita so you decided to stop short. Good for you. But if the airport had been a few miles further away you would have flamed out while in the air. So, yeah, you're a lucky son of a bitch."

I thanked Bob the mechanic and went on to fly another trip that day.

Fortunately, that airplane was scheduled to be scrapped so it was to end its career ignominiously, but not first without trying to kill Rohwedder and me. It was also about this time that the unreliable nature of the autopilot became apparent again. Another Learjet, a 24B, crashed on takeoff from San Francisco, killing all three people on board. The investigation discovered that, once engaged, the autopilot rolled abruptly to the left and caused a loss of control from which the pilots were unable to recover.

As a result of this event, I was very happy to see one of my favorites, an old Lear 25, back on my schedule. An airplane that, although getting outdated by modern standards of the day, was a reliable and old friend to me.

Chapter 48

South Caicos

The instructions from Lyndee were very clear. We were to take off immediately for South Caicos in order to pick up a large group of people, and return them to Miami. By itself, this was not a terribly demanding trip but she laid out a pressing constraint.

"You have to get there and then take off by sunset."

I looked at my watch. It was 3 PM so we had about four hours of daylight left. The flight down would be just under two hours. That gave us two hours to refuel, take care of customs, and take off again before dark.

"OK, that's no problem. We have plenty of time."

"There's one other thing…"

"What's that?"

"You have to find the passengers."

"What do you mean…find them?"

"Well, they're in jail."

And then she laughed. Not because it was funny; it was more like she was relieved that the problem was now mine.

"You're taking their attorney with you. He'll bail them out. The line boys are pulling the 25 out right now. You're flying with Inderbitzin and he's already here. You're taking off as soon as you get here. Bye." And she hung up without any further acknowledgement on my part.

As I drove to the airport, I reviewed what I knew about our destination. The Turks and Caicos Islands were located at the southern end of the Bahamas chain in a lonely part of the southwestern Atlantic Ocean. We routinely flew over them back and forth to the Caribbean but we rarely stopped there. It was an inhospitable place, hot, dry, and windy. The surrounding water was beautiful but the terrain itself was flat and stark with none of the beauty of the Antilles. They were practically the definition of desert islands. As a result, there wasn't much tourism down there; or much of any economy at all. I had an overnight there a couple of years earlier with Farmer. Our passenger on that trip was a Bahamian attorney who we had flown down from Nassau. He had told us he just had a quick meeting to conduct some kind of business with the local offshore bankers. Instead, his business stretched into two days and I remembered it as a fairly bleak place, with one exception. While we waited, we enjoyed several colossal meals of the local lobster served at a tiki hut on the beach. Each meal was accompanied by mangoes shipped in from Haiti and an unlimited supply of Heineken beer, or as the locals called them "greenies."

The economy in the Turks and Caicos wasn't always so limited. For many centuries it had a thriving salt industry that benefited from the island's two greatest natural resources, sunlight and salt water. It turned out that the weather and topography on Grand Turk was ideal for salt evaporation. Temperatures seldomly dropped below 80 degrees and constant 15 knot tradewinds made it easy to create vast fields of salt crystals. However, that particular industry didn't make for much of a life for the locals. Salt raking was pure drudgery. Laborers were dropped off to spend several months on the island. And because salt season coincided with the hottest summer months, workers suffered terribly; with their only relief being short nights in rough huts on the ocean's edge. The work first went to slaves and then to the lowest class of indentured laborers. Salt production was a lucrative trade but none of the money stayed in the Turks. Finally, the salt industry in the Turks collapsed in the 1960s due to competition from modern production techniques in North America. An American salt company still maintained a small presence on Great Inagua but mostly the modern world had ignored the Turks and Caicos. The island chain lacked every accommodation for a comfortable modern life leaving it as a hardscrabble back water where time had ceased to exist. Virtually everything had to be imported. Which is, I was soon to find out, was why we found ourselves rushing to Caicos for this urgent pickup.

The attorney showed up alone just as we were finished preflighting. Once he boarded the airplane, we held up our part of the bargain and we were airborne quickly and climbed right to FL 430. By the time we leveled off, Nassau was passing underneath us. I left Inderbitzin at the controls to get a briefing from the attorney.

His name was Molina and he was wearing a blue polo shirt with white linen pants and blue suede loafers. He was Costa Rican, about 40 years old and very clean cut. He had no luggage except for a leather satchel. It was the same type of satchel we used when carrying large amounts of cash.

He gave me an update.

"We are going down to pick up a DC-4 crew. My client owns a cargo charter service in Costa Rica. He owns the airplane and he sent it to Grand Turk three days ago, and the crew flying the airplane was arrested."

I was familiar with the DC-4. It was designed for the pressing cargo needs of the military in World War 2 and was the world's first true all weather, trans-oceanic airplane. In their day, they were the most advanced airplanes in the sky. The DC-4 was built with four powerful Pratt and Whitney Wasp engines. It could carry a much heavier load, much further, and much faster than its predecessors. She was a beautiful and strong airplane and her design pointed the way to the future. After the war, the DC-4 then became the flagship airplane in the postwar airline boom and she was regularly featured on magazine covers with Hollywood stars. However, aviation at the time was making great strides so the DC-4 was quickly made obsolete by the tidal wave of modern jet airplane designs. As a result, many of them had found their way to be of service in the Caribbean. Many dozens of them were also based in the seedy northwest section of the Miami airport. That particular parcel of the airport was known as Corrosion Corner; or oftentimes by the even more derogatory reference, Cockroach Corner. Despite its inglorious fate, the DC-4 still was a robust and reliable hauler, carrying everything from baby food to illicit drugs.

Molina continued. "They came up from San Jose, Costa Rica, a couple nights ago. They were running late trying to get into Grand Turk. Their flight plan dropped out of the system so the locals didn't know they were coming."

"That's not usually a problem, you just call ahead."

"Well, it was a problem for these guys. The control tower assumed they had to be smuggling drugs since they were flying up from the general vicinity of Colombia late at night and with no flight plan."

The well dressed attorney then also added what everyone in the business already knew.

"The Turks are a popular fuel stop for smugglers on their way to the United States."

"So I've heard. But did they call ahead?"

"Yes, but the control tower assumed they were smugglers and never answered. My guys kept on making position reports as they got closer. But it didn't matter. When the airplane got close enough, the locals just turned off the runway lights so they couldn't see to land."

"But you said they were trying to land in Grand Turk. How did they end up in South Caicos?"

"They gave up on trying to land in Grand Turk. So they tried to fly the approach to South Caicos."

"But there isn't an instrument approach there."

"Of course. But they were getting low on fuel so they made their own. They just flew outbound out of the Grand Turk navigational beacon. They guessed on a bearing to Caicos and descended over the water trying to feel their way in.

"But the airport on Caicos has no lighting. They couldn't have found it."

"Yes, they knew that but they were running low on fuel and they were getting desperate. They didn't want to ditch in the open ocean. They did have barely enough moonlight to reflect off the white sand of the beach. So they lined up to land on the water's edge. They made a relatively normal landing on the beach but the landing gear collapsed in the soft sand and punctured the fuel tanks. What little gas they still had caught fire and consumed the whole airplane. The crew got out OK but the airplane but they left behind a burned out hulk on the beach."

That was quite a tall tale but I knew enough about flying south of Miami to know that any story, no matter how outlandish, was probably true. But I was still curious. Oftentimes in the Caribbean, ignorance is the best option. And with that in mind, I should have left it at that and not have asked the next question. That's because the answer was probably something that wasn't my business, but I asked anyway.

"So, what were they carrying?"

"Beef."

"Beef?"

"Yes, 12,000 pounds of Costa Rican beef. From the ranches near Perez Zeledon."

"I didn't know Costa Rica was known for beef."

"It's not. The quality is not that good, which is why you don't see it in Miami. It mostly goes to the poorer markets in the region. Markets like Grand

Turk. Regardless, the local government was suspicious of the crew so they arrested them."

"On what charge?"

"You know as well as I do that down here they don't need a reason. But in this case, they had two: Smuggling and attempted murder."

"Attempted murder? For doing what?"

"As it turned out the airplane came to rest right in front of the Governor's mansion. They accused them of trying to assassinate the governor. He wasn't even in the country but it didn't matter."

"You're kidding? They actually thought they were trying to kill the governor?"

"Probably not, but they were just adding charges. You've been flying here long enough. You know how it works. Same with the smuggling charge. When the airplane burned up, the whole beach smelled like a barbecue. The cargo was obviously beef but they didn't care. As far as they were concerned, anyone flying a DC-4 in the middle of the night was up to no good.

"Anyway, I've got bail money. More cash than I need really in case someone wants a little bit extra. I don't know how long I'll be, but I want you ready to take us back to Miami the instant we get to the airport. You know. In case the local officials change their minds."

I returned to the cockpit to relay all of this information to Inderbitzin. He and I had known each other as fellow flight instructors back when life had been much more innocent. That was a season that seemed a very long time ago. He was an accomplished airman at the top of his game. He had also been around South Florida long enough to be suspicious and he laughed out loud.

"Beef? Really? And you believe that story?"

"It's not my job to believe it. It's my job to take them where they want to go. They paid up front to take them to Miami and that's what we're going to do. It's cash money."

Then I added the following comment. Although, I wish I hadn't because it would turn out to jinx the whole operation.

"And if they want to go anywhere else, we'll take them there too. They're good for the money. That's all that matters."

Inderbitzin, not totally convinced replied, "Yeah, I guess so."

I had to admit, though. Inderbitzin was right. Skepticism was usually the best policy in the Caribbean. After all, the name Turks came from the Spanish word for pirate. The islands that were to be eventually named The Turks were a sanctuary for pirates of all sorts. Their shallow waters were a no-go zone for deep drafted Spanish ships leaving it a safe haven for raiders, privateers, and criminals. Three hundred years later, the preferred method of transportation may have changed but the basic idea was still the same.

After a little while longer, it was nearing time to start down so we directed our attention to the task at hand. South Caicos had no navigational aids of its own that could give an accurate distance reading. As a result, we had to calculate our distance remaining using our own dead reckoning and taking cross bearings from the beacons at Grand Turk and Providenciales. There was also no control tower at Caicos, so Miami Center handed us off to Provo Control only as a formality, and they in turn, cleared us for a visual approach into South Caicos.

At roughly 120 miles out from Caicos we committed ourselves to start down. The airpace ahead of us was empty so we closed the throttles to begin an uninterrupted idle descent. And as we got lower, the earth below us appeared in greater detail.

In general, our planet provided a neverending parade of beautiful sights for an aviator to enjoy but The Bahamian and Caicos archipelagos were a special treat to the airborne observer. Its clear aquamarine waters speckled with white and green islands always left us glued to the windshield. Even astronauts, who had the best perch of all, unanimously agreed that the Bahmaian chain had the most beautiful geography on the globe.

Compared to our usual world of electronic navigation, we were enjoying the challenge of navigating by visual references as much as we were enjoying the view. But we had to be careful. The island of South Caicos is only a few miles across and therefore, easy to miss but we were confident in our calculations. As we continued to descend we lost the advantage of height for making our navigational observations, but at the appropriate time a small island did indeed appear where it should have been. There was no control tower with a fellow airman on the ground who could verify our approach so we compared the view out the window with the chart. We also carried a copy of the Caribbean Pilot's Guide. It was a more detailed handbook, which included pictures and detailed navigational notes for each airport in the region.

We compared what we saw out the window with what was in the handbook. This double checking was especially critical when navigating through a byzantine archipelago. Most of the hundreds of small islands were featureless and each had its own small runway. It was easy to confuse islands and landing at the wrong airport was considered bad form. Especially if there was no fuel available to fill empty tanks.

We finished our navigation problem and were confident everything checked as it should have. The handbook and our view out the window matched exactly. The island held just a single crumbling concrete slab for a runway. It was situated on a limestone plateau just barely above sea level, with a single concrete building on the southwest side of the airport. A marshy lagoon lay on one side of the runway and a bay on the other. That was, indeed, South Caicos and we landed uneventfully.

Chapter 49

A Change of Plans

O nce the attorney had left us to go into town, we prepared everything for a quick departure to Miami. That only took a short while and we then waited patiently, standing by the airplane in the blazing sun trying to find a cool spot in the meager shade. While we were killing time, I wandered into the small concrete block building that passed for a passenger terminal. Inside I found an enormously obese local woman who was selling oil paintings. She was sitting in a darkened anteroom on a tiny chair that strained under her weight. She was wearing a bright yellow cotton dress. The paintings on her table depicted local waterfront scenes and were done in the primitive style by a Haitain artist. They were a bargain at five dollars each so I bought two. Although, I have to admit her radiant smile helped close the deal. I returned to the airplane and continued to wait with Inderbitzin, watching the sun creep closer to the horizon.

After a while, an ancient Ford Econoline van came through the airport gate. Molina, the attorney, was in the front seat and the van was filled. I counted seven more people. And I thought we were going to be heavy getting out of here. I glanced at my watch. We had about 40 minutes to sunset. Plenty of time.

As the van passengers filed out I could see they were dirty and haggard looking. I suppose that an airplane crash and spending two days in a Caribbean jail would do that to a person.They were a mixed crew of Anglos and Latins. All of them were wearing faded dungarees with dingy, oil stained pilot shirts. That was about typical. Airplanes of the DC-4 generation were dirty and sooty affairs and their pilots wore that grime permanently on their uniforms, but these guys were dirtier than most.

They huddled around the airplane door, eager to board. Most were smoking cigarettes, and one was already inside the airplane, starting in on the scotch. As for me, I was eager to get going also.

The attorney Molina looked to me and made an announcement.

"There has been a change of plans. We're going to San Jose."

"Which San Jose?"

"Costa Rica."

"OK...Why?"

"They all just want to go straight home. Can you get off by sunset?"

This was a major change of plans. By itself, it was not that big of a deal but we had a major time constraint.

"OK, we are going to need some extra time to refile a different flight plan, and make the proper customs notifications. It's going to take a while."

I glanced at the sun. We were then down to about 30 minutes of daylight.

Inderbitzin was already in the cockpit and I stuck my head inside to alert him of the change in plans.

"But I already have the flight plan filed back to Miami."

He held up his handiwork. Inderbitzin was a meticulous planner and he had the entire flight plan back to Miami detailed to the last minute and pound of gas.

"Well, just rip it up."

I pulled up the map of the Caribbean in my head. Caicos to San Jose is one of the longest legs in the Caribbean and it was also over one of the longest stretches of uninterrupted water.

I started calculating the navigation problem.

"Dammit" I cursed to myself. We were in the 25, the short range airplane. Just to complicate matters, we were going to have to make a fuel stop.

"Get on the phone and just file a new flight plan with Miami Oceanic Control. You'll just have to do it on the fly. We'll have to stop in Jamaica for gas; so make the destination Kingston. With Montego Bay as the alternate."

I recited the route from memory.

"Just to get out of here, file direct Grand Turk, Upper Blue 882 to Benet intersection, then direct to Manley. That's close enough. It's a little over an hour flight. Don't worry about an accurate estimate for the Kingston boundary. Just use seven miles a minute for a quick time estimate. Once we're airborne we'll figure out the rest. It doesn't have to be pretty. They want to get the hell out of here before the locals change their mind."

Inderbitzin understood the urgency and he was climbing out of the cockpit before I even finished.

"While you're doing the flight plan, I'll go to the customs office and take care of the outbound paperwork."

I cursed again silently. My uniform was already soaking wet from sweat and now it was going to be a while yet before we could get to a dry altitude.

"We have enough fuel for Kingston so we're good on gas. I'll meet you back in the airplane in about 15 minutes. We gotta' get the hell out of here." I looked again at the western horizon.

"Make it fast. We're burning daylight."

Chapter 50

....

Kingston

We lifted off of South Caicos just as the top of the sun's disk sun disappeared under the horizon and we made a left turn towards the southwest. As we raced west towards the setting sun, we climbed back briefly into daylight but eventually the sun outpaced us and 30 minutes into the flight we were in complete darkness.

By now, our passengers had gone through our entire supply of scotch, vodka and rum, as well as all of our beer. When they asked for more, we then broke out our secret stash of Dom Perignon. It was usually reserved for newly-weds and high rollers but we figured that they deserved it. Thus sedated, and safely away from the Turks and Caicos airspace, our passengers fell asleep as we proceeded uneventfully towards Kingston's Manley Airport.

After landing, we parked on an empty piece of asphalt next to the passenger terminal and as we deplaned we were again enveloped in the dark and humid Caribbean night.

Fuel stops on international flights were no simple affair. Not only did we have to take care of the airplane's technical needs, we had several bureaucratic hurdles to clear such as customs and immigration clearances, flight plan approval, and security checks.

I left Inderbitzin to attend to the airplane and file a flight plan, while I looked for the customs office to clear in and out. Dealing with customs was usually the captain's job because this is where we would run into the biggest paperwork hassles. And this is where we would usually be squeezed by officials hungry to exploit weakness. I was hopeful that since this was just a technical stop there wouldn't be much fuss with the immigration officers but in the Caribbean, especially late at night, one could never know what would develop.

I walked off into the heavy night air towards the airline terminal building and entered a side door that opened into a long and dim hallway. There were no signs but this corridor seemed like it would lead somewhere fruitful and I continued deeper into the labyrinth of the building searching for the proper office.

I wandered around for a bit, turned a corner, and found another hallway, this time more brightly lit and walked down that until I found a sign next to an open doorway. It read:

"Jamaica Customs & Immigration"

The room was brightly lit with fluorescent lights and the harsh light bounced off of the stark white walls. There was a battered but formidable oak desk in the middle of the room. It looked to be a leftover from the British colonial days and was out of place against the polished green linoleum floors. The crest of the Jamaican customs service hung on the wall behind the desk. On the crest was the motto of the customs service, "Country Above Self." Alongside it was a picture of the Jamaican Prime Minister. Otherwise, the room was empty.

"Hello?" I called out to no one in particular.

I heard footsteps and a female voice called from outside the hallway. It had a Jamaican lilt and she called out. "Hello, coming!"

I turned towards the door and a female customs officer entered the room. She was tall and strongly muscled. She looked like an athlete. She was wearing a well tailored uniform dress. It was monochromatic khaki color except for the red tabs on her collar and a black web belt that accentuated her waistline. Her name tag read "Campbell."

Our eyes met. And we held our gaze for a second too long. Another second later, we both knew what could be.

She took another moment to collect herself.

"Yes, can I help you?"

"Yes, please. I am flying a private airplane and we just landed from South Caicos. We are transiting to Costa Rica. We will be leaving as soon as we get fuel. Just a crew of two and seven passengers. Here are our customs declarations."

"You know, you're not supposed to be here without an officer first accompanying you."

"The door was open."

She pursed her lips slightly as though she didn't like my assertiveness. I had hoped this was going to be easy but her body language wasn't promising. She seemed the type that put the rules ahead of expediency. I prepared for the worst but I was not in the mood to hassle with Jamaican customs.

She sat down.

"Just take a seat there and I will be right with you."

That was a typical ploy among Caribbean customs officers. Oftentimes, they wouldn't hassle you. They would just make you wait for what seemed to be no reason.

She took a seat herself and started on our paperwork.

While she was working, I couldn't help but stare. She had light brown skin and golden eyes. Her Afro was parted in the middle and combed down to her shoulders.

"Yes," I thought, "definitely an athlete. Probably track and field."

She was only about 20, but she already had sergeant stripes so I guessed she was probably also smart and ambitious.

"Purpose of visit?"

I sighed silently; I already told her. Either she didn't hear me or she is going to play the strictly by the rules customs agent game.

I wanted to say "I already told you"... but I remained polite.

"This is a fuel stop only. We are transiting from The Turks and Caicos to Costa Rica."

She continued to study the paperwork and she went through the passports of each of our passengers and compared them to the names to those on the form. I then relaxed a little. She seemed more interested in the bureaucratic accuracy of our customs documents rather than trying to find any problems to hassle us over.

After a few more minutes of methodical review, she stamped my paperwork with the same practiced efficiency of customs officers around the world. She took a rubber stamp and banged it down on a squishy ink pad, and then banged it down on each of our customers' forms and passports.

Stamp to ink pad, then over to the document, and back again; Squish... Bang... Squish... Bang

Sixteen times in rapid succession.

It was then time for her to hand the paperwork over to me but instead she paused and held her hand firmly on the papers, the papers that were my permission to leave Jamaica.

"Everything appears to be in order, but there is still one thing."

She paused and looked directly at me.

Our eyes locked again. I felt my spine stiffen for what was next. This will be where she would ask for an additional fee.

"Captain… Be careful out there tonight."

I wasn't not sure what she meant.

At first, I thought that was an unusual way to ask for a bribe. But then I realized that wasn't what she wanted.

Still not sure how to respond, I chose to be a little arrogant.

"Thanks, but, I'm always careful."

"Yes, I am sure you are… but tonight feels different. Tonight, the air somehow feels evil."

Oh Christ. I thought. It feels evil? Is this more of that voodoo bullshit?

"Well, thanks for your concern but the weather is forecast to be clear all the way to San Jose."

"I don't mean the weather."

"Well, then what?"

She had a puzzled look on her own face and her eyes looked up slightly as though she was searching for an answer. "I don't know. Things don't feel right tonight and it's just not one thing. I don't know. Just be careful."

"Well, Sergeant…"

I paused and leaned forward and pretended to look at her name badge for the first time.

"Well, Sergeant Campbell, thank you for your concern but I have to be going. Is that all?"

"Yes, Captain, all your paperwork is in order. But one other thing… if you get to San Jose… land her gently."

Now, I figured she was flirting. But that's OK. That, I can handle.

"Thanks, I always do." And I left with a wink.

However, on the way out to back out to the airplane, I realized she said, "if we get to San Jose," not when.

What the hell did she mean by that?

Chapter 51

Fire at Midnight

O ur takeoff into the pitch black sky south of Kingston was uneventful. Inderbitzin was flying and once we leveled off at 41,000 feet he reached down to the lower center control panel and pressed the autopilot engage button. We had been on duty for a long and hectic eight hours and we were eager for a break. As he reached for the autopilot, my eyes followed his finger and I saw the white "On" light illuminate. At the same moment there was a satisfying twitch of the control wheel. This indicated the autopilot was now fully engaged and was following our pre-programmed commands.

Now that we were level with the autopilot taking most of our workload, it was the first opportunity we had to relax in the past several hours. I allowed myself a moment of rest before getting back to the navigational tasks at hand. We had a two hour flight ahead of us and I still had several chores left before we committed ourselves to flying over the darkest and loneliest part of the Caribbean.

I scanned the instruments. The engines were running smoothly at a leisurely 88% RPM. The electrical and hydraulic systems were good; everything was in the green. The air was smooth and everything was rock solid. There were no airways in this part of the Caribbean so we were just flying outbound on the 230 degree radial of the Manley VOR radio beacon. If our quick and dirty navigation was right, then we should be on course for San Jose.

However, San Jose was still over a thousand miles away. That distance was within the capabilities of the airplane but it was close to the limits. And since there were no diversion airports along the way we needed to conserve our fuel. With that in mind, Inderbitzin had selected a cruise speed for max economy. With Kingston receding rapidly behind us and the emptiest part of the Caribbean basin ahead we had to make absolutely certain we could make it. There were no other alternate airports, no other land whatsoever along the way except for San Jose itself. I toggled through the indicators on each fuel tank. The tip tanks by now had drained down to half and the center tank was feeding into the main tanks. I checked the fuel remaining against our current fuel burn and then did some quick math. The numbers came out to my satisfaction so we were going to be OK to continue.

Confident then that we had enough fuel to make it to Costa Rica, the tension of the last few hours drained from my body. The cabin heat was turned up allowing the warm tendrils of hot air to wrap around my ankles and our passengers were again asleep.

Still, I was uneasy. I leaned forward and placed my forehead against the windshield and strained ahead to scan the sky. There was nothing to see. Then I turned back to look out over my left shoulder, through the rearmost part of the cockpit windshield. Nothing, except the flashing strobe lights on our tip tanks illuminating the haze all around us. Each flash of the strobe light reminded me that we were immersed in the gloom of a cirrus shield that had covered the area. That was too bad…I had hoped for a moon.

If I had been able to see directly behind the airplane I would have just caught the lights of Kingston sinking below the horizon. But I couldn't. I looked ahead again and peered into the gloomy darkness.

Over the years, I had learned that there were different kinds of dark in the night sky. Some were clear and crisp, when the pilot revelled in the joy of night flight; and others, like tonight, were fuzzy and claustrophobic. Tonight, the flying was more a duty than pleasure.

I squirmed again in my seat trying to get comfortable. I looked back to search for the crescent moon that I knew should be there but it was still lost in the murk. Finally, I surrendered any hope of celestial guidance. But that was why we had instrument ratings. We didn't need gloriously clear skies to travel. Our technology would guide us to safety and that's what we were trained to do. We were just an infinitesimal dot inside an aluminum and plexiglass bubble in the vast night sky, and it was our job to carry eight tired humans who only wanted to get home.

We continued west for a little while longer and Kingston Control then called to advise us we had reached the limit of their airspace. With their lyrical and happy English, they advised us to call the next air traffic control sector.

I said good night to Kingston as well, and paused. The next controller for this sector was in Panama City. However, I knew we were too far from the

Central American landmass to be in radio contact with the Panamanian Control Center and we would be for some time. We would be out of radio range for at least another hour. There was no rush to call them so, I just hung up the microphone in its cradle.

I double checked the fuel again. It still looked good. It had been over 30 minutes since takeoff and except for radio calls and checklist items, I spoke my first words since we had left Kingston.

"The fuel is looking good. We only burned 2000 pounds so far and at ECON speed we'll land with about an hour and a half of fuel."

I waited for Inderbitzin to respond but he was quiet.

I looked over to my right and saw him bathed in the dim red lights of the cockpit instruments. He was intent on the forward panel. I followed his eyes to where they were focused. It was the electrical panel, which contained several gauges that told us the health of our electrical system. After a second my eyes refocused on the instrument cluster and a movement caught my eye.

It was the ammeter for the left electrical generator. The needle was flickering.

Before I could register an emotion, there was a muffled buzz; the needle pegged to max, then fell to zero. In just an instant later, the instrument panel lights went dim with the loss of half of our electrical supply. And then in another instant, the cockpit lights re-brightened as the right generator faithfully picked up the load from its failed partner, as it was designed to do.

A moment later the cockpit lightened again. Except, this brightening was unwelcome. My eyes were drawn to a bright yellow light on the forward warning panel.

L GEN

Its soft light bathed the cockpit and it allowed me to clearly see Inderbitzin's silhouette across from me.

The light also told me what I already knew. The left generator had dropped off the line. But the light wasn't being completely honest with us. It was a yellow light, and yellow lights were usually only cautionary. They didn't normally signify an emergency; but right then, for us, this was a bigger problem than a yellow caution light would normally indicate. That's because it was night and we were immersed in the clouds without any visual reference.

Even though I had warmed the cabin I felt a chill deep inside my stomach. We had lost half of our electrical capability. The right system had picked up the load but it was straining doing the work of two generators. The reason why we had a problem was that the Lear 25 was designed for short hops around the United States, not long haul oceanic flights. She was powerful and quick but she was not an endurance athlete. As a result she had only minimal redundancy. The engineers when designing the airplane used the assumption that if the airplane were to lose a major system while flying in the United States, there would always be a diversion airport nearby. But here in the middle of the dark Caribbean there was no safe haven for our little ship.

At that moment, all of our electrical needs were dependent on the single remaining generator mounted on the right engine. The generator was mounted against the compressor section of the engine. One side faced the red hot turbine section; the other faced the minus 40 degree night air. It was only about the size of a small loaf of bread and had a one inch diameter shaft spinning at 7000 RPM. It was the only thing keeping us alive in the moment and it was working under enormous stress. I wanted to thank the engineers at Bendix, who worked in some nondescript building in Ohio, that their design was still holding up. Except they were 3,000 miles away and safely in bed at the moment.

If the remaining generator failed there was no other backup. We would have only emergency battery power available and that was only good for about 30 minutes. Or at least, that's what hangar scuttlebutt told us. I recalled the actual guidance from the flight manual and it was even less reassuring. It only offered the briefest of advice. It said in the event of a dual generator failure, "power will be supplied by the batteries for a short period of time."

With no electrical power from either generators or batteries, the outcome would be inevitable. In the inky black sky, we would lose our navigation radios and would be unable to plot a course to a safe haven. Worse, we would lose our attitude gyros and wouldn't be able to orient ourselves up or down. The airplane would tumble out of the sky with only the ocean surface to stop our momentum.

For now, the generator was still operating normally but we had an urgent task at hand. We had to either fix this problem or return to Jamaica. I looked at the ship's clock. It had been 45 minutes since our takeoff from Kingston.

The failed generator was a big problem but we had help close by.

Inderbitzin pulled out a thick binder by his left knee, and shuffled through it in an instant.

"I've got the Generator Failure checklist, want me to run it?"

"Yeah. Go ahead. I've got the airplane. You run the checklist and I'll verify."

Inside that checklist contained the combined wisdom of test pilots and engineers who had worked out every eventuality with cookbook-like recipes of steps to follow for most eventualities. The checklist was like having a very experienced captain sitting beside us telling us what to do.

We went through the checklist together step by step trying to get the generator back on line. At the same time, I was thinking of alternatives.

I knew Kingston was our only escape hatch. If we didn't get this reset, and quickly, we'd have to turn back. There's no way we were going to tempt fate and fly for another two hours with only one generator. But even at our economy cruise speed of 420 knots, Kingston was retreating at seven miles a minute. We would need resolution soon.

We arrived at one of the final items on the checklist.

Inderbitzin read the item.

"Generator Reset Switch - Depress momentarily."

This was the key step that would reinstate the system. We held our breaths as he obeyed the checklist and pressed the generator reset button.

"Damnit!"

Nothing.

The L GEN light still burned brightly.

We were then about 50 minutes from Kingston. If the remaining generator failed then it would then take longer to land in Kingston than the life of our battery.

I was thinking more that turning back was now our only option. We really shouldn't have been screwing around. Every minute we waited to turn back could be another precious minute we might regret having wasted.

Our first attempt at resetting the generator was a failure. But the checklist still offered us some tantalizing help so we persisted. All the while, we flew further on towards the west, and away from Kingston.

We continued through the checklist until there was only one last item.

Inderbitzin read it slowly to ensure we got it right.

"If generator does not come back on the bus,

'Set Generator switch to OFF, then back to GEN'"

We glanced at each other, knowing the implication.

This step instructed us to shut off the circuit completely. If that final step didn't work we would not get a second chance to reset. Or, worse, even if it did work, the sudden electrical load on the failed generator could either break the generator shaft, or cause a surge in the electrical system. Either one could cause another, and more catastrophic, failure.

I looked outside. Still no moon. I knew the lights of Kingston behind us were definitely below the horizon. Our lives were utterly dependent on our manmade electrical power. On just one generator. And on a battery of unknown capacity… a battery with a history of overheating if stressed.

Inderbitzin was waiting for my answer.

I felt cold on the inside. I was looking for any comfort but there was none to come. Instead, I could only offer cold guidance.

"Before we do the final reset. Just in case it still doesn't work; read the next item, just so we'll be ready."

He continued further down the checklist and read the very last step. Rather than give us console, it was more of a somber warning:

"If the generator does not come back on the bus, set the generator switch to OFF. And it must remain OFF for the duration of the flight."

The checklist then advised us of a long list of items that would be unpowered due to the failure; most of which would be necessary for night flight over the ocean.

Inderbitzin paused and looked at me for permission.

I shook my head. "Go ahead… We don't have a choice."

He reached for the switch and cycled it from GEN to OFF, then back to GEN. My eyes were glued to the left generator ammeter. He held it in the GEN position and applied extra pressure on the switch, as though body English would make an electrical circuit work better. I knew it was a useless effort but at that point, I was willing to take any help.

Nothing.

"Try it again."

He toggled the switch again.

"Damnit!"

Still nothing.

We were now 55 minutes out of Kingston. We had to turn back.

I made one last plaintive command.

"All right. Try it one more time. If it doesn't come back, we'll turn back."

He complied. And, he again wiggled the switch, hoping to use mechanical energy to close an electrical circuit.

I then heard a loud buzz along with several loud clicks as the sound of electrical relays cycled. Then the needle on the left ammeter jumped to life.

Yes!

The left generator came to life and we had full power again.

At the same time, the right ammeter dropped to show it had relieved itself of the extra load it was carrying.

I scanned the instrument panel. Everything was stable and in the green. The autopilot was unflustered and still obediently steering the course to San Jose.

We looked at each other across the dark cockpit and smiled. We were still only children who had successfully passed a dangerous moment but we congratulated ourselves as experienced operators.

"It looks like we are back to normal. I think we can continue."

Although, I said it only to convince myself. We still had over an hour and a half to make landfall in Costa Rica. I had decided to proceed, yet I didn't trust the generator. I was on high alert for any more misbehavior on the part of our recalcitrant generator and I continued to stare at the electrical panel.

After a couple more minutes, I was satisfied that the generator was stable. It was only then that I allowed myself a moment to relax and slouch back in my seat.

But then.

A foul odor curdled into my nostrils.

It was smoke.

This was the worst fear of every aviator. Fire at night, and over the water. My gut tightened, and I again tasted the dehumanizing grip of panic rising in my throat. It tasted just like it did back in Medellin on that day when death was looking for me.

However, I was well practiced in the art of facing fear and I slammed it back down.

A few minutes ago, we had worked through a generator failure and I was pleased with how we handled that. But, now, there was no defense against fire on an airplane, no amount of experience or training that made this routine.

It wasn't my imagination. Inderbitzin smelled it also and we saw wisps of smoke floating past the shafts of light cast by the cockpit instrument lights.

"What the hell!?"

"We must have done something to the electrics when we reset the generator."

"I don't know. We followed the checklist." There was no time to trouble-shoot. There was nothing more to talk about. There was only one course of action. And I had to take it now.

I had to swim immediately for the closest safe harbor.

"I'm turning back to Kingston!"

Inderbitzin nodded and he gave me some needed guidance, "OK. Turn to about a heading of zero-five-zero. That will get you pointed back to Kingston."

I reached for the control yoke. My thumb was on the autopilot disconnect switch and I began to squeeze it.

Every second was now crucial. We had to go back to Kingston. It was the only option. But God, it was so far away. We should have begun our diversion at the first hint of trouble. I was angry with myself. I should have turned back at the first sign of trouble.

Goddammit!

The silvery tendrils of smoke had now flooded the cockpit. It was likely the smoke was related to the wayward left generator but I couldn't assume that. And, I couldn't rely on my memory.

"Give me the smoke elimination checklist!"

I squeezed harder on the autopilot disconnect button. I was going to take manual control of the airplane and begin an emergency turn back to Kingston. But it hardly mattered. I had waited too long to turn back. We were going to be dead soon and it was my fault.

I considered calling Kingston Control to advise them but there was no point. It would have only been a desperate cry for help. Even if they heard us from this far away, we were beyond their help and they could have only noted our position for search and rescue teams.

The smoke filled my throat and I slammed down an urge to cough.

I decided not to waste time on radio calls that couldn't help us. I was reminded of what Coe told me so long ago, "Fight the alligator closest to the canoe."

We'd deal with the most pressing crisis first. We'd turn back and then run the checklist. Later, we could call Kingston.

That is, if we were still alive.

Inderbitzin knew what to do and had already pulled out a different binder. On the cover, in large block letters were the words:

EMERGENCY CHECKLISTS

I already knew what it said and I didn't like it. If the problem was electrical, it was going to direct us to begin shutting down our electrical systems in order to isolate the problem. And if that didn't solve the problem, then we would have to depressurize the airplane to clear the smoke. And if we did have to shut down our generators, then we'd be lucky enough to get back to Kingston before the batteries died. But if the fire continued unabated, it would ultimately consume the airplane. We were in the middle of a pitch black sky with a sick airplane, with too many ifs, and with only shitty options.

Inderbitzin appeared calm. He was not showing the inner turmoil he too must have felt. He clutched the binder tightly like a supplicant holding a prayer book. But instead of divine intervention he was again seeking the wisdom of the experts back in Wichita, all of whom were, like the Bendix engineers, surely sleeping soundly in their beds right now. His reverence towards the binder was not a meaningless gesture. If we followed its directions slowly and properly, it could save us from my own foolishness.

He flipped through the pages to find the proper checklist. My left thumb squeezed the autopilot disconnect button on the control yoke and I felt the spring in the button begin to give way to my pressure.

I squeezed the disconnect switch harder.

We were turning back. But we were still an hour away from land.

Then, a scream from behind me.

"FIRE!"

And then another scream.

"I'm on fire!"

Then the roar of more voices.

I turned to look but the passenger cabin was also filled with smoke. I only saw the shadows of men piling on top of each other.

They were all moving towards the front and the airplane lurched forward as the center of gravity shifted abruptly. I guessed they were trying to run from the fire.

I held pressure on the disconnect switch but paused. It was halfway down, the relay was just a fraction of a millimeter from disconnecting. But I hesitated. Without my final command, the electronic brain that was the autopilot; the brain that did not know fear, or have judgement, was still dutifully flying us towards San Jose.

I relaxed the pressure on the autopilot disconnect switch. It was too late now to turn back. With a fire in the cabin, we had only minutes to live. A retreat to Kingston would have only been an empty gesture at that point. Perhaps, we could radio a distress call to the empty sky. Maybe someone might have heard us and report it to the authorities. Hopefully then, the accident investigators would have some idea of what happened to us. At least people would know that we didn't screw up and get into Mach tuck. Our disappearance would be attributed to a fire, and not our fault.

Inderbitzin turned back towards the back of the cabin. From his seat he had the best angle to witness first hand what was happening.

There was one more scream and then a grunt.

The commotion died off quickly and the crisis passed.

"What the hell happened?"

Inderbitzin saw it all.

"The guy in the first row? His chest caught on fire."

"What do you mean his chest caught fire? That was the smoke?"

"Yeah, after we took off, he found our secret bottle of scotch and finished that off. He then reclined his chair and was smoking a cigarette. Then the stupid shit fell asleep. Or passed out, more like it.

He passed out with a lit cigarette still in his lips. It fell onto his chest hair and caught fire. It was smoldering for a while. That's what we were smelling. Everyone was asleep so no one smelled the smoke except us. We thought it was an electrical fire. It wasn't until the guy felt the pain of his chest on fire that he started screaming and woke everyone up."

"Jesus! You're shitting me. He really caught himself on fire?"

We weren't going to die after all.

My thumb was still resting on the disconnect switch and I pulled it away.

The cabin had quieted down and I called back to our passengers.

"Jesus Christ guys. Do me a favor, and no more smoking until we land."

I turned to Inderbitzin.

"Fuck! I can't take this shit."

I scanned the instruments again. All the systems on the airplane, including the left generator, were stable and running true. Nothing was wrong with the airplane. And we knew smoke was harmless. For the fourth time that night, I allowed myself to relax.

I asked Inderbitzin, "Everything seems OK. You good to continue?"

He responded with a laugh. "Yeah, just as long as you keep them from smoking."

I smiled and checked the fuel again. It all looked good and we pressed on through the dark night.

Chapter 52

···

A Woman's Intuition

We continued to fly southwest towards the Central American isthmus, and as we did, the sky above us slowly cleared. Our spirits raised a bit as the stars became visible, although we were still concerned about San Jose weather. Our forecast was several hours old and San Jose was notorious for developing late night fog banks.

When we were about an hour out from San Jose, we heard a Pan American jet on the frequency, heading to Miami. Their radio call sign was "Clipper" which was a modern day salute to their ancestors, the 19th century clipper ships. Those sailing vessels were strong and muscular and considered some of the most beautiful ships ever built. They were relatively small and designed to get valuable Chinese tea to western markets as fast as possible.

Clipper ship captains had one goal, and one goal only: speed. They were known to carry full sail day or night; in weather fair or foul, and they were constantly setting records across all the world's oceans. In airplane parlance they were always traveling at redline and probably had their own go fast switches. Despite their glamour, many of them disappeared without a trace while enroute. Then, their reign was cut short by steam power. Afterwards, the word "clipper" entered the lexicon to describe speed.

PanAm was equally as glamorous. They pioneered transoceanic air travel and had become the world's premier airline. They held a mythical status among most aviators and their pilots were like demigods, even more so than the Eastern pilots.

I knew the PanAm pilots had a modern suite of long range radios onboard and could pull up the weather for anywhere in the world with a finger's touch. This late at night, the frequency was quiet so I queried them for the latest San Jose weather. A friendly voice responded and a moment later they advised us that the weather waiting for us in Costa Rica was good with no changes expected for the rest of the night.

I could, of course, have gotten the weather from the Panamanian controllers but it was somehow more comforting hearing an American voice. They were so much higher than us in the aviation hierarchy but in the moment we were brother airmen passing in the sky. And even though I briefly envied the Pan Am pilots, I loved the Learjet and I was pleased to be her captain.

I knew they were off to our left and below us; and we would be crossing paths on perpendicular airways. I studied the sky in a direction where I thought they might have been.

The night, by now, was ablaze with the white swaths of the late night constellations filling every inch of the sky. And then in the immensity of the heavens, their red rotating beacon stood out clearly, moving rapidly to the north. I continued to watch their movement. Once they got close enough we could see their tail logo light was on, which illuminated the famous blue ball Pan Am logo. For a thousand miles in either direction, the only color in the sky was the blue Pan Am logo and their red beacon.We watched them pass in silence until they disappeared over the northern horizon and then, we were, once again, alone in the sky.

Our night had now become sweet but nonetheless, I was still eager to get this flight over with. We still had about one hour to go. Our passengers were all asleep again and a sense of calm came over the whole airplane. For the first time in several hours, my breathing had slowed, and I felt like talking.

"Back in Kingston, the customs officer? She was a woman."

"Oh yeah?"

"She was a young woman, and good looking too."

"That's always nice but what about it?"

"She said something funny."

"What do you mean funny?"

"She said for us to be careful."

"Careful?… Of what?"

"I don't know. She just said the sky was evil tonight. Just like that. Like she knew something we didn't. I thought she was flirting."

"Evil? That sounds creepy. How can the sky be evil? You think she was into that Rastafarian stuff?"

"You mean voodoo? They're different things. But no, she was too clean cut."

"She did say she was a brownie, though."

"What's that?"

"She's mixed race. Half white, half black. That's what they call them in Jamaica, although I think it's not meant as a compliment. She said her grandfather was white, an Irishman."

"You were pretty chatty with her, was that what took you so long?"

I didn't feel like answering, so I lied.

"I got lost on the way back."

"Well, does that mean she is supposed to have some kind of special powers?"

"No, I don't think so. But she did seem to have a sixth sense. Just more like woman's intuition."

"What else did she say?"

"Well, she said when we got to San Jose, we were supposed to land the airplane gently."

Inderbitzin laughed. And his quick retort was the false bravado pilots are known for.

"Well, I always land the airplane gently."

We both laughed again, but it was just more bravado and our laughter didn't help our confidence as we whistled past the graveyard.

Just prior to top of descent, the clouds below us eventually parted allowing us to see the glow of San Jose far off to the west. And I finally got my moon, a thin crescent hanging low over the horizon.

The city of San Jose lay in the Central Valley of Costa Rica. It was not as challenging as Medellin or Guatemala but since it was the first time there for either of us, we still approached with caution. Inderbitzin made an uneventful instrument letdown into the valley, which had us fly over the airport and then make a teardrop descent back to the airport.

It was a wide curving letdown with idle power and 210 knots. It was my favorite phase of flight. The engines were quiet and we just glided down at high speed. This was the type of powered flight that most approximated the pure flight of birds. As we turned back towards the runway, we put the gear down and we felt it thunk as it locked into place. At this point every pilot's natural focus was on the landing gear indicator lights to get a visual confirmation of the gear being in position for landing. The normal indication was for three green lights. One for each gear. But instead, the indicator panel remained blank.

"Now what?!"

I reflexively checked the fuel. We had about an hour left. Enough to work a gear problem. But not a whole lot more.

We entered a holding pattern over a sleeping city while, for the third time that night, we dutifully read through an emergency checklist. This time, we quickly determined there was only a problem in the indicator circuit. We were confident that the landing gear was safely locked down; but just as a precaution I instructed Inderbitzin to land the airplane as gently as possible to test the landing gear before putting the full weight of the airplane on them. Inderbitzin was a talented pilot and he was known for smooth landings so he was the right man to do the landing.

We circled around and descended towards the runway and he did, in fact, land her gently. Our touchdown in San Jose was met by cheers from our passengers. Their relief to be home was palpable.

Once we parked the airplane, we were met by a large convoy of black Chevy Suburbans. A few men got out. They looked American. They were physically well built, were wearing cargo pants, and had short haircuts. Our passengers jumped into the cars and departed the airport grounds without even clearing customs, leaving Inderbitzin and me standing alone.

He turned to me.

"Do you still believe that bullshit about them flying beef?"

"What do you mean?"

"I don't know exactly. But if they were really just a ragtag group of tramp freighter pilots they wouldn't have been greeted with the VIP treatment. Those guys who picked them up were with the government. No doubt."

"Well, whatever they are, we did our job and got them here."

I really wasn't interested in knowing anything more about them so I used that statement to signal the end of the conversation.

As for us, we spent the night in San Jose and slept soundly before heading back to Miami the next morning. We were also given some additional rest when the scheduling gods rewarded us with a few weeks of uneventful daytime flying in the American Midwest. All the while, I thought of the admonition that night from the Jamaican customs agent; and also of the truism that the guess of a woman is much more accurate than the certainty of a man.

Chapter 53

Providenciales

The orange sun was setting behind a distant white thunderhead as we approached the island of Providenciales. We were flying an empty Lear 24 up from Caracas so we were light enough to have climbed up to 450. We were flying in perfect conditions and the airplane was behaving well. Normally, I would have liked to have lingered in the air but this evening, I was eager to get on the ground. The reason was that we always had pleasant overnights on Providenciales. Our favorite bar was just a tiki hut on an isolated beach where the fish was superb and the beer was cold. Because the sky was benign, I instructed the copilot to hand fly the airplane and speed right up to the redline, the airplane's maximum Mach speed. It would get us in a little early and it would be good for him to get the experience. Flying at the maximum speed and maximum altitude would place us right at the extreme knife's edge of the airplane's performance envelope, high up in coffin corner. It was good practice for times he might need to do it for real.

The copilot on this trip was Chipman. He had been intently listening to the identifying signal for the Non Directional Beacon (NDB) on Providenciales, or as it was commonly called "Provo." He was one of our better copilots, same as Inderbitzin and Rohwedder, and he took to Lear flying like a natural. We had all been instructors at the same flight school and he was about a year behind me in his aviation path. He was just a bit shorter than me and had black wavy hair with a lush black moustache. Chipman was not only an excellent pilot but he had an infectious laugh and was popular with everyone in the flight department.

He lowered the volume on the receiver.

"The beacon is identified. I'm getting a little static from those distant thunderstorms but other than that, it's a good strong signal. If it's OK with you, we should probably start down about 150 miles out."

The NDB was an ancient piece of technology that had survived into the modern era and was the simplest form of radio navigation. It was a ground based radio that would transmit a constant signal in every direction. Our receiver on the airplane then would simply point a needle on the instrument panel directly towards the station for us to home in on.

It seemed easy enough to use, but the NDB was prone to errors and had a couple limitations. One, was that it was difficult to fly accurately the closer an airplane flew to the station. As a result, it didn't have the necessary precision for approaches in very low visibility. It could only guide the airplane to within a few miles of the airport, and then the pilot would have to proceed visually. The second was that it was prone to error when there were electrical disturbances in the atmosphere. But it was effective over very long distances and the ground transmitter was inexpensive to install and maintain, making it ideal for tropical airports with limited budgets.

It was always difficult to navigate in a byzantine archipelago like The Bahamas or Turks. The area was a labyrinthe with several thousand square miles of islands, islets, cays, atolls, and sand spits. Few of which had any true defining landmarks and many of the shapes undulated with the daily tide. It was very easy to confuse islands even in good weather. The NDB, while not perfect, would guide us in well enough.

It was Chipman's leg into Provo but as the captain, it was my call to commit to landing there. I had already done the math in my head and also decided we needed to start down about 150 miles out. Satisfied that our math agreed, I made one last check of our fuel before making the decision to start the descent. I clicked through all five fuel tanks. We had plenty; enough to make an approach in Provo; and if we had to, enough to divert to Grand Turk, about 50 miles away.

"Everything looks good. You can start down whenever you want."

For the past 30 minutes, I had also been looking to the northern horizon. About one hundred miles ahead, there were several active thunderstorms but they were far away and wouldn't affect our approach. Chipman reduced the power to idle and as he pushed the nose over, he clicked in a unit of nose down trim. As we descended he continued to fine tune the pitch to keep the airplane right at the redline. The air between us and our landing airport was clear and smooth, which was going to allow us to keep our speed up. I looked below us and saw the blue ocean had become a dull gray. Night was coming and Provo was an unlit airport. Speed was now no longer a training exercise but an imperative. We had to land before nightfall. But it wouldn't have mattered even if we were early. That's just how we always flew the Lear. Always at the red line, always on the edge.

I recalculated our ETA in my head.

"It looks like we'll get there right at official sunset."

Chipman was a trustworthy pilot but as part of the descent checklist, I confirmed the Morse Code identifier for the Provo NDB myself. Authenticating the other pilot's work wasn't done to question their ability. It was just a normal safety check. When safety was at stake, we constantly double checked each other's work, and then double checked it again.

"You're right, it's a strong signal but the static interference from those storms on the horizon is getting worse."

"Is that going to be a problem?"

"Shouldn't be. Electrical storms always interfere with the signal but they're pretty far away. But the thing is, at night the low frequency radio waves bounce off the ionosphere so as the sun sets we might get some interference from another station far away. Expect the needle to fluctuate, but the conditions are visual and we only have to get close enough to pick up the landmarks around the airport."

As we descended through 10,000 feet, I kept an eye on the storms ahead. In the waning daylight, we could see the cloud to cloud lightning was flashing with increasing frequency. I looked again at our direction finder needle. The electrical interference was getting worse and the needle was becoming more erratic as it was disturbed by their electrical discharges.

We had descended to 3,000 and we became fully immersed in the twilight. The earth below us had by then lost all color as I searched for the airport.. It was Chipman's leg but it was also his first time into Provo so I coached him through it.

"OK, we're about 20 miles out. Just like we briefed, fly direct to the beacon and pass overhead at 2,000 feet. Once we cross it, turn to a 280 heading and descend to 800 feet. Don't chase the needle. Just average out the swings. There's no crosswind so that heading should line us up with the runway."

We continued on a bit longer and I calculated that we were about 10 miles from the navigation beacon, but that was mostly just a guess on my part. Provo didn't have any distance measure electronic navigation aids so we were navigating now not much different than the sailors from an earlier age. I was just using a compass and a clock to hold a heading towards land. I glanced down but the irregular maze of islets below us offered no visual clues. I was fairly certain we were on course, but we would only know our exact location once the main body of Provo came into view.

The sky around us was smooth but the lightning from the distant storms was causing even more interference to the direction finder. I was still monitoring the Morse Code identifier. Each time there was a lightning strike in the invisible distance, the radio receiver would crackle sharply. I would lose the signal briefly and the needle on the instrument panel would swing wildly, 30-40 degrees left and right.

Chipman knew what to do and was doing a good job of hand flying the airplane but I added a little more guidance.

"Everything is looking good." And I then repeated my earlier guidance. "Don't chase the needle. Just average out the swings and hold a heading. It is visual at the airport so it doesn't have to be exact. We just need to get close."

Chipman's flying was precise but he still deadpanned, "Now I know why it's called a non precision approach for a reason."

We had now descended to 2,000 feet and slowed to 180 knots. We continued patiently on course until the needle on our instrument panel swung around to show the NDB was now behind us.

That was the Final Approach Fix and it was time to start down. Chipman made a turn to a 280 heading. At the same time he commanded me to lower the landing gear and select full flaps. He slowed to our final approach speed and began a steady descent to the airport, which was still invisible to us. I punched the stopwatch on the instrument panel clock.

"Two minutes and thirty seconds on this heading and we should pick up the airport."

It was getting increasingly dark. Not only was the sun setting but with each foot of descent we were flying deeper into the earth's shadow. I could still see the silhouette of the island shoreline along with a few lights along the beach but mostly we were immersed in the twilight gloom. We were going to barely land by sunset. That was, if we could find the airport right away. We had slowed to 130 knots and were now skimming the surface at the minimum allowable altitude of 800 feet. We could descend no further until we saw the runway. Chipman remained focused on the instruments while I searched for any visual clues. He was doing a good job flying the airplane so I was able to concentrate on the outside with only a few brief cross checks inside.

I turned on our landing lights and two powerful shafts of light stabbed the primordial landscape ahead of us.

He queried me, "See the runway yet?"

"Not yet. Just some ground contact. Hold 800 feet and maintain this heading."

Another few seconds went by and as I tried to compare the irregular coast-line with the shapes on the map. It was sort of making sense and then the shadow of a runway came into view.

"Runway in sight. Straight ahead!

Chipman, looked up. He instinctively pulled back the power slightly to begin a descent again.

"In sight, landing!"

He continued down and then made a faultless landing at the empty airport. By the time we cleared customs and buttoned the airplane up for the night, we were completely enveloped in the tropical night.

Chapter 54

Tranquility

We drove along a dark and rutted gravel road to the hotel in a fossilized Ford sedan that had only one operating headlight. It was a brief ride to the northern side of Provo where we pulled up to the darkened hotel. Of course, calling it a hotel was a stretch. It was a simple affair consisting of a small concrete block building with a corrugated tin roof. More of a hovel than a hotel, it was located on an empty stretch of flat beach where for most of eternity it was populated only by seagrass, sea turtle nests, and ocean waves. The main building was only a few yards from the water's edge and had only two small rooms. In the front, was a makeshift lobby, housing a pine table as a front desk. In the back was a kitchen with a stove powered by a rusty propane tank. Both rooms were dimly lit by a single bare bulb hanging from frayed electrical cords. The so-called lobby was ostensibly cooled by a decrepit ceiling fan, rotating only fast enough to wobble but not move any appreciable amount of air. Alongside the main building was a row of five outbuildings. Each was a one room plywood shanty, which is where we to be lodged for the night. More importantly, and the main reason why we selected this seaside inn, was that off to the side of the lobby was a tiki hut, which is where Chipman and I agreed to meet.

A few minutes later, I was sitting under the thatch roof of the empty tiki hut sipping my first Heineken, which I had by now realized, was pretty much the national beer of the Caribbean. A sole kerosene lantern hung from the middle of the ceiling lit the area. The lantern looked like it was attached to the ceiling more by cobwebs than by the single rusty nail from which it hung. The tiki didn't need a fan because a breeze was coming on shore. Chipman showed up and we sat at a rusty pink linoleum kitchen table that was in the style of mid century America. The tiki had no man made floor so I dug my bare toes into the cool sand.

The front desk clerk, who also doubled as bartender, waiter, manager, housekeeper, and cashier, was barefoot himself. His name was Dennis and he came out from the kitchen and served us two more ice cold Heinekens. He was wearing shorts, and a T-shirt advertising his devotion to the Jamaican reggae star, Gregory Isaacs. I slipped back into my chair and enjoyed this moment in my life. The beer went down smoothly and I melted into my chair. I had, in my own eyes, become an accomplished aviator. I flew the airplane well. I respected the copilots I flew with; and they, in turn, respected me.

Chipman was a cheery flying partner and our conversation was lighthearted but after our second beer, the conversation went silent. We watched the thunderstorms continue to light up the northern horizon with the only sound being the hiss of the kerosene lamp and the gentle waves kissing the shoreline and then pulling themselves back out to sea.

The waiter again came out of the kitchen then walked over to a make-shift wooden cupboard. Sitting on the middle shelf was a Zenith shortwave radio. Its black Bakelite cladding was mildewed on the corners. On the top of the console was a map of the world etched into the plastic, a pamphlet of radio station frequencies, and a makeshift compass to orient the antenna properly. He flipped a switch and the vacuum tubes inside came to life, glowing a soft orange.

After the electrodes in the receiver were properly warmed up, he began scrolling through the dial, stopping at various stations that represented the various outposts of the old British Empire. The first was a BBC news broadcast. The announcer spoke English with a heightened pronunciation; you know, the sort of accent used by imperturbable and very important men who had led an empire.

"Foreign ministers from 12 countries including the United States and the Soviet Union met today..."

But that broadcast was cut short by a squall of static. That was because the shortwave radio used frequencies very close to our NDB frequencies. As a result, the faraway electrical storms that had affected our navigation radios when we were trying to land were also affecting the short wave reception.

The crackle of the static died off and the broadcast then came back into tune.

"Representatives from the National Front for the Liberation of Angola."

And then broadcast was again interrupted by a crackle of static from the storm. The waiter, then scrolled to another frequency.

"A meeting regarding the Congo rebels opened today…" But interrupted again by the crackle of static.

He scrolled again to a new frequency.

"This is BBC World Service"… crackle… "A powerful storm struck the island of Tonga yesterday"… crackle… "loss of life is said to have"… crackle…

Our host continued in this fashion until he found satisfactory reception from a station transmitting a cricket game between South Africa and Sri Lanka. Satisfied with the reception on this frequency, he left to get us two more beers. As they clunked down on the table he gave us a lesson in international politics.

"You know man, you are listening to a rebel game."

"What's a rebel game?"

"The South Africans? They've been banned from international cricket competitions due to apartheid."

"So, how come they're playing now"?

"Sri Lanka is a fledgling team. They're willing to play anyone just to get publicity. Too bad, though for Sri Lanka. They're a good team and don't have to play South Africa to get exposure. Now, the entire cricket world is ostracizing Sri Lanka just the same as South Africa."

The bartender seemed good natured about the whole thing but he then exposed the raw nature of how sports wasn't completely insulated from politics.

"The Sri Lankans? They're traitors for defying the ban. They're going to be banned for life."

"For life?"

"Yeah, man. We gotta' break from the imperialist past. A clean break, ya' know?"

We were now into our fourth or fifth beer. Dennis the bartender/waiter/front desk clerk/reggae aficionado had joined us at the table and tutored us on the wretchedness of the imperial damage done to the Caribbean people over the centuries. It was his dream to recreate a new Caribbean; built for the Caribbeans. Or a "cultural reconstruction" as he called it.

I watched the dying electrical storm continue to flash lightning against the black horizon as I absorbed Dennis's wisdom until he said his piece. I was tired but not yet ready for bed. There was nothing else to do on that lonely beach so I listened silently to the cricket game late into the night wondering how the whole world was much more connected than I had ever thought possible.

After a while, sleepiness, along with a chill wind, drove us back to our rooms for the night. They were equally as simple as the hotel lobby. It contained a tired old bed, a dim battery powered lamp, and that was it. I cranked open the jalousie windows and the thin curtains blew inward from the ocean breeze.

Provo was just a tiny outpost, a flat spit of sand, located at the tip of a lonely archipelago, which itself was on remote sea, but it was comforting to be here. I had faced many challenges in the past and I had survived. I had become confident in my craft. I loved being in the air and I loved my airplane. However, for right now, I was happy to be here on the ground rather than in the sky fighting those nighttime storms. I slipped off into a satisfied sleep, unaware of even greater challenges ahead.

Chapter 55

Iquitos

I opened the door of our airplane and stepped into the humid night. Chipman was again my copilot. He joined me at the foot of the airplane stairs. He was new to South American flying but I was glad to have him on this trip. He was a good stick and a steady and calm operator. In addition, he had an intuitive understanding of our style of flying.

"What now?" he asked.

I looked at my watch. It was 3 AM.

I took a deep breath and the fetid air from the neighboring river bank filled my lungs. I waited to answer, partly to calm my nerves, and partly to collect my thoughts. I had never been to this lonely airport before so I was unsure of what to expect from the local officials. I peered into the darkness but there was nothing to see. All the lights at the airport had been turned off. I didn't think things were going to turn out well here; and I instinctively clung to the small pool of light from our cabin door entry light.

"I don't know."

An hour ago, we were level at 43,000 feet making good time to Lima. That was, until Lima Control ordered us to land short in Iquitos. All they said was that Lima was closed due to weather below landing minimums.

The night sky over the Amazon had been silky smooth as we had passed through the Intertropical Convergence Zone. The ITCZ, as it was known, was a broad area straddling the equator where the opposing weather patterns from the Northern and Southern hemispheres clashed to create an area of intense thunderstorms. But tonight, the entire region had been silky smooth.

We were, as usual, in a rush to respond to a last minute call. Chipman had the flying duties on the leg to Lima and because of the unusually smooth air, he was able to run the engines hard and flew the airplane right at the red line. We were flying a Lear 35 that night, probably the best of all the Learjet models. It had increased range, modern navigation aids, and most importantly, it had much more docile handling characteristics than the earlier models. It was a pleasure to fly; but now, we were standing on a barren ramp in Iquitos, at the far western edge of the Amazon River Basin.

"Well, we still need to get to Lima. We need gas and to file a flight plan. But we have to wait for Lima weather to clear."

"How long do you think that will be?"

"A couple hours probably... maybe longer. The Lima airport sits right on the Pacific Coastline. The cold ocean currents come up against the dry mainland air and they get a lot of morning fog. Just like in California. You just have to wait for the morning sun to burn it off. I thought we could beat the weather but I guess not. That's why the controller had us stop here."

Those steps were the obvious ones. But then I mentioned the harder part.

"First thing, though, is we have to find a customs officer to clear in the country but they're not going to be happy we dropped in unexpectedly, especially in the middle of the night. They're going to levy a hefty fine."

"A fine? I thought clearing flights was their job?"

"It is. But sometimes they can be difficult."

"What do you mean difficult?"

At that point, I found myself repeating what my earlier captains had told me when I was new to the game.

"They don't get paid very much. Airplanes like ours dropping in are like manna from heaven. They're going to find something wrong with our paperwork or give us grief for not having a proper clearance since we were supposed to be in Lima. Whatever. They'll just come up with some bullshit reason to shake us down. They will expect us to offer to pay a fine."

"Isn't that a bribe?"

"Not really, it's just a handling fee to smooth over any discrepancies."

"That sounds like a bribe."

"Well whatever you want to call it. It's nothing personal, just the cost of doing business. 'Mordida' they call it, 'the bite.'"

"How much?"

"Depends on their rank. Middle of the night, we might get lucky and just get a sergeant. Just a few bucks. If it is a lieutenant, maybe a couple hundred dollars. Cash. American money, of course. We might even be able to negotiate a little. Toss in a few cans of Coca-Cola and maybe a couple of issues of

Playboy, and everyone's happy. But if a Major or Colonel smells blood and shows up, forget it.

"How much do they want?"

"Five hundred, maybe a thousand. The sky's the limit, it's all negotiable but you just don't know. It depends on how well connected they are politically and what kind of mood they're in. They might even impound the airplane. Two years ago, they took Bobby Harris's airplane up in Cartagena. It was a really nice 24. It's still sitting there off in the grass. He's still trying to get it back. Although, there's not much left of it now. It's been stripped clean."

I peered out into the abyss and still saw nothing. My eyes had not adjusted to the night, because this far up the Amazon, there was no light at all in which to adjust. Instead, my eyes just swam out of focus and I leaned against the cool aluminum fuselage for reassurance.

A stray mosquito buzzed past my ear. The swampy Nanay River was just on the other side of the airport fence. It was a sinuous tributary of the Amazon and our scent has already made it to the riverbank. A couple of the mosquitoes already knew we were here and surely there would be more to come.

Chipman was eager for some movement.

"Let's see if we can find someone."

"Where? I can't even see beyond the nose of the airplane. We'll get lost and then if the National Police find us wandering around, that will just cause more trouble. Those guys don't answer to anyone."

The dark was oppressive and getting claustrophobic. The airport was so quiet that I could hear my own ears ringing. Dark and quiet, a death pall surrounded us. The hot and humid air had enveloped us now for only five minutes and my skin was crawling. I knew it would only be a matter of time before something other than the mosquitoes also smelled us. And I didn't have long to wait.

From out in the darkness, I heard a muffled roar. It was the sound of a heavy diesel engine straining under acceleration. It seemed like it was heading towards us. The sound fell off. Then, the sound of gears grinding as the driver shifted into second gear. The engine sound rose again, still straining under a higher gear, still heading our way. I looked out again but the black revealed nothing. The heat, humidity, mosquitoes and uncertainty weighed me down. The roar was still rising but we didn't know from what direction. The black night was overpowering, made worse by the ominous roar heading our way. Chipman and I shifted closer together, clinging to our small pool of light.

Suddenly, a set of headlights turned on and showered us in white light. A large truck swung around from behind the tail of the airplane. It was painted olive green and it came to a swift and squeaking halt just in front of us. A thin man jumped out of the right seat. He was wearing khakis. He was hard to see in the dark but he was looking straight at us. He turned his back to us and barked some commands in Spanish to the driver. We heard a muffled "Si Señor!", followed by the sound of boots hitting the pavement hard.

The khaki clad man turned towards us again, paused, and was joined by two young armed soldiers. From the dark he walked towards us and his form took on a more definite shape.

I saw the insignia of a Colonel in the Peruvian National Police. And twenty minutes later, I was in his office.

It was now close to 4 AM. I should have been home in my bed. Instead, I was alone, standing in the Colonel's office under the harsh glare of fluorescent lights. He was of medium height and thin but well muscled. He wore his khaki uniform tightly tailored. He wore a thick thick black belt highlighting his thin waistline to show he had not a bit of body fat. He was close to 50 years old but his close cropped hair was jet black and his aquiline nose highlighted his native heritage. If we had met five hundred years earlier, he would have been an Incan knight battling the conquistadores.

He took a seat in a squeaky office chair while I continued to stand. Unlike my inquisition with Ragsdale, there was no cold air conditioner blowing on my neck. The room was hot and stifling.

I was hesitant to speak first. I thought about offering him mordida but I was uncertain. I felt for the wad of cash in my pocket. It had always been a reliable friend that had gotten me out of trouble before. It was waiting for me again and I was ready to count it out. However, as I stood there I got the sense something bigger was in play. So I waited. But my usual security blanket of cash didn't make me feel any better.

His English was excellent.

"Why are you here?"

"Lima was fogged in. The airport was closed so air traffic control told us to stop here."

My answer didn't satisfy him as he sat ramrod straight in his chair.

"I understand that but what do you have to gain by coming here?"

"I am on a commercial flight. I have nothing to gain. We are supposed to go to Lima to pick up a passenger."

My answer still didn't satisfy him.

"Why do you come here and meddle in our lives?"

I didn't like this line of questioning so I tried to avoid his eyes but I could see his gaze tightening on me.

"I don't understand Colonel. I am not meddling. I would just like to pass through."

"You say that. Just like all the others have said that. But then they stayed. And they destroyed us."

I just wanted out and searched my mind for a solution but I couldn't find one. I wasn't sure what he wanted so I retreated to my old reliable exit strategy.

"I am sorry if I violated a law. If there is a fine, I would be glad to pay it now."

And I hated myself as soon as I said it.

He shook his head.

"That is exactly what I mean. You come here and you find the weak members of our society. You bribe them and you promise them power so you can take over. But after you take over, you enslave everyone. The Spanish did it first. They were only a tiny force of men. It would have been impossible for them to overthrow the Inca. But they took advantage of our differences and convinced some of our own people to join them in defeating the emperor.

"That was the worst. The Spanish conquest of South America was the greatest geopolitical disaster in the history of the world. And we were betrayed by those closest to us. Then you, the North Americans, with your Monroe Doctrine, decided you could humiliate us at your will."

I noticed he referred to me as a North American. I had learned earlier that everyone else in the hemisphere considered themselves Americans as well. They resented that people from the United States kept that appellation for themselves. This was also not the first time I heard about the Monroe Doctrine. The people here also resented how the United States claimed rights over South American without, in turn, taking much responsibility for it.

"Then the Germans came. They didn't care about us either, they only had designs on their own American empire. And then with the Cold War, the Russians came. None of them cared about us. They only wanted to control what we had. We have been fighting the Europeans for centuries."

I thought about responding but I didn't want a replay of the scolding I got back in Guatemala. So, I just shut up.

"Now, your so-called businessmen come here with enormous amounts of money to feed your country's drug habits. They make themselves rich but leave us with death and corruption."

I had held back long enough. Then, as usual, I couldn't help myself. And I told him the justification I had used before. I had used it so many times before. It was very believable. Who knows, maybe I even believed it myself.

"Colonel, you are a soldier. You must understand this. I am just like you. They tell me where to go and I go. It is only a job for me."

"It's not so easy young man. You surely know who it is you are carrying? His picture is in all the newspapers. And I have seen him on your airplane before."

I had, long ago, stopped being the righteous American. I had also stopped trying to understand people's motivations. And even less, I stopped trying to get people to see matters as I did. I just wanted to survive the day and move on. So, I gave him what I thought was a satisfactory response.

"He's just a passenger, just like any other. We only fly him to his vacation home. That is all we do. Nothing more."

He smiled.

"Yes. Just keep telling yourself that. Maybe you will eventually really believe it yourself someday. You are just trying to justify your actions. You are only deluding yourself and you must accept your role in all of this."

I wasn't sure where any of this was going but I knew I could no longer defend myself under his scrutiny. That's because I realized that I was face to face with the fourth type of customs official. The rarest one of all. The one Gal-Nur had warned me about… the most dangerous one.

Here was an honest man. A man who couldn't be bought. And, I had no defense against his honesty other than to admit he was right.

I also remembered my conversation with the vodou priestess back in Port-au-Prince. Back when I had not yet lost my idealism. I told her that even if a person had only a small role in an injustice, they still couldn't deny any culpability. She disagreed and said people had to do what was necessary to survive. At the time, I spurned her point of view. Now, I realized, I had become like her.

I stood silently for I had nothing left to say.

The colonel's mood then shifted.

"Your passenger? I know him. We went to school together. We were once friends and I am sad to see what he has become. I know he is waiting for you in Lima. And I would like to stop you here. I would like to stop him, but your paperwork is all in proper order. I am sorry for what has happened to my country. Someday, you will go home and you will be fine. But we will be left to deal with the problems. I am sorry for my country but I am even more sorry for you. You don't understand what you are doing, my friend. You must learn to differentiate between right and wrong."

He paused and he slumped down slightly in his chair.

We both waited in silence while he collected his thoughts.

"That is all I have to say. Once the weather clears you are free to go."

And I left him alone in his office.

Shortly afterwards, we did take off again for Lima. It was just a short hop and I let Chipman fly that leg also. I wasn't in the mood for flying. Actually, I wasn't in the mood for much of anything. My bag of cash intended for mordida was unmolested, but my conversation with the Peruvian colonel deep in the Amazonian swamp had left me enormously sad.

Chapter 56

....

Some Deaths Come Slowly

Tito Ascano was dying and it was my job to get him back home. At the time, it was to be my furthest venture deep into the heart of South America. But Lyndee assigned me the trip almost casually.

"We have a trip to Asuncion. It's an air ambulance trip."

"OK."

"The patient is in Aruba. So you'll have to pick him up there first."

Before she finished her sentence, I began to plan the flight in my mind. In the 35, we could make Aruba non stop, and then from Aruba, we could then make Asuncion with only just one stop, probably in Manaus. It would be a long trip but not a big deal.

Lyndee interrupted my mental calculation.

"It's a long trip so we are assigning three pilots, all of them captains. Since you've had more time flying in South America, you'll be the pilot in command. You'll be going with Benny and Doc Miller. Benny is the first copilot and Doctor Miller will be the relief pilot when he's not tending the patient."

I wasn't happy about the crew selection.

"You're assigning me with Benny?"

"Yeah, sorry about that but he's the only other captain available. Anyway, Doc Miller is in Key West right now and you'll have to stop there first to pick him up.

This was another complication and another fuel stop. The trip was already going to be long and grueling. An extra stop just to get Doc was an extra stop that was neither necessary nor welcome.

"Dammit Lyndee. Do we have to detour to take the doc? Isn't someone else available?"

"Can't do it. It's Doc Miller's patient. You know the deal. He gives us the charter and in exchange he gets some pilot time in the airplane."

She was right. Doc Miller was a licensed pilot and wasn't a bad stick but when we were carrying his own patient, he got distracted from his flying duties. If we wanted the trip, then he had to come along. Otherwise, he'd charter it out to someone else.

"Oh yeah, and there's one other thing."

She was about to reveal even more unwelcome news.

"The 35 isn't available, so the trip is in the 24."

"The 24! You're kidding? You know that means we'll have to hopscotch our way down. That's going to require two or three extra fuel stops and a lot of extra work You're sure we can't take the 35?"

"Sorry, the owner has it booked this weekend."

And before I could protest further, she wished me good luck and hung up. I was then left to fret over the flight as I packed my bag.

An hour later I was at the airport where Benny and I met each other warily. He was polite but his resentment was seething below the surface.

"You know, I should be the captain on this trip. I have more time on the airplane than you."

"Yeah, I know. I'm sorry about that, but that's what they decided. But, anyway, I'll need your help; this is the farthest south either of us have been and it's a long trip. Doc Miller will probably be busy with the patient so it will mostly be just me and you. We'll have to support each other. You can fly the first leg, if you want."

This didn't seem to satisfy his ego. He stomped one foot and responded with a curt "whatever" and turned away to finish his preflight checks.

We prepared the airplane quickly and when it was time to go, I closed the door behind me and looked back into the cabin. It was crowded with medical supplies. The entire right side of the cabin was taken up with a stretcher and we had several oxygen bottles secured around the remaining passenger seats with enough medical oxygen to last for the long trip. Every other storage compartment in the airplane was filled with enough food and water to last us so we didn't get delayed waiting for catering anywhere along the way. I also ordered three extra cases of Prist for the journey. Prist was an anti-icing fuel additive and the airplane ate it up like candy. It was as if we had our personal car packed for a long road trip. In addition to medical supplies and food, I was also carrying enough cash to pay for fuel for the entire round trip, and to cover any other eventuality along the way. Just for good measure, we had also loaded a case of scotch to help negotiate with any willful bureaucrats we might meet along the way.

It was just after 4 PM when we finally took off for Key West to begin our odyssey into the deep south. After a 45 minute hop down to Key West we found Doc Miller already waiting for us at the tiny passenger terminal. He was wearing green scrubs and had a small tote bag. He was standing under a large sign on the terminal building that that read "Welcome to the Conch Republic."

He walked to the airplane. Doc Miller was in his 50s and had a slight limp. But like many physicians he was full of energy and acted much younger than his years. He had a very busy practice in Miami and although he may have been a doctor preoccupied with medical matters, he was still an instinctive aviator who knew how to prioritize things.

"The fuel truck is on its way and I already cleared us out with customs. Are you ready, otherwise?"

We had left Fort Lauderdale with a full tank of gas so we only needed about two hundred gallons in Key West to top off again. While we waited for the fueler to add gas, we quickly briefed the first leg. It would be a two and a half hour flight to Aruba. We would pick up the patient and then press on further south.

"Doc, once we board the patient, you'll be busy. Why don't you fly the first leg? Benny will be the copilot and after that we'll swap legs."

Benny didn't say anything. I could tell he chafed at the prospect of pulling gear for Doc Miller but that was tough shit. We were all rated pilots and we had a long marathon ahead of us. We had to put our egos aside and row together as a team.

With our fuel tanks filled for the long flight across the Caribbean, we were back in the air in short order, and level at 410. From the back I watched Doc Miller fly the airplane. The truest test of pilot competency in the Learjet was the ability to fly the airplane solo if he had to, and Doc could certainly do that. Doc was a pretty good stick but, like some other doctors and businessmen pilots, he was so preoccupied with his other duties, he really needed a strong copilot to help keep him out of trouble.

Doctors and pilots. It was an interesting dynamic. Both were very smart guys who had a desire to do something different than the rest of society. Many doctors pursued aviation as an avocation and many pilots would tell you they considered being doctors. Each just gravitated to the career that suited them best. However, despite their career divergence in early life, pilots and doctors tended to be simpatico partners later in life.

As we cruised to Aruba, I had tried to rest but I was too restless. Complicating matters was I couldn't find a comfortable spot anywhere in the cabin among all the medical supplies. Instead, my curiosity about our patient won over. I crawled back up to the cockpit and sat on a crate of water bottles just behind the two pilots.

I watched Doc for a while. Like many other early model Lears, the auto-pilot had been acting up lately so it was deferred inoperative leaving Doc to hand fly the airplane. That was another pearl. A flight all the way to Asuncion with no autopilot. I didn't want to distract Doc but things were quiet and he was doing a good job holding altitude within 20 feet.

"Hey Doc, What's the deal with our pickup?"

Doc maintained his concentration flying the airplane and remained glued to the instruments. He wasn't being impolite. It's just what pilots would often do. We could converse while maintaining eye contact only with the instruments.

"Our patient? He is a petroleum engineer for Esso. He's an interesting guy. I've flown him before on regular charters. He's from Paraguay. Over the years, he has traveled the world, and being in the oil business he has been to some really remote parts of the world. During his free time, he visited the local in-digenous people around the drilling operations. He's a semi-professional an-thropologist and he's amassed quite a collection of ethnic memorabilia. It's all museum quality stuff."

"Lyndee said he was dying."

"Yes. It's pretty bad. He has a rare blood disease and there is no treatment available. He probably only has a couple of days left. Maybe even less time given the stress of traveling on the airplane. There's not much the hospital can do for him, and even less on the airplane. But he wanted to get back home to see his wife one last time. The thing is, that once we get going, I expect his condition to worsen. He may not even live to see Asuncion."

"Really? It's that bad? Since we're in the 24, we're going to have to make three stops on the way. That's probably going to add another 3-4 hours. What's worse, is with this many fuel stops on the way, anything can happen."

I had earlier studied the chart for South America and had already made the final decision on our route.

"After Aruba, we'll stop in Caracas, Manaus, and Santa Cruz, Bolivia."

Doc Miller turned to look at me.

"Santa Cruz?…You're kidding right? You know they're notorious for causing problems."

"Yeah, I don't like it either but we're flying over the emptiest part of South America. If we were in the 35 we could have overflown Bolivia altogether. But in the 24, we have to get some fuel. There really is nowhere else to stop unless we detour east to Brasilia. But from what you tell me the patient doesn't have that kind of time. So Santa Cruz it's going to have to be. Hopefully, it won't be too much of a hassle."

"Yeah, hopefully."

I then went to the back of the cabin to try to rest a bit more before our long marathon south. Doc was certainly right about one thing. There wasn't much medical care we could provide on the airplane. Calling us an air ambulance was a stretch. Any patient would likely have gotten better care in the back of a pickup truck. Air ambulance flights in the Lear were mostly just a way to get someone home before they died.

Once I sat down, I tried several different unsuccessful contortions trying to find a comfortable spot in the overflowing cabin. Ultimately, I was able to find a suitable position using an oxygen tank as a footrest. And so situated, I looked out the main window. The sun was already low in the sky and we would be doing most of the trip in the dark. Not ideal, but nighttime flying was the nature of Lear charters in South America, and we were all used to it. We still had about ten hours of flying ahead of us and I was able to catnap a bit until the pressure change of our descent into Aruba woke me.

The pickup and turn in Aruba was lighting fast and we were already airborne for our short hop to Caracas. I was back in the left seat; with Doc Miller now in the back tending to our patient. I was mostly concentrating on flying but I did get a chance to examine Tito for myself. He was about 45 years old but he looked boyish. When he was lifted through the door of the airplane he sat up in the stretcher and greeted me with a toothy white smile and a strong handshake.

When I closed the door of the airplane in Aruba, I wanted a private moment with Doc Miller. I was looking for his assessment of whether we could take the extra time and avoid Santa Cruz. But he looked worried as he was setting up Tito on oxygen so I didn't bother him. After we took off, it was only a 45 minute hop over to Caracas. Doc was still busy but I wanted to talk about it anyway.

I mentioned to Benny. "Maybe if the patient is doing better we can detour over to Brasília."

"Whatever you want to do but it's probably Doc's call."

"We could maybe stretch the next leg as far as Corumba."

"That wasn't the original plan. Why do you want to change it?"

"I'm dreading dealing with the Bolivian officials."

Benny's advice was no advice at all. "Well, you should have thought of that before. But if you want to change it, then it's on you."

"Yeah, we'll decide in Manaus. That's still about 5 hours away. By then we'll have a good idea of how he is doing. I really don't want to stop in Santa Cruz."

The fuel stop in Caracas also went quickly and we were back in the air with Benny at the controls again and Doc Miller still in the back tending to our patient. The sky was then fully dark as we headed further south towards our next fuel stop.

As per our flight plan, we were headed in the general direction of Manaus. The reason why I say that we were flying in the general direction was that in this undeveloped part of the world, there was, ahead of us, a 600 mile gap in modern air traffic structure. And as a result, we had no precise way to navigate. We started out flying outbound on Upper Mike 417. It was an airway that would guide us directly to Manaus. However, the radio beacon we were tracking outbound from Caracas was a VOR radio that used a VHF frequency. And being VHF, it was designed for short range navigation only. As we continued south at seven miles a minute, the signal from Caracas became increasingly weak. Until finally at 200 miles south of Caracas the navigation instruments gave up completely.

On both sides of the cockpit, all four navigation needles went limp and red failure flags dropped across their faces, signifying they were done assisting us. Our little airplane had been transported back in time to the 1920s when the earliest aviation pioneers navigated across hostile distances using dead reckoning, which is to say, nothing more than with a compass and a watch. There was also no radar coverage to watch over us. Outside the airplane our red rotating beacon was the only thing that signaled our position to an otherwise empty sky.

I had triple checked my navigation and announced to Benny.

"I figure we just need to hold a heading of 161 degrees.There's no cross wind so we don't need to account for drift. It's 900 more miles to Manaus so we should pick up their VOR in about an hour and a half, maybe a bit longer. Once we pick up the Manaus radio beacon, we can correct for any drift that I didn't account for."

"That's kind of half ass, isn't it?"

I wanted to remind him that was just how we did it. But he knew. He was purposely being difficult so I saw no need to justify myself. If we had been in a Lear 35, we would have had the luxury of having long range navigation onboard. But we were not in a 35. We were in a first generation Lear 24 equipped only with short range electronic navigation capabilities which, in this lonely part of the planet meant we had none. So, we made do with dead reckoning.

Adding to our workload, the autopilot was out of service and we were hand flying. Benny was an exceptionally good pilot but he had one human deficiency shared by every pilot. When hand flying over long periods of time, fatigue would set in and one's flying became less precise. That was important because not only did the autopilot relieve our workload, it could hold a course much more precisely than a human who was hand flying. With a human at the controls, over the course of the next hour and a half, it was likely that our navigation would get sloppy.

Benny was very sensitive to critique but I offered it as a form of encouragement.

"Our heading is drifting to the right slightly. But it should work out. We're high enough that by the time we pick up the Manaus VOR it will be early enough to correct any course errors easily."

"Don't worry about me. You gave me a heading and I'll fly it. If your navigation was correct, then I'll get us there." And we continued in that manner for the next 900 dark miles without any further conversation.

And it was exactly 90 minutes later when we picked up the first flicker of life on the VOR navigation receiver. A few minutes after that, the red failure flags retracted and the directional needles locked onto the signal from Manaus showing we were exactly on course.

Manaus, itself was another lonely outpost in the middle of the vast

Amazon basin and it was a relief to see the lights of the city on the horizon, a lone galaxy in the middle of the unpopulated Brazil hinterlands. After calling Manaus Control on VHF, we began our descent into the notorious Brazilian bureaucracy. You see, the Brazilians weren't interested in mordida, just proper paperwork. Therefore, once we landed, every official, at every step of the process, had to examine our paperwork in great detail. Everything had to be in triplicate and once a particular bureaucrat was satisfied that everything was in order, they then had to check and recheck with every other fellow bureaucrat to ensure that each bit of minutiae was painstakingly accurate. And then each of those bureaucrats had to check with their peers. It was a slow and aggravating process. I had to admit, maybe those other countries that took a little bite had it right. A little cash could speed the wheels of commerce and help everyone out.

However, there was one thing that the bureaucrats throughout the region had in common. And that one thing gave us an advantage. They loved to have each document stamped with some kind of seal from a government agency. If you could produce a piece of paper that had a stamp, or, better yet, a raised seal on it then it became carte blanche. As though stamps had some sort of magic power.

One of our workarounds was that we would carry blank flight plan forms. We would stamp them with our own rubber stamp that said simply, "AP-PROVED: MIAMI, FLORIDA, USA" and then fill out the remarks section with whatever information the bureaucrat seemed to want at the time and hand them in. We, of course, had an ample supply and freely handed out those forms with the meaningless stamps. These forms would look as if we had received some sort of official approval when leaving the United States and they made many of our fueling stops go smoothly. That night in Manaus the ersatz approval forms worked as usual and we were on our way again quickly.

Doc Miller was flying the leg to Santa Cruz and Benny was on break in the back. By now the sun had risen and we were again in a section of empty airspace. Without much to do, I was fighting off a bout of drowsiness without much success. I knew that if I could hold off the urge to sleep for another hour my body will then be fully back on its circadian wakefulness. I wasn't in the mood for more caffeine so I turned to conversation.

"So, Doc, how is he doing?"

"Not great. He's getting weaker. It's a good thing you decided to flight plan us straight through Santa Cruz. Going around Bolivia would have taken too long."

"Will he make it?"

"It will be close. How far are we?"

I did some quick math in my head.

"Another hour and a half to Santa Cruz. Hopefully, we can turn the airplane in just an hour there. Then another two hours to Asuncion..In total? Five hours, maybe less."

Doc Miller frowned.

I looked at the Mach meter. The morning air was still and we were going about as fast as we could, speeding down to the Tropic of Capricorn.

"I wish I had better news, Doc, we've been flying at the redline the whole trip. There's not much more we can do and we're still a long way from Asuncion."

I wanted to give Doc Miller more speed but the Lear was notoriously unforgiving if pushed past her limits. As it was, hand flying all night long, at max speed, and with three tired pilots was pretty risky. We were, ourselves, running at our own limits.

"I've done everything I can do medically. We're just racing the clock now."

I looked back. Tito was lying face up on the stretcher. The window shades were all drawn and in the darkened cabin I could see his face. He was asleep and ashen; or maybe he was already dead. I couldn't tell.

"So, what's his deal? This charter wasn't cheap so he must be pretty well off if he can afford it."

Doc pressed his lips tight to suppress a smile but the corners of his mouth still turned up.

"Yeah, Tito… he's a good guy. We met in Paraguay when I was down there as a medical student doing relief work. His family are Guarani Indian. You know, the Guarani had a shit experience with the Europeans."

"Well, I didn't think any of the indigenous had it easy. What was so special about the Guarani?"

"Well, when the Spanish showed up, there were two separate groups of Guarani. One group were nomadic and warlike so they were able to defend themselves. But the ones that lived in the area that is now Paraguay were more sedentary and agricultural. The Spanish saw the Guarani as an easy source of slaves and let Portuguese pirates come in, to go on slave hunting expeditions. The agricultural Guarani were easy pickings. The pirates usually came on Sundays during the church service. It was easier to capture an entire village all at once that way. The Jesuit missionaries tried to put a stop to it, but the Spanish priests who put up too much resistance were usually just killed outright."

"Where did they end up?"

"Usually in Sao Paulo, and Rio. Almost the entire population ended up in slavery. But then, some Jesuit priest got the Pope and the Spanish king to forbid their enslavement.

"Well, I'll bet that was easier said than done."

"Yes. Of course. The bishop of Asuncion and the provincial governors opposed it. They made a nice living out of the slave trade. But here's the thing. The Spanish king also allowed the Guarani to arm themselves and they ended up forming a militia headed by the Jesuits.

Things change, of course, when you have guns to defend yourself. Over time, the Guarani repelled all the Portuguese invasions and formed the modern Paraguayan state as we know it. Most of the citizens of Paraguay are Guarani. They make up the whole merchant class and many of them are politically powerful; pretty much as it was before the Spanish ever showed up. But the problem is the full blooded Europeans in Paraguay still rule the country. And, just like in colonial days, the Spanish ruling class and Guarani are still at odds."

Doc Miller went on about the history of Paraguay but I had stopped listening to him. My mind was preoccupied worrying about our transit in Santa Cruz. That was, until he said something that caught my attention.

"Which is why I didn't think they'd let us in."

"What do you mean, 'You didn't think they'd let us in'... Who isn't going to let us in?"

"The Paraguayan government."

"Why wouldn't they let us in?"

"Tito. That's why. Paraguay is run by Alfredo Stroessner. It's one of the harshest dictatorships in South America and his family are dissidents. Any opposition to the government in Paraguay, no matter how mild, is met with prison, torture, or death; usually a combination of all three. You did get landing permission ahead of time from their Ministry of the Interior, with Tito's name on the manifest, right?"

"No. I was just going to file a regular flight plan once we landed in Santa Cruz and then just list him as a passenger on the custom's declaration once we landed in Asuncion. Nobody told me about getting prior approval."

Doc sighed.

"Tito is persona non grata with the Stroessner regime. Well, I guess it's too late now to do anything about it. We'll just have to deal with it when we land there."

Of course, by saying, "we," he actually meant me. And I just added it as just another item on my list of unpleasant things about this trip as we came in range of Santa Cruz.

Chapter 57

Purchasing Safe Passage

We landed at the old Trompillo Airport in Santa Cruz and we parked the airplane in front of the airline terminal. Trompillo was slated to be closed in a few weeks in favor of the new Viru Viru airport under construction. As a result, the locals had let the airport and runway go to seed.

As we pulled in, the sound of our engines scattered a family of chickens that had been feeding on the grass percolating up from the cracks in the tarmac. The terminal itself was a small brown building built in the stark brutalist style favored by the Germans who came to South America in the early 20th century. Those German settlers were investors and businessmen but for many, their main goal was to spread National Socialist ideals throughout the region. And sadly, many of their policies regarding torture and human rights violations took hold among the local ruling class.

Santa Cruz was the largest city in Bolivia and far different from La Paz, which was only 300 miles away. Whereas, La Paz sat in the thin air of an arid high altitude plain, Santa Cruz was in the steamy tropical lowlands. The city was located on the muddy banks of the Piray River, which fed into the Amazon basin. The air in Santa Cruz was thick and once we shut down the airplane, it was dripping with condensation; and we, ourselves, were drenched in our own sweat.

Even the local people were different. In La Paz, the residents were mostly Aymara people. The weather was cold and the women favored the warmth of the traditional colorful pleated skirts and bowler hats. Here, in Santa Cruz, we were close to Paraguay and in the historical range of the Guarani. In the debilitating heat of the local climate they wore western garb that leaned towards hand-me down shorts and T-shirts.

A large group of locals clung to the airport fence observing the airport's comings and goings. We were an unusual diversion for the onlookers, flying an airplane that didn't pass through Santa Cruz very often. Our sleek white jet contrasted sharply with the ramshackle terminal and the usual derelict air freighters found so frequently in South America. We looked different, we dressed different, we didn't speak Spanish very well; and worse, we lacked appreciation of the local culture. In short, we were in a neighborhood where we didn't belong, and I was eager to get going.

It took a little while to get the fuelers to come out, and to take care of the necessary flight planning. But, overall, things seemed to be progressing faster than usual so I was pleased with my decision to chance a transit through Bolivia. I had delegated the customs processing to Benny. He was taking a little longer than I expected but he eventually came out of the terminal building.

"There's a guy in there who says he's from Civil Aviation, whatever that is. He won't clear us out of the country. He says our landing permit isn't correct and he wants to see you."

"He asked for me personally?"

"Yes, he mentioned your name. He had a copy of the flight plan and you are listed as the pilot in command of record. As soon as he saw your name, he got really difficult."

"Yeah, what's wrong with the landing permit? We cleared out of Manaus properly."

"I don't know. He didn't say. You're the captain. He wanted to see you. You go in there and deal with it."

I left to go find the office and Doc Miller followed me. Once I got there, I walked into the office and looked at the officer behind the desk.

"Damnit!"

It was the same officer who harassed Farmer and me last year and forced us to go back to Rio de Janeiro. That was the trip where one of our passengers fell from a hotel balcony...or was pushed, depending on who you wanted to believe. It's a long story for a different day but we were detained by the Brazilian police for several days pending an investigation.

The Brazilians eventually released us to leave. We got out of there as fast as we could but we had to make a fuel stop in Santa Cruz. By the time we did get to Santa Cruz, the Brazilians changed their minds and called ahead to the Santa Cruz authorities to order us back to Rio. The Bolivian officer who gave us that order was now sitting in front of me.

We both looked at each other and I knew what I had to do.

"Hey Doc, do you mind going out to the airplane to check on the fuel?"

I knew the fuel was fine. But, I had some negotiating to do. And I just wanted some privacy. Doc left the room.

The officer behind the desk was a bureaucrat with the Civil Aviation authority. He was about 40 years old and wearing a tan uniform. He had a full head of hair that was graying prematurely. Over his left breast pocket was the insignia of the local Civil Aviation authority. It was the Bolivian national crest surrounded by a wreath; and an embroidered Andean condor with its wings spread menacingly above the crest.

He smiled.

"Hello, Captain. You didn't think you would see me again?"

The guy was trouble for us last year and I knew he would be trouble again, but I also knew he had a price.

This time, we were in a rush and he knew it. I figured about a thousand should do it. But if it was more, I didn't care; I wasn't in the mood to negotiate. I was willing to peel off whatever the toll was going to be in order to get Tito home, but I still had to play hard to get.

I ignored his question. We were beginning a game of poker and I opened the pot.

"Good morning, Señor. I understand there is a problem with our landing permit. I am very sorry about the misunderstanding. If there is a fine, I am willing to pay it right now… to you… in cash."

He nodded and didn't say anything. I pulled out a wad of $100 bills. I flipped out two of them and looked at him.

He raised the ante and shook his head.

I flipped out a third bill. He wanted more and raised the ante again.

"Captain, this is the second time you have landed here without proper permission. Remember, the last time? We made you return to Rio to get the proper papers."

I thought about it. There was no way he was going to send us back to Manaus with a dying patient on the airplane.

I flipped out a fourth bill and I then called his bluff.

"I am sorry for the problem. This seems to be a violation that maybe you can't handle. Perhaps we should call the airport director?"

At that suggestion, he stiffened and I knew the balance of power had shifted. If I insisted he call in his boss, one of two things would happen. The boss would either take a large share of the mordida for himself; or if his boss were honest, he would reprimand the official and send me on my way.

While he was thinking about it, I was willing to give him an extra incentive. I flipped out a fifth bill.

And he nodded his approval.

A few minutes later, I came back out into the daylight. Doc was inside the airplane tending to Tito, who was looking much worse. Benny was standing by the airplane.

I asked, "Are we ready?"

"Yeah, just waiting for you. What happened in there?"

"Nothing. We're cleared to go. Let's just get the hell out of here as fast as we can."

And then, we were airborne again for our last leg to Asuncion. This portion of the trip was only about an hour and a half. However, the airways between Santa Cruz and Asuncion were circuitous so I decided to speed things up a bit by flying direct to Asuncion. All the airspace over this desolate part of Paraguay was non radar so no one would know. It was fine. The sky was empty anyway and it saved us about 10 minutes.

Chapter 58

A Good Death

We landed in the furnace that was Asuncion a bit earlier than even we expected. I taxied over to the airline terminal under the direction of the control tower and we shut down the engines. It was 18 hours after leaving Fort Lauderdale and 3800 miles away from home.

I opened the door onto an empty ramp area. I had heard that Paraguay was the American Outback and as I scanned the far horizon I believed it. Asuncion was located on the edge of the region known as the Gran Chaco, which was an arid savannah known for scorching summers. It was mid afternoon and the temperature was well over 100, with a humidity level as bad as Miami. Unfortunately Asuncion didn't have the advantage of cooling trade winds and the hot concrete shimmered all around us.

We were parked next to a large and modern airline terminal building but it was empty. Everything was hot and quiet. And the silence roared in my ears.

We continued to wait outside the airplane for the customs officials to meet us, while Doc remained inside the airplane and attended to our patient. I had closed the door to preserve what little cool air was left in the cabin. I wanted to run the air conditioner but we had to conserve the batteries. There was no guarantee we could find a power cart so we had to hoard battery power for our engine start. And that was just as well. The batteries had a locking circuit anyway preventing them from powering the air conditioning for that exact reason.

And then, a woman appeared. She was wearing a blue linen dress. She was dark complexioned and had black wavy hair. Her cheeks had some scarring from a childhood pox and they were swollen from crying. She fingered a gold crucifix on her necklace. She said her name was Zully and she was Tito's wife. She was also in her mid 40s. Like Tito, she also looked young for her age, although she appeared tired. I didn't know how she got into the airport but there she was, and she wanted to see her husband.

Benny was unsympathetic.

"Don't let her in. We are quarantined. You know that. We can't have any contact with anyone until we get a customs clearance. If they see her, they'll probably arrest her and maybe even us. You heard what the Doc said about the government here."

However, I didn't care about bureaucratic niceties.

"So what? We'll just add her to the declaration and pretend she came in with us. They'll never know the difference."

"Don't let her in the airplane!" And then he walked off to attend to some other matter, leaving the decision to me.

I opened the hatch and looked to Doc Miller. He shook his head in a silent no. We were quarantined but I didn't care and I let her in the airplane. If the customs agents got upset, then I would just have to deal with it later.

Zully climbed in the cabin and Doc Miller left the airplane to make room for her. She lay down next to her husband; both squeezed in on the narrow stretcher. He opened his eyes and they started sobbing while in each other's embrace. I looked away and as I was about to close the door, Benny reappeared and saw that I had let the dying man's wife in the airplane. He was furious that I let her board, especially since he already warned me not to allow her in.

"Get her out of here," he hissed.

I returned his stare. "Just get away from me."

"If we get in trouble with customs it will be your fault."

"I said... go... away."

And he stomped off.

I was 27 years old, and despite the four stripes on my shoulders, I was still just a boy. Who was I to say who could spend time with whom, especially if they loved each other. My father warned me that blind adherence to a bureaucracy was only for the stupid, or for the frightened. It was an easy concept for me to grasp because I naturally resisted authority. I reached up and gently lowered the cabin door so Tito Ascano, an engineer, a student of humanity, a dissident, and a loving husband, could spend his last minutes on earth with his beloved wife.

By the time the Paraguayan customs officers had shown up, Tito had already died. And despite the quarantine violation, they were entirely sympathetic to Señora Ascano's loss. After Tito's body was taken away, the three of us, Benny, Doc Miller, and myself, stood around the airplane that was waiting patiently. Normally, we would have straightened the cabin and wiped the soot off the engines but that seemed a vanity. Instead, we stood in silence. We had successfully completed the charter but it felt more like failure.

I was tired and emotionally drained, and I just wanted to get home. The entire trip had unnerved me and I wanted to get back. And not just back to home. I wanted to get back to how I was. I wanted my innocence back.

"Well, gentlemen, there's no reason to stay here. Unless you have any objections, let's head back." Everyone nodded and, it was without any enthusiasm, we retraced our steps back home to wait again for the next phone call.

Chapter 59

Into the Black Hole

It was 4 AM in Port-au-Prince and chaos had descended over the city.

The Duvalier regime, which had been putrefying for years, was now in its final death throes, and the Haitian elites were getting out any way they could. The best way out... the only way out, really... was through the international airport in Port-au-Prince, which was why I had again been summoned to this mournful island.

Marsch was with me and we had been waiting in anticipation of the arrival of an unknown passenger. We had parked near the passenger terminal and although we were inside the relative safety of the international airport, the crack of rifle fire had been getting closer.

Our dispatcher had assigned two captains to this trip in anticipation of trouble. She chose Marsch and me. He was just 25 years old, making me the old man, but he was wise, well beyond his age. It had been an hour since we had said anything to each other, but we didn't have to. Although we had only known each other for a few short months, we were like minded on almost all matters.

I took a draw from my last cigarette and tossed it aside. Marsch was not one who used an excess of words but he took this opportunity to make an observation.

"This feels like Saigon."

I glanced at him. His pink scalp was visible beneath his thinning blond hair and it was beaded with sweat.

"You're kind of young to have been in Vietnam."

Even in the dark I could see his jaw tighten and the tendons in his neck pulse. He looked away so I decided to drop that line of questioning and instead pondered what had brought me here.

The phone call for this charter came at 11 PM. Of course, that was, by itself, not unusual. There was always some crisis brewing and by the time someone decided on the need for a Lear charter, it was usually late in the evening when we were notified. I was asleep when I picked up the phone and the voice on the other side of the line was a familiar one. Although we had never met, we had done business several times before. I didn't even know his name but he was representing some agency in Washington, D.C. That much, I was sure of. Or, at least, as sure as I could be of something like that. His requests were always shrouded in some mystery but over time, we had developed an implicit relationship. The voice on the other side of the phone would always explain how to perform the charter in exact detail. And we would always complete the charter exactly as prescribed. In exchange, his payment was instantaneous and it was always wired from an account in Grand Cayman. Probably not by coincidence, he always sent us to a city that was getting heavy press coverage in the Miami Herald; always a city in the throes of some political turmoil. And no matter where we went, we had plenty of strangers who showed up willing to help expedite our transit; and without expecting the usual bribes. The passengers on those flights always looked to be in some kind of trouble and needed to suddenly and quickly get out of wherever it was they happened to be. And, like with all of our customers, we never asked any questions.

Right after the phone call, I had rubbed the sleep out of my eyes and drove to the airport through the dark streets of Fort Lauderdale as quickly as I could, with the exception of that one quick stop for a carton of cigarettes.

Marsch had already arrived at the airplane and had finished the preflight. During our quick briefing we agreed that I was to fly the leg down in the left seat and then we'd swap seats and Marsch would fly us back.

We knew that we had to fly down to Port-au-Prince for a pickup. That was about all we knew, so that was the extent of our briefing. It was only a two hour flight but we did agree to taking a full tank of gas. I learned a long time ago that when flying into lonely airports in the middle of the night that extra fuel was always my friend. We filed a flight plan with Miami Center, and then we were on our way.

We were at the International Airport at Fort Lauderdale and we taxied out to the end of Runway 9 Left. The airport was quiet at that hour and I reached the runway with no delay. Once on the runway, I held the brakes. I toggled through the fuel selector panel one last time. Satisfied we had enough fuel, I scanned the cockpit. The warm yellow lights of the instrument panel in our little cocoon were all reassuring. I looked down the cold runway. We were pointed down a black slot of concrete outlined by the bright white runway lights. Beyond the runway end lay the coastline and the dark Atlantic Ocean. The engines were idling patiently as we then reviewed the last checklist items. Everything was good. I toggled through the fuel selector panel one last time. It was time to depart. We were the only airplane movement on the field and the tower had already cleared us for takeoff while we were still taxiing out. At this point, we only needed our own permission for takeoff.

"Ready to go to Haiti?"

Marsch nodded.

"OK. Let's go to work."

I released the brakes and advanced the throttles about halfway and paused to let the engines stabilize.

We began rolling slowly and I took one last scan of the engine instruments. Everything looked good so I pushed the power all the way up to 100%. With that increase to maximum power we then roared down the runway and lifted into the night sky.

We quickly switched to Miami Center. The night sky was empty so they immediately cleared us to climb unrestricted to flight level 410. Once we were at cruise altitude, I reduced the power and let the speed stabilize just below the redline. We had both been rushing for the past two hours and this was our first opportunity to assess our situation.

Marsch spoke first, "Any idea what this is about?"

"Not really. The Miami Herald says the Haitian government is in trouble but I didn't pay too much attention to it. The guy who called for the charter said we would get further instructions once we landed. He was kind of nebulous. The only thing he said for certain was that we had to get in and out of Haiti as quickly as possible; but definitely no later than sunrise."

Marsch glanced at his watch. It was 1:30 AM.

"The TV news said the Air Force might send down a transport to rescue Duvalier. To get him and his buddies out of town."

"Well, if that's the plan," I asked, "then what the hell are we doing coming down?"

Marsch peered ahead into the grim sky and retorted with a dull "I dunno," signalling the conversation was over.

There was nothing more to say. We only knew a few facts. And that's all we needed to know. Anything else would have been speculation or a distraction; and therefore, a waste of energy. The night air was smooth, but the calm air only allowed my thoughts to stray as we raced on to the south.

Our airplane that night was a very old Learjet. A model 23. Serial number 3 to be exact. The registration number emblazoned on her tail lionized her lineage: 3BL, for Lear Jet number 3, and BL being, of course, Bill Lear's initials. At the time, 3BL had the dubious distinction of being the oldest Lear still flying. Its two predecessors having met completely different fates. Serial number 1 had crashed during a test flight in Kansas. And serial number 2 was prominently displaced in a Washington museum.

Twenty three years after the death of her oldest sibling, and despite her own glamorous youth, 3BL had eventually found herself in the Caribbean trade. Like so many other airplanes, ships, and even people, the Caribbean was the place for things to live out their remaining days after they had been all used up by the richer developed world.

I myself had gotten used to the Caribbean trade and was accustomed to flying to remote airports in the middle of the night without knowing what was waiting for me. Tonight was about the same and I assumed this would be no different. We would get in, then get out, with only the usual amount of bother. But I wasn't too worried about it. Once we would begin our instrument let down in the misty unknown we would find out soon enough.

The Miami Center controller broke the silence with a radio call. We were approaching the invisible line in the sky that demarcated the southern edge of Miami's airpace. Miami was 500 miles behind us yet the signal was strong and clear because we were passing by their repeater transmitter in Provo.

"Learjet 3 Bravo Lima, I show you approaching Joses intersection. Contact Port-au-Prince on frequency 124.5. Radar service is terminated."

And then from one airman to another, he added.

"Have a good night."

Marsch dialed the frequency for Port-au-Prince Control. He paused and keyed the microphone.

"Hello, Port-au-Prince, this is Lear 3 Bravo Lima, Joses intersection. Level 410."

He released the mike key and we waited for a response but we were greeted with nothing but dead air.

He tried again..."Hello, Port-au-Prince... Lear 3 Bravo Lima, Level 410."

Still nothing.

"Is that the right frequency?" I asked.

Marsch had the high altitude chart folded over and tucked between the glareshield and the windshield. He pulled it out and flipped on the map light.

"Yeah, that's right, 124.5. I'll try it once more before I go to the secondary."

He tried a third time.

We then heard a microphone key onto the frequency but there was only a carrier with no voice. The voiceless transmission happened a second, and then a third time.

Someone or something was also on the frequency.

A few eternal seconds went by. I looked at the distance counter showing miles remaining to Port-au-Prince. 180 miles and it was counting down at seven miles a minute. I looked far ahead to the horizon. Even on a normal night, Haiti did not have a lot of surface lights visible from altitude. But tonight the country was completely dark. We had less than 30 minutes to landing and I was getting eager to begin our descent. After a few more long seconds, a voice came over the frequency.

"Roger…"

Another long pause…

"Learjet 3 Bravo Lima, Port-au-Prince Control…"

And then another long pause as though the controller was distracted.

"You are cleared to the Port-au-Prince airport. Cruise 4,000 feet."

Even though the autopilot was flying I was holding the control yoke lightly and I nervously tapped the top with my finger.

"A cruise clearance?! What the hell?"

Marsch raised one eyebrow, "Well, I guess we're the only airplane in their sector tonight. Or… they don't give a shit. Or both."

A cruise clearance was a throwback to the very earliest days of air traffic control. Before the skies became congested and controllers would sequence your flight every step of the way, a cruise clearance was a way to give a pilot unrestricted authority to fly any way they wanted. A cruise clearance was only given in empty skies and when the controller couldn't be bothered to provide better oversight.

"I haven't ever gotten one of those in real life, just in training."

"Yeah, me neither. Do you remember how that works?"

"Kind of, but that was a long time ago. It was one of those obscure questions the examiners would ask to trip up a student. No one ever actually received that clearance."

"I think it means that we can continue on our own all the way to the airport without further ATC instruction."

"Sounds right, but it basically means they don't want to talk to us anymore and we're on our own"

"Yeah, basically."

Appropriately confused, and like so many of our other late night approaches into unknown airports, we continued on, counting more on luck and our raw skill rather than on definite knowledge of what we were doing. We thus began our descent towards the dark and empty horizon without any further guidance from air traffic control.

As we passed through 5,000 feet, Marsch tuned the frequency for the Instrument Landing System and I was encouraged to see the needles that we needed to guide us to the runway immediately jumped to life.

Marsch raised the volume on the navigation radio and dutifully checked the Morse code identifier for the Port-au-Prince Runway 9, and reported, "Localizer identified!" With that verification, we knew we had a good signal for electronic guidance to the runway.

I turned onto a twenty mile final toward Runway 9 and Marsch switched the number one comm radio frequency to call the Port-au-Prince tower. But that frequency was silent as well. After three tries, he gave up with a self-evident observation.

"Nobody's home."

I turned on the recognition light and a shaft of powerful light stabbed the darkness ahead.

"Well, screw 'em. If they don't answer, I'm landing anyway. We got the cruise clearance so somebody knows we're here. We'll just continue using no comm procedures. With all of our lights on, if anyone is down there, they'll see us coming."

"Sounds good, at least the runway lights are on."

The runway was visible in the distance. It stood out as a lonely sentinel against the black sky. But without any other references, we were flying into a classic black hole phenomenon. It was an illusion that made a pilot's eyes lose focus in the featureless background. And a black hole was almost as sinister as its cosmic namesake. It was a common circumstance that happened near airports with dark surroundings and the result was often a wrecked airplane just short of the runway.

To prevent that, I knew I couldn't trust my own depth perception. Instead, I was concentrating mostly on the flight director to guide me down. It was the best and most reliable instrument and source of information. It combined the information from our attitude gyros, compasses, and navigation radios to give us reliable guidance all the way to touchdown.

But there was a distraction. I noticed a bright white light oscillating in my peripheral vision. It was like a strobe light, intermittently flashing in my right eye. At first I ignored it but it became increasingly bothersome. I shifted in my seat to move away from the light. Thus re-situated, I was able to ignore it but it then the light beam altered its projection. The vexing beam then began to alternate between my eye and the flight director itself.

"What the hell?"

I asked Marsch. "Do you see that?"

"See what?'

He wasn't able to confirm my observation.

I glanced outside. Maybe, the control tower was trying to signal us with a light gun, or maybe it was another airplane flying nearby. My glance revealed nothing so I lingered looking outside a bit longer than I should on an instrument approach.

Then, another flash in my eye.

The air was smooth and the airplane was flying rock steady so I figured it was OK to continue. I glanced outside and down. Maybe a boat was flashing a light at us. However, there was nothing but the black sea below us.

I locked my gaze back on my instruments. We were only a few miles from touchdown and I committed myself to landing despite the distraction.

I sensed motion to my right so I looked over. I saw another flash of light. This time from inside the cockpit. I saw Marsch's left wrist moving. I looked at him directly. He was smiling widely. He had been caught and let out a cackle.

"You shithead!" As I laughed as well.

He had been using the crystal of his watch to reflect the map light beam over to me. It was a practical joke we had been playing on each other for months and he got me again.

"OK, that's enough. Stop screwin' around. I gotta fly this stupid approach."

We were by then about five miles from touchdown, about two minutes, and we had given up on calling the control tower for landing clearance. They knew we were coming and the runway looked empty. Our landing and recognition lights filled the sky so no one could say they didn't see us coming.

With just a minute before landing, the Communications radio came to life.

"Lear Jet 3 Bravo Lima, this is Port-au-Prince. You are cleared to land."

Marsch read back the clearance over the radio and commented to me.

"Well, at least someone knows we're here."

"Yeah, but I'm not sure that's a good thing."

The last few hundred feet before touchdown were routine and I felt the tug of the asphalt as the wheels touched the ground. Once we slowed to taxi speed, I glanced at the clock on the instrument panel. It was 3 AM.

Chapter 60

A Puzzle with No Answer

Once we turned off the runway, the tower gave us terse instructions to park in the cargo area near the passenger terminal. I saw an open area next to an Air Haiti C-46, which was another tired old relic pressed into service for the Caribbean trade.

I approached the parking spot and swung the airplane around pointing straight towards the runway. It was a habit that experience had taught me. It allowed for a quick getaway, if necessary. We shut down the engines and they both gave up with their usual descending whoosh.

Marsch left the cockpit to open the door while I finished the parking checklist. As he was exiting, I called out to him.

"I don't think we'll have a power cart available so I'm shutting down the whole airplane to conserve the battery."

I took one last look at our fuel before I shut off the battery switch. I toggled through the five fuel tanks. The tip tanks were empty and so was the center tank. The main wing tanks had 1,000 pounds each. That was plenty of fuel to land with but not really enough to go anywhere else. Until a fuel truck showed up to top us off, we were prisoners on this island; just like so many others. I reached for the battery switch and the airplane went dark.

That was two hours ago. The fuel truck we were promised had yet to show up. More surprisingly, the customs officials looking for their usual little bite never came out to meet us. We had earlier walked across the dark ramp to the airline terminal to find someone to process our flight but the functionaries of the Duvalier regime had already run away into the night. The airport was unattended and we now had only about an hour before sunrise. If we were to depart before dawn we had to come up with a plan. But we had none. Instead, we just stood by the airplane, alone and soaked in our own sweat.

However, I was still trying to formulate a plan.

"We have about 2,000 pounds of fuel on board. I suppose if we get desperate we could make it over to Santo Domingo."

Our roles had switched and Marsch was now the pilot in command. It was his decision on what we should do.

Marsch only grunted an indistinct "Maybe."

He didn't seem to want to talk but I broached an old subject again, "So, what's the deal with the Saigon thing?"

Marsch looked into the distance and he decided to satisfy my curiosity and answered.

"I grew up in Asia. My dad was with the State Department. He was stationed in Vietnam right after the war ended in '73 and he brought the whole family to live with him. I was twelve years old at the time."

He paused to wipe the sweat from his forehead.

"When the Communists rolled into town, we had to evacuate with hardly any notice. The State Department evacuated us. We were the last airplane out. We would have been next to last but a Communist rocket vaporized the airplane just behind us."

He trailed off.

I tried to lighten the mood a bit, "I guess that explains why you speak French so well."

He ignored me and went on. "The people on that airplane were the lucky ones. There were thousands more left behind and they learned quickly about communist justice."

My chest tingled as I remembered what my dinner mates in Guatemala said about Communists and then I calculated the odds of that happening here… to us.

Marsch then turned and looked directly at me.

"You know, it's right about now when things are the worst. It's during the time just after the government collapses and just before the rebels take over full control. That's when all the old scores are settled. And the best part for the killers is no one asks any questions. After all, what's a few more bodies in the overall murderfest? That's probably what's happening right now on the other side of the airport fence."

I looked beyond the airport perimeter. The eastern horizon was beginning to lighten. In the still air I could see wafts of smoke hovering over the city and I got a whiff of my own sweat.

Marsch had his back up against the side of the airplane and wiped his sweaty palms against his pant legs. We then had a back and forth analysis of our situation. I forget who said what exactly but it went something like this:

"We need to be out of here before sunrise."

"Trust me, I'm ready to get the hell out of here too but we need gas. I walked by the Shell office but it was locked up tight. Nothing to do but wait."

"This is bullshit. Let's just get the hell out of here. We'll just leave under visual rules, no clearance needed. We could make Santo Domingo no problem, maybe even Grand Turk."

I stuck my head back in the airplane and half crawled towards the cockpit. I flipped on the battery switch to double check our fuel load. I already knew what it said but maybe the fuel fairies came and gave us a few extra hundred pounds. I toggled through each fuel tank indicator. Still just 2,000 pounds. I hesitated. The brightly lit instrument panel was familiar and it offered a sense of security. Every part of it was my good friend but we needed to conserve our batteries. I flipped off the switch and I was again enveloped in the gloom.

After my Medellin experience I was a lot less less inclined to fly around the dark Caribbean with only fumes in the tank.

"We only have two thousand pounds. Yeah, we could make Santo Domingo but we'd land with maybe 10 minutes of gas. And Grand Turk is definitely out of the question."

"So, what should we do?"

"I don't know but if we sit here, what's the worst that could happen? We could wait for daylight. Someone should find us and they'll help us get some fuel. Even if the rebels take over the airport, we'd be OK. After all, Papa Doc never let the Tonton Macoute mess with Americans so maybe they won't care about us."

Neither of our plans, stay or go, offered much comfort. Instead, we both clung to the airplane without a good answer.

Chapter 61

Escape from Haiti

I was startled by a voice from near the nose of the airplane.

"Gentlemen! Hello!"

A man appeared and I turned towards him. He was white man, about 70 years old. He was short and had a full head of curly white hair, He was wearing khaki pants and a thin white cotton shirt. His shirt was sticky with sweat and it clung to his sinewy biceps.

He apparently had been standing on the other side of the airplane for some time. In the dim light, his appearance was unassuming but I found his presence comforting rather than intimidating. I moved closer to him for protection.

"You are here to pick up Philippe Emmanuel."

It was a statement, not a question. He spoke English with a European accent. It was possibly German… but not quite.

Marsch responded, "We don't know. We were just told to wait here for instructions. Who are you?"

"Yes, of course. Excuse me for not introducing myself. My name is Edelman. And you are Marsch. I am here to give you instructions."

"How do you know my name?"

"I am with the Israeli Embassy here. We have been asked to help you. Monsieur Emmanuel is a high ranking member of the Duvalier regime. He was to have been evacuated earlier this evening with President Duvalier. They left a few hours ago on an American Air Force C-141. Baby Doc and his wife are already on their way to France. Unfortunately, Monsieur Emmanuel was left behind."

Like many Jewish men of his age, Edelman was avuncular but he still had enormous dignity and power. You had to hand it to the Israelis. They built one of the most vibrant economies in the world. They did it with no oil money and with their neighbors trying to kill them. They were both lion hearted and gentle at the same time and our friend here was a perfect example. I felt safe with him.

"Things have been getting worse here for the past few days. No one knows yet that the president has left the country. Once word gets out that Baby Doc is gone then things will get much worse."

A sound of a truck in the distance broke the silence.

He paused and looked past my shoulder.

"No one knows the whereabouts of Monsieur Emmanuel. He has a lot of enemies both within the Tonton Macoute and outside of it. It may already be too late for him."

Edelman was wary but calm as glanced behind our airplane. I looked that way also. A gate in the airport fence had been opened.

"None of that concerns you though. It isn't safe here for you anymore. I suggest that you just leave without him…immediately. A fuel truck is coming now. I will ensure you have a flight plan filed. Don't worry about customs processing; just leave, the sooner the better. Your airplane is out of place here and it is already getting the wrong kind of attention."

And our Israeli friend disappeared into the night leaving us alone again.

The fuel truck then pulled up by the airplane, Marsch turned to me.

"It's going to take twenty minutes to fuel. I'll start filling the center tank. Once the fuelers are done, you pay them; just jump in and we'll go."

I stayed outside and monitored the fueling but it took an extra long time. I anxiously watched the eastern horizon, wishing for a cigarette, as the first streaks of orange peeked over the horizon.

When the fueler was done, I paid him and watched him pull away.

I looked again at the horizon and took a deep breath. It looked like we were going to leave empty handed when a silver BMW came out of darkness and lurched to a stop alongside the airplane. The front license plate displayed the numbers "22." The numbers that were code for the Tonton Macoute. A man in a dark blue silk suit tumbled out. He came straight to me screaming.

"I am Philippe Emmanuel! Take us to Miami!"

His black skin was shiny with sweat, and it contrasted sharply with the immaculate white of his starched shirt. I didn't know who he was but my guess was that he was someone important, or at least he was important until a couple of hours ago. Things had turned out badly for him.

Inside the car was a light skinned woman sitting in the rear seat. Despite the heat, she was wearing a fur coat. Her arms were crossed across her chest;

but her right forearm was bent at the elbow, allowing her to hold a long ciga-rette in front of her mouth. She looked familiar.

Monsieur Emmanuel had turned back to the car and began pleading with the woman in Creole. He had every right to be agitated. He would know as well as anyone that in Haiti it was not uncommon for people to be executed on the airport ramp just as they were about to board their flights to freedom. Mr. Emmanuel had lived by the sword and now he fully expect-ed to die by it as well.

However, Madame Emmanuelle, or whoever she might have been, was in no hurry. She looked determined not to show any fear or urgency. Perhaps she thought it better to die a regal death rather than escape as a sweaty ref-ugee. By now the driver had gotten out of the car and was holding her door open. Their driver was dressed in military khakis and he looked to be a high ranking officer. I watched the lady pull a last leisurely draw from her cigarette.

However, Mr. Emmanuel was not so collected and he screamed at her.

"Please, hurry!"

On the other side of the airport, where the gate had been opened, I saw a white pickup truck had entered the airport.

I yelled to Marsch. "Turn Two!"

It was my call to start the right engine while we were still boarding. It would have only saved us a few seconds but my main hope was the whine of the engine spinning up would create a sense of urgency.

The noble lady then got out of the car and walked to the airplane like a runway model. She paused at the foot of the stairs while her driver loaded two heavy leather bags in the cabin. Once the stairs were clear she looked at me and her mouth turned down in a scowl. She began to speak but the rising din of the starting engine made it hard to hear her.

"You were told not to come back to Haiti."

That was odd. That was what the vodou priestess at the Hotel Oloffson had told me. But how would she know that? Then I realized it was Michelle and I remembered her warning to me.

No matter. I shrugged one shoulder slightly.

"I'm not good at taking advice. You said so yourself."

She shook her head.

"Just what I feared. My fate again to be determined by a fool."

And without a second look back at me or her homeland, she glided into our richly appointed cabin.

I climbed back into the airplane myself and prepared to close the door. I looked back to the driver and he returned my gaze. It was likely he also had a death warrant waiting for him back in the city. Our eyes remained locked and I saw his chin was trembling.

We had enough room for the driver and I thought about it for a half a second. I looked to the back of the cabin and to our two passengers. One looked fearful, the other glared at me.

Well, to hell with them.

The right engine was still accelerating so I had to scream to the driver.

"Goddamnit! Get in!"

He couldn't hear me so I beckoned him with my arm. He scrambled into the cabin and I slammed the door shut behind him.

I jumped into the right seat and I saw the right engine was now idling.

"There's an army truck out there! I don't know what he wants but he is heading our way."

I craned my neck as far back as possible and looked over my right shoulder. The first truck was then joined by a second. They were several hundred yards away but they were accelerating toward us. The second truck had a few men in the back. They looked more like bedraggled rebels than soldiers. One of them was wearing a Miami Dolphins jersey. No matter; whatever their pedigree, I could see they were carrying rifles.

Marsch collected his thoughts and he commanded to me:

"Call for taxi clearance!"

We still only had the right engine running so at the same time he reached for the left engine starter switch. Once he moved the switch, the cockpit lights went dim with the extra strain on the electrical system and I saw the left tachometer begin to slowly rise. Rather than wait for the left engine to stabilize before taxiing, Marsch pushed up the right throttle, hoping to escape with partial power.

The control tower had now come awake, commanding us to stop. I gripped the hand microphone and looked to Marsch, unsure of how to respond. Monsieur Emmanuel had moved up from his seat and was now kneeling between the two pilot seats. He banged on our shoulders, yelling, "Go!"

I glanced back and saw Monsieur Emmanuel's expensive suit was now soaked in his own sweat. Further back in the cabin, Madame Emmanuel was impassive, taking a slow draw from her next cigarette. The driver who we just rescued was sitting in a side seat rocking back and forth with his hands clenched between his knees.

Marsch advanced the power on the single running engine even more and we began moving faster. But this was a risky ploy. The Learjet was a powerful airplane. Each engine, alone, provided enough thrust to push us through the air at over 300 knots. However, while we were still stubbornly attached to the ground, we had a weakness. We were not an airplane. We were just an overpowered tricycle.

Just like with every multi engine airplane, the Lear had a strong tendency to yaw when only one engine was producing thrust. This pulling motion was easily countered, but only in flight with lots of airflow over the rudder; not on the ground and certainly not at taxi speed. We would need to accelerate to about 120 knots before there was enough airflow over the rudder so we would control the airplane. However, we were moving at only 30 knots. Marsch was coaxing as much power as possible from the right engine without us flipping over.

Marsch was a solid aviator and not someone prone to recklessness. At any other time this stunt would be foolhardy. However, given the alternative approaching us from behind it seemed sensible... even wise. I decided not to answer the screaming tower controller and hung up the microphone.

We were like a drowning man flailing but, instead of air, we wanted more speed. Marsch was furiously working the nose wheel steering control to counter the asymmetric thrust; but he was asking too much from the airplane. I felt the rubber scrubbing off the nosewheel from the sideways strain.

We had a dilemma. We needed more speed to control the airplane but we couldn't control the airplane until we had more speed. Our only hope was for the second engine to light off and spool up quickly enough so we could again have balanced thrust. In the meantime, we were playing a balancing act as the airplane accelerated.

The engine was accelerating but not fast enough. We were up to 25% but we needed the engine to get to a minimum of 50% for idle. At that point, the engine could stabilize momentarily and then the engine could then be further accelerated to full thrust.

Marsch saw the taxiway leading to the runway and he angled towards it. At this point, his ploy to escape was turning into a circus stunt. He wasn't just going to taxi away from our pursuers but he was actually planning a takeoff and I could see he was timing his acceleration just so. He was adjusting his trajectory so that just as he lined up onto the runway, the full thrust of the second engine would be available. And we would take off from there.

He hoped.

And this was the first time I thought I might die before I even took off.

One of the trucks was gaining on us, almost parallel to our wingtip. There was a man standing on the back of the bed of the truck. He was wearing shorts and an unbuttoned officer's tunic. He was waving at us and I wondered briefly if our windshield was bullet proof. Monsieur Emmanuelle was still kneeling between our seats and still banging on our shoulders.

The left engine was then up to 35% RPM. But we needed 50%. Marsch was working three different controls at the same time. Like an organ virtuoso he was using every appendage to jockey the nosewheel steering, the rudders, and the thrust on the good engine. Not one of those controls alone could have kept us under control but under his adept hands he was able to give us the fastest forward speed without flipping the airplane over on its back. Thus situated, we careened our way in the general direction of the runway.

There was nothing I could do but watch.

40% RPM. The tower was now yelling at us over the radio in a full throated scream to stop. I didn't really have anything to say to him and considering we already had enough in the way of distractions I snapped the comm receiver off.

The truck was still in my peripheral vision but slowly falling behind. This should have given me some relief but the hardest part was yet to come. It looked like the engine would start in time but we still had to make a skidding turn onto the runway.

Marsch, by now, had the airplane under better control and added some more left rudder to turn onto the runway. We skittered onto the long groove that was our escape path, straining the wheels and tires to their limits. He lined the airplane up with the runway centerline facing west. However, since we entered the runway at mid-field we only had about 3,000 feet of runway ahead of us.

I called out "70 knots!"

The left engine by then had reached the magical 50%. That was idle speed and the engine needed to stabilize for a few seconds at idle before the fuel controller could open up fully. But it was a few seconds we didn't have. And Marsch wasn't waiting any longer. Then, with no pretense of finesse, he pushed the left throttle all the way up in one swift movement to match the right throttle.

Following our command, the fuel controller slammed high pressure jet fuel into the combustion chamber and the left tachometer flashed from 50% to 110% in just two seconds. The airplane lurched back to the right as the push of the left engine balanced with its partner.

Marsch was still working the rudders furiously to keep the airplane stable and pointed down the runway centerline. Our speed was increasing and I called out.

"80 knots!"

At that point, we transitioned from a skittering toy to a real airplane again. Just after that, the left generator was also up to speed and came back on line with a jolt. We were back to 100% of electrical power… but that wasn't our main problem. I looked down past the end of the runway and saw the dull outline of the slums lining the airport perimeter. It was Cite de Soleil, one of the grimmest and most incongruously named neighborhoods in the world. And we were closing in on it rapidly.

The acceleration was coming more quickly then.

"110 knots!"

We were almost at flying speed and I could no longer see the army truck in my peripheral. We had left them behind.

"120 knots!"

Then I had a sudden and dreadful realization. In our haste, I never had a chance to calculate our takeoff speeds and the required takeoff distance.

I admit that it was my job as the copilot on this leg but I sort of got distracted.

Even worse, we turned onto the runway with only about a third of the usual runway ahead of us. As a result, not only did we not know the proper lift off speed for our takeoff but we didn't even know if we had enough runway remaining ahead of us to accelerate to flying speed.

Marsch knew we couldn't stop. I noticed his knuckles were white from pushing the throttles hard against the stops. He was trying to squeeze every possible molecule of thrust from the engines. At that point, we probably didn't have enough room to stop before hitting the hovels at the end of the runway. We were committed to take off. The alternative to a successful takeoff was not a firing squad for our passengers, but a fireball at the end of the runway.

As the airspeed needle passed 120 knots I felt that transition that every pilot knows. The wings were starting to generate enough lift and the airplane was getting light on its feet. I relied on my instinct and made a wild guess. "You're approaching flying speed!"

But Marsch knew this was just a guess. And he only gingerly pulled back on the yoke just to test the airplane. The weight on the nose wheel lightened and the nose strut extended ever so slightly. We had just enough air flowing over the elevators to raise the nose but not quite enough yet to support the weight of the whole airplane. The airplane wasn't ready to fly yet.

Marsch pushed the nose back down to streamline the airplane and aid acceleration. With so little runway left, it was an agonizing decision but it was the right one. Trying to lift off too soon would have guaranteed disaster by adding drag and lengthening our takeoff run.

"125 knots!"

We need just a little more speed.

He tickled the yoke back again, just a fraction more. He was not telling the airplane what to do; he was asking permission.

I again tasted the awful metal taste of panic rising up from my throat. This time I was too busy to ram it down or to have a philosophical discussion with death so I just ignored it.

Then, a thought flashed into my mind:

The pilot's prayer! Yes, of course! "Please God, don't let me screw up!"

But this time it was already too late. We had already screwed up. We were going to die and it was going to be our fault. Now we had to pray for another type of divine intervention. But to which divinity? To the demigod Bill Lear, the genius who designed the Learjet? How about to the ancient gods, or perhaps, the modern ones? Maybe, since we were in Haiti, the vodou spirits?

Instead, I made the decision to appeal the airplane herself. And I prayed silently.

We are crass and foolish aviators, not worthy of your genius, not worthy of your beauty. You are the perfect machine and you know what we want. Come on! Please... Help us!

"130 knots!"

The muddy slums at the end of the runway were now clearly visible in the stark power of our landing lights. The airplane was surging ahead of its own volition and we were now riding the back of a wild animal. The wings by now were making enough lift to support all of our weight. But we were still rolling on our wheels with the airplane only waiting for us to give her permission.

There was a road at the other side of the airport fence. Alongside it, I saw a young girl coming out of one of the shanty huts carrying a water pail. We had about five seconds before we would hit her. And I thought that maybe death had finally come to collect his debt.

We were fast enough to fly but we still had one problem. We were not yet assured of clearing the buildings ahead. I briefly thought of the airliner hitting the gas station in St Thomas. Cite de Soleil was already wall-to-wall squalor and we were about to make it even worse.

The yoke was light in Marsch's hands and it was fully alive. The airplane was giving him permission to fly. And just in time, for there was no more runway left.

I urged him on again.

"Rotate!"

Marsch waited a half a second to build up more kinetic energy. We were at the point of release. It was now time… fly, or die. He couldn't hold back any longer and pulled the yoke back deep into his lap.

The airplane obeyed and leapt into the air as the abyss of Cite de Soleil flashed underneath us.

Chapter 62

....

The Journey Home

"Gear up!"

The wheels we so badly abused moments ago, obeyed our command to retract and locked up with a satisfying thunk. We were a sleek thing of beauty again. The airplane was fully in her element and accelerated quickly past 170 knots.

"Flaps up!"

With the airplane aerodynamically clean, we then accelerated to 250 knots. As we climbed over the Gulf of Gonave, we were again plunged into darkness. Regardless, I felt light. We had been guilty men doomed to the gallows. But we were given a last second reprieve and I was grateful to gulp the underserved air of freedom.

I wanted to savor the moment and let the relief sink in but I had a serious realization. We were out of the fire but we only had jumped back into the frying pan. We still have to get away from Haiti and we never received a clearance from Port-au-Prince Control.

Marsch reported his intentions to me.

"I'm staying low until we get away from the city. I don't want anyone taking shots at us"

I glanced at the fuel flow meters. We were consuming fuel like water through the rapids. I silently concurred but we were going to have to climb soon to have any hope of making Miami non stop.

Once we were a safe distance out from the city, Marsch began a climb and we leveled at 16,500 feet, the highest we could go without an instrument clearance.

Our immediate goal was to get to back to the Joses intersection, the northern boundary of Haitian airspace. It was there that the airspace of Haiti met with the boundary of the Miami control area; and just beyond that, was home. Joses was only an invisible point in space but it shone brightly in our minds like a lighthouse for stricken sailors.

I tuned the VOR navigation radio and set up the proper course for display on our flight directors. It was a 330 course inbound to Joses. We still didn't have any permission or guidance from Haiti control so I just made another guesstimate.

"Fly a heading of about 360 to intercept. We'll angle in shallow, almost direct. Just fly a speed of about 270 knots for max economy until we get to altitude."

Marsch turned the airplane to the right and the orange glow of sunrise rolled into our view filling me with some hope.

Marsch was still hand flying the airplane and doing an impeccable job so I didn't have to worry about monitoring his flying. However, we needed each other to think this through and he was still fixated on the airplane. I needed to unload him.

"Autopilot is available if you want it."

He snapped out of his trance and reached for the button marked "A/P engage" and it clicked on without protest. The autopilot then took over flying and navigation duties while we figured out our next step.

"We're going to have to get a clearance from Miami Center before Joses to climb into their high altitude airspace. Although, the Haitians are super pissed. And by now have probably called ahead to report us."

"Well, we could just not call Miami. We have enough gas to land in South Caicos. We can refuel, file a flight plan to Miami and just pretend nothing ever happened."

"I'm not sure landing in The Turks is cool. I don't think they'd take kindly to us just dropping in there either without a flight plan or a customs declaration. Remember that DC-4 crew?"

The Miami boundary was now only 100 miles ahead and at seven miles a minute we had to make a decision soon.

"We have enough gas to make Miami if they let us climb right away. Let's just call Miami and take our lumps. I think our passengers would rather deal with the US State Department rather than the Grand Turk officials."

"OK. Miami it is."

But we were still too low. At only 16,000 feet, we were burning deeply into our fuel reserves. We had to get up to at least 410.

We needed to contact Miami and not just to climb to a more efficient al-

titude, but to also alert the air defense authorities. Without identifying ourselves to Miami Center and with no flight plan, we would be a UFO, and not
the kind from outer space. We would be a fast moving unidentified flyer coming from the general vicinity of Cold War Cuba. We would surely gain the
attention of Air Force interceptor jets patrolling the southern US border.

As we approached Joses intersection, I called Miami Center's deep ocean
controller on a VHF frequency with our call sign and altitude and then held
my breath. The controller in the dark air conditioned room in North Miami
responded immediately.

"Roger, Lear 3 Bravo Lima. This is Miami Center. You are loud and clear.
Standby.

After a brief pause, he came back and and half queried/half stated,

"We just got a call from the control tower at Port-au-Prince. They said you
were kind of doing things on your own down there and you departed without
a clearance."

Marsch remained his calm self but the controller's question had my
stomach twist. Marsch looked at me and in his usual stoic manner just lifted
one eyebrow. As the pilot in command, he would normally have responded
to these sort of queries that had legal implications. Instead, he was indicating
that I was on my own.

I decided to be clever. "Well, sir, there may have been a miscommuni-
cation with the tower, but our understanding was that we were cleared for
takeoff."

Again, Marsch and I exchanged a glance wondering if this time we didn't
overstep too much. Most of our charters were on the very ragged edge of le-
gality. Most of the time, the US authorities looked the other way. Hell, half
the time we were doing charters for some government entity. Maybe, this
time, though, we would bear scrutiny once back in Miami.

There was a pause on the ATC frequency. And then we heard a different
voice on the frequency.

I recognized it immediately. It was the same voice over the phone. The
one that set up the charter. "Learjet 3 Bravo Lima, confirm that you have Mr.
Philippe Emmanuel on board."

Hearing that voice and hearing that question, I knew that since we had
done our job all would be forgiven. I responded with a lightning fast:

"Affirmative!"

The voice of the original controller came back over the radio and we were rewarded with our second lifeline that day.

"Roger, this is Miami Center, you are radar contact. You are cleared to Miami via Upper Amber 222. Climb and maintain flight level 410."

I read back the clearance and Marsch climbed quickly to altitude. Once level, I again toggled through the fuel tanks, and noted with relief we would have enough gas to make Miami.

In the safety of cruise flight I leaned back in my seat. I stared for a long time down at the blue waters of the lower Bahamas. The jewel of Great Inagua was on our right but it held no charm for me.

A wave of fatigue swept over me and I was looking forward to getting home, more than usual. I always loved hearing the Miami controller tell us we were back in radar contact, especially after a long trip in South America. I would be tired and dirty but it meant we were under the watchful eye of people like me, and almost home. At that point, our safe landing in Miami was assured. But I knew tomorrow there was going to be another call waiting for us... and then another...

I was not tired of flying. I still loved the visceral feel of flight, but instead I was tired of everything else; the uncertainty, the dark nature of the passengers waiting for us, the people in cities who didn't want us, the corrupt customs officials, the oligarchs. Tired of not being in control of my destiny. This was not the life I wanted.

They say that the lives we live really just reflect our true desires and that everything is how we subconsciously planned it. But was that really true? Were we truly masters of our destiny? Weren't we sometimes just victims of circumstance? Did Monsieur Emmanuel want to be escaping with his life? Did the colonel in Iquitos want to be the protector of Peruvian sovereignty in an obscure river town? How about Mr. Taguchi? Did he really want to spend five years in a Soviet gulag?

The Panamanian captain reminded me that the day you are born you are given a nationality, religion, and family name, and are expected to defend all three. For the rest of your life.

It seemed that in order to learn new things, it was first necessary to unlearn old things. But it seemed ideas were a very hard thing for people to give up, especially those views that one has cherished for so long. Maybe the people I had to deal with over the last few years didn't have any choice. They lived in rigid societies with no real freedom to be themselves. Maybe that was the most unappreciated freedom that Americans had, the freedom to break free of old things.

As we passed Inagua, we were flying over the shelf marking the steep drop off between the shallow salt flats of the Grand Bahama Bank and the deep Atlantic. It was a windy day on the surface and the sea was disturbed and covered with white caps. I looked at one large white mark on the ocean surface. I thought it might have been a large cruise ship. I focused my eyes on it and saw it was just the crest of a whitecap. For a brief moment in time, it was frozen on the sea's surface. And then it melted into the greater ocean, never to be seen again.

Yes, I was tired of working in the dark shadows of aviation. It was time to move on. Time to fly big, fat, slow airliners to places like Orlando, Louisville, and Sacramento. Places where they had long flat runways and we could land with lots of gas and not have avaricious customs agents waiting for us.

As we sped home, the airplane was flying beautifully like a speedboat on a flat calm lake. The engine's drone was hypnotic and there was not so much as a flicker on the instruments. Everything was as though we were suspended in space by a wire. The sun was well over the eastern horizon and the cockpit was warm. The fear and sweat from an hour ago had been swept away in our slipstream. I melted into my seat.

I used to be enamored of the Learjet; then as I got closer to her, I got to know her true nature. In the beginning, I feared her, but I had shown myself to be her equal. The Learjet had demanded much from me and, as a result, I learned much from her. We had reached an agreement. I treated her with respect and she didn't kill me. I was now a fully proficient Learjet pilot and I was alive to prove it.

I glanced back at the Emmanuels. They were sitting at opposite ends of the rear settee with their arms crossed and were looking out opposite windows.

Why was it, that people who had everything were oftentimes still so unhappy? Maslow's famous hierarchy implies that the more you had, the happier you should be; but the opposite seemed true. The poor people I met seemed the happiest. Were the poor just resigned to their fate? Or were the rich just fundamentally unhappy, constantly striving to get to the top and then jealously guarding what they had?

Over the last three years, I had been exposed to a world so much different than the world where I grew up. I initially resented the people in that world; but eventually, I had become like them. Or maybe… I was really like them all along.

The island of Stella Maris passed by the right wing. It was near there that Columbus first landed in the Americas, setting into motion the events that brought me, the grandchild of Italian peasants, to the most unlikely of places. My grandparents were doomed to a life of poverty in Italy but they broke away from their fate and came to America. And in order to honor their legacy, I knew I had to break free from my circumstances and become master of my own life.

I looked to Marsch and made an announcement.

"I'm tired."

"Yeah, it was a long night. You want to take a nap?"

"Not that kind of tired. I'm just tired of this. I miss home."

Marsch raised one eyebrow. I wasn't sure if he was skeptical or agreeing. I had fallen in love with the Learjet. And flying the Lear all around South America was where I learned to truly be a pilot and a survivor. Flying the Lear had been a great adventure but she was only just a way to get what I truly loved. I was still eager for the adventure but I now needed some stability in my life.

Marsch was still looking at me, waiting for me to finish my thought.

"I've been doing this for three years. That's enough."

One side of his mouth turned a half smile and turned to look straight ahead without saying a word.

The shadow of the Florida coastline was visible on the horizon. We were approaching the next air traffic sector responsible for the sector close in to Miami. I tuned the new frequency on the VHF radio and called them without any emotion. The controller responded in a crisp voice, "Roger, this is Miami Center, you are radar contact. You are cleared to Miami via the Biscayne VOR. Report when ready for descent."

Yes, there was that expression again used by Miami Center, "Radar contact." It meant that I was home… home to stay.

Epilogue

After landing in Miami, the customs agents were unusually understanding about our indiscretion in Port-au-Prince, and the matter of not having any outbound paperwork from Haiti also seemed of no consequence to them. Like the Miami air traffic controller, they were mostly interested if we had our passenger safely delivered to the United States.

We made the short hop back to Fort Lauderdale. And as it turned out, that was to be one of my last trips in the Lear. It had been a privilege to have had a relationship with the Learjet for three stormy years but I was determined to keep a promise to myself.

Over the following years, my fellow Learjet pilots all made it back home in one way or another. Ragsdale returned to his boyhood home in Indiana and Walpole retired near his grandchildren in rural Florida. The story for all the others was pretty much the same. Farmer was recalled from furlough and went back to his airline and eventually retired as a 777 captain flying glamorous trips to Europe.

Coe, Rohwedder, Chipman, Marsch, and Inderbitzin also achieved their dreams and were hired by the airlines as well. Although, I must admit that the airlines were no safe haven from human discord. The 1980s were a time of rancorous labor strife, bankruptcies, and unhappy mergers. Andrews and Marsch continued their careers flying private jets for the wealthy but in decidedly less unsafe environments. In the end, almost all of us found homes in happy places. As for me, I began a new love affair and ended up with a long and happy career flying airliners around the world.

On a more somber note was the fate of Allen, my captain who was with me on that descent into Medellin. You remember? The afternoon where we put aside our panic and saved each other's lives? He also made it home. But not in the way most of us hope. Death caught up with him while flying a Lear 25 over Saudi Arabia. The accident report attributed the cause simply to loss of control from a high altitude and the airplane impacted the ground near Medina. Whether the cause was simple or not, the end result was still the same, and both Allen and his copilot were killed that day. His body was transported back to the United States and he was buried near his home in Connecticut, in a plot overlooking his beloved Long Island Sound, the same waters he had sailed as a boy.

Glossary

Accelerate-Go Distance. The distance required to accelerate to the Go/No Go speed then suffer an engine failure and continue the takeoff safety on the remaining engine

Accelerate-Stop Distance. The distance required to accelerate to V1 with all engines at takeoff power, experience an engine failure at V1, and abort the takeoff and bring the airplane to a stop using braking action only (use of thrust reversing is not considered).

Adjustable Stabilizer. A stabilizer that can be adjusted in flight to trim the airplane, thereby allowing the airplane to fly hands-off at any given airspeed.

Ailerons. Primary flight control surfaces mounted on the trailing edge of an airplane wing, near the tip. Ailerons control roll about the longitudinal axis.

Aileron Buzz. A high frequency oscillation of the ailerons caused at high speeds by turbulent airflow over the trailing edge of the wing.

Airfoil. Any surface, such as a wing, propeller, rudder, or even a trim tab, which provides aerodynamic force when it interacts with a moving stream of air.

Air Route Traffic Control Center (ARTCC). An FAA function, radio call sign "Center" provides ATC service to aircraft operating during the en route phase of flight.

Airway. An airway is an imaginary centerline that extends from one navigation aid to another navigation aid. It is used to establish a known route for airplanes to track.

Angle of Attack. The angle of attack is the angle at which relative wind meets an airfoil. The angle of attack changes during a flight as the pilot changes the direction of the aircraft and is related to the amount of lift being produced.

Automatic Direction Finder (ADF). A navigation receiver that operates in the low- and medium-frequency bands. Used in conjunction with the ground-based non directional beacon (NDB), the instrument simply points to the associated ground station.

Boundary Layer Energizers. Small strips installed on the top of the wing designed to maintain a smooth flow of air over the wing. See vortex generators.

Coffin Corner (Also known as aerodynamic ceiling.) A region of flight where an airplane is close to its critical mach speed. At this speed, it is difficult to keep an airplane that is designed for only subsonic flight under stable control. An increase in speed will cause the airplane to pitch down abruptly. And a decrease in airspeed will cause the wing to stall. The term "corner" refers to the triangular shape at the top of the flight envelope chart.

Critical Mach Number. A speed at which airflow over the aircraft reaches supersonic speed.

Cruise Clearance. An ATC clearance issued to allow a pilot to conduct flight at a block of various altitudes. It also authorizes a pilot to proceed to and make an approach at the destination airport.

Decision Altitude (DA). A specified altitude in the precision approach at which a missed approach must be initiated if the required visual reference to continue the approach has not been established.

Drag Curve. A pictorial representation of the drag an airplane experiences at various speeds.

Dutch Roll. A combination of rolling and yawing oscillations that normally occurs when the dihedral effects of an aircraft are more powerful than the directional stability.

Empty Field Myopia. Induced nearsightedness that is associated with flying at night, in instrument meteorological conditions and/or reduced visibility. With nothing to focus on, the eyes automatically focus on a point just slightly ahead of the airplane.

False Horizon. Inaccurate visual information for aligning the aircraft, caused by various natural and geometric formations that disorient the pilot from the actual horizon.

Flight Director Indicator (FDI). Provides steering commands that the pilot follows.

Instrument Landing System (ILS). An electronic system that provides both horizontal and vertical guidance to a specific runway, used to execute a precision instrument approach procedure.

Knot. The knot is a unit of speed equal to one nautical mile (1.852 km) per hour, approximately 1.151 mph.

Mach Number. The ratio of the true airspeed of the aircraft to the speed of sound in the same atmospheric conditions, named in honor of Ernst Mach, late 19th century physicist.

Mach Tuck. Mach tuck is an aerodynamic effect whereby the nose of an aircraft tends to pitch downward as the airflow around the wing reaches supersonic speeds.

Minimum En Route Altitude (MEA). The lowest published altitude between radio fixes that ensures acceptable navigational signal coverage and meets obstacle clearance requirements between those fixes.

Minimum Obstruction Clearance Altitude (MOCA). The lowest published altitude in effect between radio fixes on VOR airways, off-airway routes, or route segments, which meets obstacle clearance requirements for the entire route segment and which ensures acceptable navigational signal coverage only within 25 statute (22 nautical) miles of a VOR.

Missed Approach. A maneuver conducted by a pilot when an instrument approach cannot be completed to a landing. Missed approach point (MAP). A point prescribed in each instrument approach at which a missed approach procedure shall be executed if the required visual reference has not been established.

Phugoid Oscillations. Long-period oscillations of an aircraft around its lateral axis. It is a slow change in pitch accompanied by equally slow changes in airspeed. Angle of attack remains constant, and the pilot often corrects for phugoid oscillations without even being aware of them.

Spoilers. High-drag devices that can be raised into the air flowing over an airfoil, reducing lift and increasing drag. Spoilers are used for roll control on some aircraft. Deploying spoilers on both wings at the same time allows the aircraft to descend without gaining speed. Spoilers are also used to shorten the ground roll after landing.

Tropopause. The boundary layer between the troposphere and the stratosphere which acts as a lid to confine most of the water vapor, and the associated weather, to the troposphere.

Vortex Generators. Small vertical plates extending vertically from the top of the wing. They are designed to maintain a smooth airflow over the wing providing better lift and controllability.

V Speeds. Velocity Speeds used to define air speeds necessary for safe operation such as go/no go speed, minimum takeoff speed, approach speeds.

CPSIA information can be obtained
at www.ICGtesting.com
Printed in the USA
LVHW022003210523
747630LV00002B/148